THE DEVELOPMENT
AND USE OF
POLYESTER PRODUCTS

THE DEVELOPMENT
AND USE OF
POLYESTER PRODUCTS

E. N. DOYLE
Plastics Consultant

McGRAW-HILL BOOK COMPANY

New York   San Francisco   Toronto
London   Sydney

THE DEVELOPMENT AND USE OF POLYESTER PRODUCTS

17765

1234567890 MAMM 754321069

Preface

A great number of fine books, treatises, and technical articles have been
written and published concerning polyester resins and their manufacture, processing, and uses.

The majority of these publications have been dedicated to the general-
purpose resins and their uses for processing into the Fiberglass Reinforced Plastics (FRP) so well known in boats, translucent paneling,
storage vessels, automobiles, aircraft, trays, and other such uses.

Very little has been written about the host of applications where
polyesters can be utilized to such great advantage without the use of a
reinforcing fiber or fabric.

Reinforced polyester resins have a well-defined place in industry.
Their use is steadily growing and expanding to such applications as
tooling, structural members, tubular goods, pipe, large storage tanks,
silos for grains and feedstuff, and many other end products.

An effort is made here to make the industry aware of the many applications in which reinforcing materials such as fiberglass, can be replaced with very low-cost fillers, such as limestone, clay, silica, barytes, and other well-known fillers. In these applications, tensile strength is not a priority factor in the end product.

The author feels that the construction industry will provide the largest and most profitable market for polyester products in the foreseeable future. Recent building-materials surveys show that the plastics part of the building industry is a very small part of the total and that it mostly consists of the vinyl and vinyl-asbestos flooring materials.

In order that polyester products may be able to compete with more conventional types of building materials, resins, processes, and techniques must be developed to turn out top-quality merchandise at the lowest possible prices. This calls for large, well-equipped plants, with all the automation possible. Mass-production requires large capital investments; however, the investment in this type of manufacturing plant is the only way polyester building materials will be able to gain any appreciable segment of this market.

This is not to say, however, that there are not many end products that can be produced and marketed profitably with modest capital investments. Some of the products discussed in Chap. 10 can be manufactured with small- to medium-sized investments and still compete well in today's markets.

In the following chapters an attempt will be made to discuss almost every conceivable type of polyester product. A very short time ago, such products would not have been possible simply because the materials were not available at prices that would allow these products to be competitive. Much credit is due to the petrochemical industry, which has made the raw materials and intermediates available to resin manufacturers. Even more credit is due to the resin manufacturers themselves, who, through extensive research, are meeting the ever-increasing demand for better polyesters for specific processes and products. Much credit must go also to the manufacturers of equipment, who today are spending large sums in research and development of equipment to process these polymers into finished end products at the lowest possible price.

Thus, in effect, the progress of plastics and polyesters, in particular, into these new fields will be a joint effort of every phase of the industry. The cycle starts, for the most part, with the basic petroleum from which the plastics are derived. The petrochemical industry takes these petroleum products and turns them into intermediates, which the resin manufacturer processes into a finished polymer. Hundreds of other manufacturers turn out additives and ingredients that make the finished formulation for the end-product manufacturer, who is the crucial part of the joint effort. The whole sequence depends entirely on his investment, foresightedness, technical skills, and ability to market the finished product. The industries below him in the sequence cannot market their products unless the end-product manufacturer can successfully market his products to the consumer.

Marketing alone will be a great challenge. Consumers do not readily take to change. Many of these new products will be so vastly different from conventional products that good, solid selling will be necessary as to how and why they are advantageous to the consumer. Once these materials are understood and appreciated, the selling will consist mostly in the performance of the materials themselves.

The challenge to those in the polyester industry is not only to find new markets for their present products, but to find the means to manufacture polyester products to compete with conventional materials and other plastic products and to conceive completely new products for marketing.

It is very doubtful that anyone has realized the full potential of these polymers or can visualize even a small part of the many applications to which they can be put.

The basis for progress in this industry (as is the case in any industry) must be quality and cost to the consumer. All this is possible through good, solid research and development. Marketing is of no less importance. Here, truth in advertising will be perhaps the biggest asset for the industry.

This book attempts to give the reader many new ideas with which to begin and suggests processing methods and means with which to work. It is sincerely desired that renewed efforts in the industry will be sparked, and that perhaps completely new trends of thought along these lines will be inspired.

Progress is the lifeblood of any industry. To stay in existence, it must forge ahead. To stand still is fatal. In this rapidly changing world, industry must project its ideas many years ahead.

This book contains no bibliography or references. However, the Appendix lists names of all manufacturers and suppliers available to the author, as well as all materials and equipment discussed in the text.

Trade names have been purposely omitted, with the exception of instances where generic names are not available.

Any infringement on the patents, copyrights, trademarks, or statutory and proprietary rights of others is purely coincidental.

E. N. Doyle

Contents

THE DEVELOPMENT
AND USE OF
POLYESTER PRODUCTS

One

WHY CHOOSE POLYESTERS?

Among the many organic polymers on the market today, why choose polyesters for use in so wide a study of manufactured products?

First, the polyesters that we have available and that are possible to manufacture today are very different indeed from the polyesters of only one or two years ago. In the past a resin manufacturer limited his variety of resins to a few basic polymers, ordinarily including a rigid, general-purpose resin, a resilient molding resin, and a flexible resin, usually based on adipic acid, which was to be used to modify the other two basic resins. By utilizing different monomers and different promoter systems, the manufacturer had a catalog of perhaps 10 resins. This at the time supplied the rather limited need for polyester resins.

Then the presses of competition, particularly from epoxy resins, caused the manufacturers to amplify the selection of resins. The isophthalic polyesters were developed, which gave better chemical resistance, better bond to various substrates, and were very adaptable to making resins, ranging from very flexible to very rigid, just by varying the amounts of unsaturated and saturated acids. The epoxy resins were far superior to any polyester in alkali resistance, so again, pushed by competition, the polyester manufacturers developed a polyester derived in part from bisphenol A, a major ingredient also used in epoxies.

The need soon became apparent for polyesters with higher heat resistance and resistance to burning. Chlorinated polyesters were developed to meet this need. In order for the resin manufacturer to develop these resins, intermediates had to be furnished by the petrochemical industry. Chloromaleic anhydride, chlorohydrophthalic acid, and various chlorinated monomers were especially developed for this purpose. In addition, the resin manufacturers fell back on some already available materials which had been used principally as epoxy curing agents: HET acid, pyromellitic acid or dianhydride, and other intermediates. The manufacturers of catalysts have played their part in the effort as well. They developed chlorinated peroxides to assist in the overall effort to upgrade the finished product.

In short, the polyester manufacturers realized that in order to expand the total volume of resin market, they had to offer resins custom-made for specific purposes. They have done, and are doing, a superb job of supplying the right resin for the specific end product.

Different manufacturers are concentrating on different phases of the end-product market. One may be doing most of the development in the field of high-temperature and flame-resistant resins, while another may be researching new fast-cycle resins for molding compounds. Still another may be working exclusively on resins for coating materials. A few of the larger manufacturers are working on a number of special resins at the same time, but the smaller manufacturers usually concentrate on one new development at a time.

Pigment manufacturers have done their part by developing colorants that resist chemicals and weathering far better than the old types. Filler processors have gone to greater lengths to supply well-graded fillers and fillers with very low moisture content. Joint research has shown that certain pigments and fillers can vastly improve the properties of a given finished product.

The total effort by all those involved in the industry has been great. There is much to do yet in order to realize the ultimate potential of polyesters. The total volume of resin market is only limited by the amount of end consumer goods that can be sold. In order to increase the volume of resin market, many new products will have to be manufactured with polyesters to compete with goods already on the market.

Versatility of Polyesters

Products designed around polyester resins can compete very well with more conventional materials in a great number of fields because of the tremendous versatility of these resins.

The term polyester encompasses a very wide selection of polymers. A polyester resin can be made up of one or more dihydric or polyhydric alcohols, one or more saturated dibasic or dicarboxylic acids, and one or more unsaturated dibasic acids. Of each of the three basic components, there are literally dozens from which to choose, and when combinations of one or more of each are used, there are many thousands of completely different resins possible, each with properties unique within itself.

Now, from these many thousands of possible resin compositions, a cross-linking monomer is to be added. Here again, there are several dozen from which to choose. These may be used singly or in combinations of two or more. Each monomer will change somewhat the properties of the finished product.

Even such ingredients as promoters and catalysts will in some way affect the properties of the cured resin. There are many additives, usually used in minute quantities, that also have quite definite effects on the properties.

Only a very experienced person in this field can possibly visualize the extensive number of distinctive polymers that may be formulated. A polymer may be manufactured to fit the need of almost any given end product; it may be processed by almost any number of methods and utilized in almost any given environment.

At the present time, there is no other organic polymer or group of polymers that have this wide versatility. This is not to say that polyesters are the answer to every end product, however. There still remain many applications where the proper epoxy, phenolic, urea, melamine, or urethane formulation will surpass the polyesters for a specific use. These resins just do not have the wide range of application possibilities that the polyesters possess.

Cost Advantages

Quite apart from the versatility of properties obtainable with polyesters, are the advantages of the manufactured costs of goods utilizing these resins. This becomes of particular importance when contemplating new products to compete with more conventional materials.

Low cost is probably the biggest advantage of polyesters. The cost of a finished resin may range from about 22 cents per lb, to well over $1.00 per lb, depending on the intermediates used. Most of the products discussed in this book can be manufactured with polymers in the range of 25 to 40 cents per lb.

In this price range, only the phenolics and ureas can be competitive, and although they possess properties particularly suited to many uses, because of their inherent characteristics, the number of products that can be manufactured is rather limited in scope.

The epoxies, melamines, and urethanes all possess properties that make them superior to polyesters for use in certain applications, but their cost and other drawbacks would make them unsuitable for use in most of the products discussed herein.

Processing Advantages

In almost any method of processing contemplated for a given product, polyesters present many distinct advantages.

One of the important advantages is the ease of handling these resins. Their viscosity is usually such that they may be pumped, proportioned automatically, mixed easily, and handled with minimum precautions. Also, they lend themselves readily to a highly automated system so necessary for mass-production procedures. Toxicity, with the exception of the catalysts, is very minimal. Plant fire hazards are about the same as with other polymers.

Polyesters have excellent wetting properties. With these resins, very high filler and pigment loadings may be obtained, yet ease of handling remains. Formulations of molding compounds which are 90% low-cost fillers and only 10% resin by weight are commonplace. Even higher filler loadings are possible with some materials. No other resin, with the possible exception of epoxies, can be formulated with such low percentages of polymer.

Molding compounds such as these are further processed at minimum costs. In compression-molding, these compounds can be easily handled at pressures of 300 to 400 psi. They may be injection-molded, transfer-molded, calendered, and pressure-cast with ease. With sufficient vibration, they may even be cast at atmospheric pressures.

Cycle-time Advantages

Because of the wide range of properties available in polyesters and the wide selection of catalysts, promoters, and other additives from which to choose, no other thermoset polymer can match these resins in production cycle time.

The faster a manufacturer can produce his product, the higher his production per working shift, and the lower his cost per manufactured unit. Short production cycle time is perhaps the most important advantage of these resins over other thermosets.

In compression-molding, an automated system can produce medium-sized products at a total cycle time of 30 sec, which includes loading, compressing, curing, and unloading the dies. In injection-molding, cycle time can be even shorter. In many other processing methods, such as casting, pressure-casting, cell-casting, calendering, hand lay-up, gun lay-up, or any other known methods and techniques, cycle time can be adjusted to fit the needs of the manufacturer more easily than with any other polymer available to the processor today.

Ease of Mold Release

In conjunction with all the other advantages of polyester, cited above, these resins offer another great advantage to the processor; of all the thermosets they are the easiest to remove from molds, dies, and other forming equipment. Most formulations for compounds will include an internal mold release, which gives fast, easy parting from the forming surfaces. In some casting operations where internal mold release does not give the desired results, low-cost external releasing agents are readily available, which will give many cycles per application. All these mold-release materials are now available in forms that will not interfere with subsequent operations, such as laminating, coating, bonding, and printing.

In the use of epoxies and other thermosets, the most widely used mold-release compounds are derived from silicone. In the use of silicones, few cycles per application can be obtained, and this material almost always interferes with any subsequent operations if not properly cleaned off the surfaces affected. To date, there have not been any successful internal mold releases developed for these thermosetting polymers. A number of research people are working in this direction, but as yet they have been unsuccessful in their efforts.

Availability of Polyesters

Certainly there is no other thermoset polymer as available on the market as is polyester. There are some 20 major manufacturers, with some 30 plants well located around the continental United States.

Many large end-product manufacturers make their own resins because they formulate custom resins for their products, and the volume used in these large plants often warrants the capital investment involved.

Some of these plants will make their resins available to others when they are not in direct competition.

In addition there are about 25 smaller polyester-resin manufacturers in this country, many of whom only offer a small line of specialized polymers for marketing to certain industries. Some of these resins are of excellent quality when used for the purpose for which they are intended.

Forms of Resins Available

Although most polyester resins are shipped with the monomers already added because of the ease of handling these low-viscosity materials, not all resins are furnished in this form for a number of good and valid reasons.

A growing number of resins are shipped in a high-viscosity state, which is almost a paste. Many processors prefer this form of resin when they have a monomer supply close at hand. Sometimes considerable reductions in cost can be obtained in this fashion. Also a processor may have several products that are manufactured with the same basic resin but necessitate different monomers because of the varying environments to which the end product will be subjected. Also, a resin is much more stable in paste form, with longer shelf and storage life. It is more difficult to handle because of the viscosity, but this presents no problem when piping and storage facilities are heated.

In addition, a number of manufacturers offer resin in dry, powdered form. These are usually the bisphenol resins and a few other very high molecular weight resins. These resins are friable when removed from the reactor and cooled, and are crushed and ground into a fine, powdered form. Packaging and shipping present no problems whatever. Shelf life on these resins is indefinite, and they may be modified with whatever monomers the user desires.

Limitations of Polyesters

About the only major limitation of finished polyester resins, to which the monomers have already been added, is shelf life. In this respect, polyesters compare unfavorably with most other thermosetting resins.

Polyesters will polymerize in varying periods of time, even without the presence of initiators or catalysts. The necessary element is temperature. In hot summer months, resins may travel for some time in tank trucks or railway-tank cars, with long periods in the sun. Then they are unloaded into purchasers' storage facilities, often also in the sun without the protection of insulating materials. Although resins are somewhat protected with inhibitors, most resins subjected to such circumstances as these must be used within a period of less than two months, and some resins must be used within a month or less. However, when transported in insulated facilities, and stored either in cooled or well-insulated tanks, most resins will have a shelf life of six months or more.

The resin manufacturer will always have reliable data at hand as to the shelf life of any particular resin, and his recommendations should be followed explicitly.

In choosing a polymer for such a wide range of products as discussed in this book, there could be only one possible choice—polyesters.

Besides the advantages stated before, there is no other polymer that is so adaptable to so many different methods of processing. Formulations can be made to cure under almost any given conditions and to withstand the hazards of almost any environment.

Building materials and other end products to be discussed seem to be the best outlets for polyester resins in the foreseeable future. The building-materials field, in particular, can provide a market for many millions of pounds of polymer per year, for many years to come.

Many new polymers will be developed, and there will be many improvements in already existing resins. Costs of some of the competing polymers will undoubtedly decrease as total volume increases, but, at the same time, costs of polyester resins will continue to decrease as volume increases. New intermediates from the petrochemical industry will appear on the market. New improved monomers, catalysts, and inhibitors will be developed, and polyesters will not only be able to keep pace with other polymers, but should widen the lead on them for such applications as these.

Polyester resins are not prescribed as the answer to all problems and processes in the plastics field. Far from it. There are many processes and end products for which polyesters simply would not be suitable. A processor must choose the polymer that best fits his needs. However, the vast group of resins known as polyesters is capable of supplying polymers to fit a much wider range of processes and end products than any resin known today.

Two

FLOOR-TILE MANUFACTURE

According to available statistics, over 1 billion sq ft of manufactured floor covering were marketed in 1967 in the United States alone. This figure did not include carpeting, natural-wood flooring, nor did it include such manufactured-in-place flooring such as poured terrazzo, urethane seamless types of flooring, and such materials as flagstone.

This volume was made up of manufactured terrazzo tile, vinyl tile and yard goods, vinyl-asbestos tile and yard goods, rubber tile, asphalt tile, and linoleum. The statistics on cork tile are not available.

Flooring materials have not changed much over the past 10 years; because all the manufacturers have been so well supplied with orders for the existing materials, there has been little incentive for developing new types of materials. This period has been a suppliers' market, with sufficient sales backlogs to keep production lines busy, so little thought has been given to research on new and better materials.

Carpet manufacturers are perhaps the only exception. Keen competition between synthetic fiber and wool fiber has kept the synthetic researchers working on new developments. This work has paid off, and some excellent materials have been made available during the past 10 years. New polyester fibers have come to light that are excellent for carpeting and clothing manufacture. Polypropylene fiber and new types of polyamide fibers have been developed, which are far superior to those of 5 years ago.

The manufactured flooring materials made of vinyl, vinyl asbestos, asphalt, terrazzo tile, brick, quarry tile, and most floor coverings today give excellent service, but the cost of maintenance of these floors is a continuing problem to the owners. Some types of tile are almost impossible to use at grade or below grade because the types of adhesives used for these materials will not withstand the moisture and hydrostatic pressure in such installations.

Architects and owners have for years longed for more permanent flooring materials that necessitate a minimum of care to keep them in good condition. Waxing and polishing is expensive, and on many of these materials both must be done many times per month in heavily trafficked areas. After continuous waxing for a period of time, the old wax must be removed completely, or wear patterns will form. Areas which get maximum traffic will have only the present coat of wax because no wax buildup can occur in these sectors, while around the walls, where little traffic occurs there will be many coats of wax. These light and dark areas are most unsightly on a floor, and the only cure is to remove all wax and start over again.

Many types of polyester floor tiles have been researched, and a few of them are ready to go on the market in the very near future. Architects, builders, developers of housing projects, and home owners have shown much interest in these products.

In cost, these products will be able to compete on the market in the middle price range of present floor coverings, which will place them slightly above vinyl-asbestos tile but well below pure vinyl tile.

A limited number of test floors have been installed with these new materials. Widespread interest has caused them to be watched very closely for a period of some 6 years. While the actual installations were being tested, extensive laboratory testing has been carried out. These materials look very good, indeed, and plans are in progress to manufacture such materials by several processing methods. A number of patents may be issued or still be pending on many of these processes, so any company contemplating the manufacture of one or more of such similar materials would be well-advised to check carefully into the patent situation before spending too much time and money in development.

These flooring materials have beauty, excellent durability, and require a very minimum of maintenance to keep their appearance at its best.

The properties of these materials make them entirely suitable to lay over almost any existing substrate.

Small-pattern Terrazzo-type Tile

One type of this tile, which has had extensive testing both in the laboratory and in use, is a polyester-terrazzo type of tile. It is roughly the same as manufactured terrazzo in appearance, but is much lighter in weight because it is not as thick.

This type of tile can be manufactured by a number of methods, but the most practical and economical process for mass production would be compression-molding with flash dies. With some slight alterations in equipment, it could also be transfer-molded. Very possibly, equipment can be developed to injection-mold such a molding compound as well.

A typical molding compound for this type of tile would consist of the following:

1. Flexible isophthalic polyester	7.0 lb
2. Styrene monomer	1.5
3. Monochlorostyrene	1.5
4. T-Butyl peroctoate	0.1
5. Internal mold release	0.1
6. Pigment	0.4
7. No. 1 marble chips (any color combination)	50.0
8. No. 0 marble chips (any color combination)	20.0
9. 40–200-mesh limestone filler	10.0
10. China clay (aluminum silicate)	6.0
11. Barytes, No. 1 bleached	3.4
	100.0 lb

Such a formulation will give a very good quality tile, with extremely low shrinkage. This particular mix will give a shrinkage of 0.34%. Matched dies will have to be designed to compensate for such shrinkage.

All liquid components should be premixed in a high-speed dissolver-type mixer. All dry materials must be premixed in a heavy-duty double-arm mixer, with dispersion, sigma, or nobbin blades. When the dry materials are thoroughly blended, the liquids are added as the mixer rotates, allowing only sufficient mixing time for the fillers and aggregates to wet out completely. Overmixing will cause friction-heat buildup and can easily cause the premix to gel.

All mixers must be stainless steel to avoid color pickup from the mixers themselves. The pot life of this compound will be at least 24 hr at

75°F. It can be made up in batches of any size, limited by the size of the double-arm mixer.

The consistency of this premix will be about that of a very heavy putty. It will be reasonably dry to the touch, yet will have enough flow so that it can be automatically proportioned into the proper-sized charges for dies with extrusion-type proportioning equipment.

Press pressures of 300 psi are sufficient to give good quality tile, or about 25 tons per cavity on 12 × 12 in. tile. Large presses, mounting 16 or more dies per press, are highly recommended for this type of production as labor costs are reduced. Heated platens for both male and female dies are a necessity, and such a process should be carried out at die temperatures of near 300°F for best results.

A highly automated system can produce excellent tile on 30-sec cycles, which include loading the dies, press-travel time, compressing, curing, and unloading the dies. Diagram 1 gives a typical layout for this type of production.

Many variations of this formulation can be made to produce tile with either more or less flexibility. A much higher resin content will produce tile with much lower flexural modulus, but a higher resin content than that given in the formulation presents some problems. First, the percentage of shrinkage will increase, which makes holding the finished tile within limitations of specifications more difficult—dies will have to be slightly larger. A tile with 25% resin content, instead of the 10% above, will have a shrinkage of approximately 2.4%.

In order to obtain a molding compound of the proper consistency with such a high resin content, a very different type of formulation will be necessary. Highly absorptive fillers will have to be substituted for the limestone and for the barytes. Such fillers as asbestos shorts, wood flour, and either treated natural silicas or synthetic silicas will all do the job.

A tile with higher resin content will cost more to manufacture; thus a total study should be made so that the finished product will have a balance as to cost and flexibility.

Many of the other ingredients of the formulation may be changed without affecting the properties of the tile to any great extent. A multitude of different materials, such as mold releases, catalysts, and other additives, are commercially available and may be substituted. The Appendix gives sources of all such materials; Chap. 11 presents proper materials for given processes and procedures.

The most important factor to consider in selecting fillers and aggregates is that they be as near moisture-free as possible. A moisture content of 0.02% is about the maximum that can be tolerated. More complete data is given in Chap. 11.

Colors and color combinations are almost without limit because so many different natural marbles are available at low cost. Background colors are limited only to the imagination of the formulator.

Uniformity in fillers and aggregates is of utmost importance, both in size and color. Suppliers of these materials must be made to understand the importance of these factors.

In production, the molding compound which goes into the cavity is referred to as the "charge," and the part, when removed from the cavity, is called a "blank." It does not become a tile until it has been ground to expose the marble-chip pattern. Diagram 1 shows the sequence

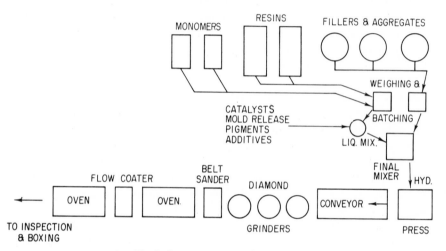

DIAGRAM 1.   *Typical compression-molding plant for floor tile.*

in the production line, from the time the raw materials go into the mixers until the finished tile is packaged and ready to store or ship.

In the process, the time which elapses from the time the part or blank is removed from the dies to the time it is ground is of considerable importance. The blank is very hot when demolded and must be ground before it cools completely to room temperature. It must not be ground too soon as it is likely to lack the strength to withstand the grinding process. The time which elapses should not be less than 12 min nor more than 30 min for optimum grinding conditions.

The grinding stage of the production line is of utmost importance because the quality and the cost of grinding can be critical.

The thickness of the blank is limited by the size of the largest marble chips used in the formulation. If ¼-in. stones are used, then the blank must be a minimum of ¼-in. thick.

The amount of grinding will now depend on the desired thickness of the finished tile. A thickness of less than 0.125 in. is not recommended for reasons of strength. A thickness more than 0.140 in. is not recommended because flexibility reduces with any increase in thickness, and because in this range maximum exposure of the stone pattern is obtained.

When a finished thickness of 0.140 in. is desired from a blank ¼-in. thick, a total of 0.110 in. must be removed. All grinding must be done while wetting with a very high flow of water, and the equipment should be designed to grind at much higher surface-feet per minute than normal equipment for metals, terrazzo, and other materials. A proper defoaming system should be added to the water. It may be a chemical system, or it may be one of the newer, very successful ultrasonic systems. A good settling tank setup can save a great amount of water because the same water can be used over and over again.

An economical and practical way to grind large amounts of this type of material is to first put it through a three-headed diamond grinder. The first head should be fitted with 60-mesh diamonds, the second with 120-mesh diamonds, and the last with 200-mesh diamonds. The first head should remove approximately 75% of the total material, the second approximately 18%, and the third some 5%; the remainder should be removed in a high-speed belt-type sander, with possibly two heads—one a 300-mesh, and the second a 400-mesh.

This five-head grinder system will give a tile with excellent finish at very high rates of production. Everything can be completely automatic. Production rate is limited only by the diameter of the diamond heads and the belt width of the sander. All the necessary equipment for this kind of production line is listed in the Appendix, together with the names and addresses of all manufacturers and suppliers.

Among engineers who are familiar with this type of work there is some disagreement as to whether such a tile should be ground totally on one side, or whether part should be removed from both sides. From an economy standpoint, there is no disagreement. It is much more advantageous costwise, to grind only one side. Less equipment is involved.

Those who disagree have legitimate reasons for their points of view: Those in favor of grinding both sides maintain that closer dimension specifications can be held in this manner. They maintain that by grinding both sides equally either side of the tile can be used, thus reducing rejects. Those in favor of grinding one side only maintain that apart from the cost factor, a much more desirable tile is obtained because a maximum exposure of the marble-chip pattern is a primary objective. Both viewpoints are worth consideration.

After the tile is ground, it must go through a short oven for drying the excess moisture left over from the grinding process. It is then ready for finishing. Since marble chips are porous to some extent, a good sealer should be applied. Many are suitable for this purpose. The sealer may be a polyurethane or an acrylate lacquer, or it could be such a material as a polycarbonate, a polyamide, or an allyl coating. All these sealers can be dried very fast, so the finished tile can be packaged.

Costs on a tile made by a process similar to that which has been described will be very close to the following figures. (All labor, equipment, power, building and plant costs, plus all raw materials are included. No overhead or profits are considered.)

Labor	$0.0120 per sq ft
Materials	0.1380
Supervision	0.0033
Utilities	0.0150
Grinding medium	0.0150
Equipment and building depreciation	0.0166
Sealer coating	0.0100
Boxing	0.0100
Total plant cost	$0.2199 per sq ft

Of course the costs set forth here can vary slightly from location to location because of transportation costs of the raw materials. However, the above figures will be a very close estimate anywhere in the United States. Should increases in resin content be desirable for any of the

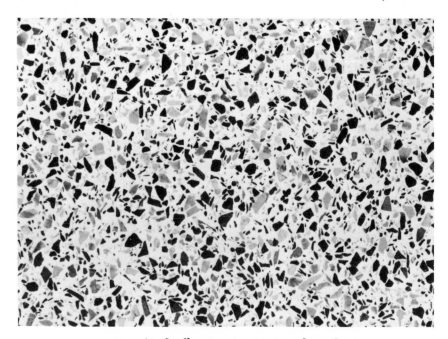

PHOTO 1. *Small-pattern terrazzo-type floor tile.*

PHOTO 2. *Polyester terrazzo flooring, Koppers Co., Inc.*

reasons set forth, then costs will rise in proportion to any added resin percentages.

A number of additional methods of producing a similar tile are presented for consideration; however, the method just described lends itself more to automation than the alternate methods which follow.

Alternate Method 1

A compound such as that which has been described, but with slightly higher resin content, can be cast in open molds.

A continuous conveyor belt, with a section enclosed in an oven, can be set up in place of the hydraulic press. Multiple molds can be mounted to the belt; the molds, charged at one end of the conveyor system, pass through the oven for curing, and can be demolded at the other end of the conveyor.

The mix must be vibrated and must have some mechanical means to spread it evenly into the molds. This may be done by mechanical screeds, by rollers in which some pressure may be applied, or in a variety of ways.

The advantage of such a process would be that it requires less capital investment. The disadvantages would include somewhat higher costs because more labor would be involved. Also, this tile would be porous, containing small pinholes, which would have to be grouted after partial grinding, and then followed by finish grinding.

This method of production offers some interesting possibilities, and at a later date techniques may be developed whereby the grouting stage could be eliminated. If so, very probably production costs could compete with the compression-molding process. Another possibility in this type of production could be the utilization of some of the newer methods of curing which are now being developed. Among these is radiation curing. A more simple curing method than the conventional oven would

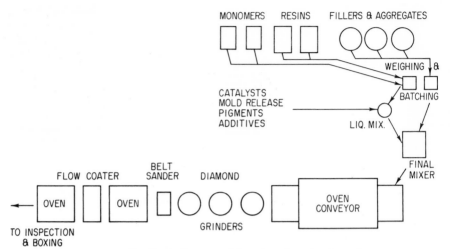

DIAGRAM 2. *Typical open-mold casting plant for floor tile.*

greatly enhance the possibility of this method competing successfully. Diagram 2 shows a typical equipment layout for this type of production.

Alternate Method 2

Pressure-casting, sometimes known as the autoclave method, would be another method of producing such tile and is well worth consideration.

A pressure chamber fitted with heating elements would be the major change in technique. This would be merely a section of pipe, about 24 in. in diameter, fitted with quick-opening pressure heads, of the hinged type. Heating elements, pressure-control safety devices, and a rail system for handling the large molds would be necessary.

The molds themselves would be long, metal cavities, divided vertically with divider panels at ¼-in. intervals. All sides would be entirely closed except the top, from which it would be filled. These molds would be 12 × 12 in. by perhaps 6 ft or more in length and could produce up to 300 or 400 blanks per casting if desired. The molds would be filled with the semiliquid compound, with intense vibration to eliminate as much entrapped air as possible. When filled, the molds would be rolled into the pressure chamber, and an air pressure of 90 to 100 psi would be applied, together with a temperature of 250 to 300°F.

Tile made by this method would not have to be grouted, as pressures in this range eliminate porosity and pinholes. The quality of this tile would be superior to that made by alternate method 1, and costs should be considerably lower. Production rates can be very high, limited only by the number of molds and the pressure-chamber space.

In production by this method, the only basic difference in formulation

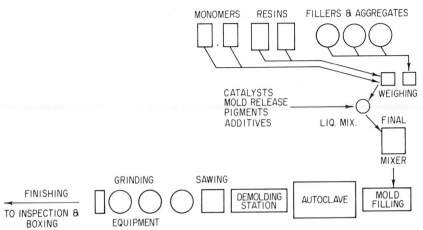

DIAGRAM 3. *Typical pressure-casting or autoclaving plant for floor tile.*

would be in the resin and catalyst system. Since polyesters in very large quantities in these molds result in very high exotherm temperatures, a resin and catalyst system will have to be selected that will give minimum top exotherm temperature in order to prevent internal stresses and possibly cracking. Such a system presents no unsurmountable problems, as resins can be designed that will give peak temperatures of 300°F or less. These are safe temperatures with which to work in this process. Catalysts and promoter systems can be selected which are an asset to the overall system.

Pressure-casting is undoubtedly the most promising of the alternate methods because it lends itself to mass-production schedules and volumes. The labor involved would be somewhat more than that in compression-molding processes, but the difference should be very minimal.

Linear dimensions of the tile would present some problems in order to maintain very close control, but once a final formulation has been selected, shrinkage would always remain the same. The molds would be sized to compensate for linear shrinkage.

Alternate Method 3

Another method of producing good-quality tile is by a variation of the process described in alternate method 1.

The same mold and conveyor system would be used and the heat-curing system would be unchanged. The basic difference would be in the formulation procedure. The liquid components would be mixed into only the finer dry fillers, giving a very liquid mix which can be poured, or which can flow directly into the open molds. A minimum of vibration would level this mix completely into every part of the mold.

The conveyor belt would now carry these partially filled molds on under an aggregate spreader, which would deposit the proper amount of the sized and blended aggregates into the mold. Due to the liquid state of the material already in the mold, only slight vibration would be necessary for the aggregates to settle down into the bottom of the mold before passing on into the oven for curing.

This method offers much to be considered by a tile manufacturer. It can have many slight variations in techniques. The proper equipment setup can produce a tile that will not be porous or have pinholes because of the sequence of adding the aggregates.

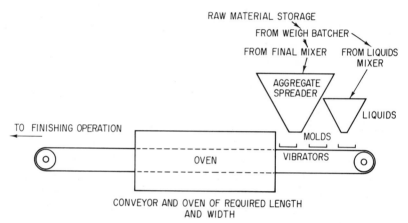

DIAGRAM 4. *Casting, aggregate-spreading. This equipment would usually be combined with that shown in Diagram 2.*

The amount of liquid to be placed into the molds can be varied so that the aggregates are not completely immersed in the resin-filler mix. The part of the marble chips extending outside the matrix can be ground, with very little waste-material cost since mostly marble chips will be removed in the grinding process.

Also, this method can allow the tile to contain marble chips that are somewhat larger than those produced by the other alternate methods without too much additional grinding costs. Chips could conceivably run to ⅜-in. sizes, giving a more pronounced pattern to the tile. Diagram 4 gives a typical equipment sequence for this type of process.

Besides the three alternate methods of producing a small-pattern terrazzo-type tile described above, there are other methods that a manufacturer may wish to consider. Competition and possibly patent situations may force the development of a number of processes.

Many manufacturers of injection-molding equipment are modifying their equipment to handle thermosetting-molding compounds. Some additional work may have to be done in order to handle these compounds, but it is entirely possible and feasible to do so. Injection-molding will possibly give the highest production rates of any process yet discusssd.

Mixes such as these compounds can be successfully transfer-molded. Again, present equipment will have to be modified to be able to accurately handle such materials.

Calendering is another possible method for the manufacture of this tile and should not be overlooked. Although a calendering line would be rather expensive to set up, the production rates could more than compensate for the added expenditures.

High-viscosity polyester filler could be calendered into a continuous sheet of proper thickness, cured, and then cut up into appropriate-sized tiles with automated diamond saws. The tiles would not necessarily have to be 12 × 12 in. They may be made 18 × 18 in. or even 24 × 24 in. The grinding of these larger sizes should not present any problems, as the grinding equipment discussed earlier can handle up to 72-in. material.

Another possible method that should be considered is extrusion. A screw-type extruder would probably not stand up well in use with such a highly filled compound as this, but a ram-type extruder should do the job very nicely.

A wide sheet of the compound could be extruded directly onto a continuous conveyor belt, passed through a curing oven, and then into the saws for cutting into tile. Here again, grinding would present no unsurmountable problems.

Should the sheeting of such a compound present a problem by either of these processes, a scrim could be added to hold the material in place until cured. Such a scrim would add very little to the overall cost of production. It would add strength to the tile, which could compensate for the added cost.

Marbelized Floor Tile

By any of the methods discussed thus far, a marbelized tile can be manufactured with the same equipment and the same dies, and the same sequence of process as that used to produce the terrazzo-type tile.

Marbelized tile has roughly the same properties as the terrazzo tile and has an appeal to perhaps an even greater segment of the market.

It is much cheaper to produce than the terrazzo-type tile, because no grinding is necessary. The tile can be removed from the dies or molds ready to box, or a manufacturer may decide to grind a few thousandths of an inch off one surface to enhance the appearance. This may be necessary in any open-mold process, and may be advantageous in any of the other processes.

A typical formulation for marbelized tile by one of these methods would be as follows:

1.	Flexible isophthalic polyester	8.00 lb
2.	Styrene	1.75
3.	Monochlorostyrene	1.75
4.	t-Butyl peroctoate	0.12
5.	Internal mold release	0.12
6.	Pigment	0.40
7.	No. 00 marble chips	50.00
8.	No. 000 marble chips	20.00
9.	40–200-mesh limestone filler	10.00
10.	China clay	6.00
11.	Barytes, No. 1 bleached	1.86
		100.00 lb

Mixing procedures for this compound would be exactly the same as for the terrazzo-type compound. Here again, many substitutions may be made as desired. Crushed quartz may be substituted for the No. 00 marble chips, and silica sand may be substituted for the No. 000 marble.

Using this mix will give a tile with even better wearing qualities, but it should not be used when the manufacturer contemplates grinding because of the difficulty of grinding these materials.

The marbelized veining or variegations are accomplished as follows: When the large batch is mixed and ready, one or more veining colors are added and only partially blended into the large batch.

A veining formulation would consist of the following materials:

1.	Flexible isophthalic resin	1.000 lb
2.	Monomer (styrene or other)	0.300
3.	Catalyst	0.015
4.	Internal mold release	0.015
5.	40–200-mesh limestone	6.000
6.	China clay	2.000
7.	Pigment	0.670
		10.000 lb

As many as two of these veining colors may be added to the large batch in order to get multicolor veining effects. Different amounts of these colors can be added to the mix to get the desired amount of veining, but a fine starting point will be 1 lb of the veining color per 100 lb of the master batch. This will give a surprising amount of veining.

In order to partially blend the small amount of veining color into the large batch, a good procedure is to streak the surface of the batch

PHOTO 3. *Marbelized floor tile.*

with about half of the veining color. Turn the mixer on, and let it revolve about five revolutions. Streak the remaining veining color onto the surface of the batch, and let the mixer turn another four or five revolutions.

This procedure will thoroughly streak the entire batch with the veining color or colors, and as the material is extruded into the proper charge sizes each charge will be found to contain a sufficient amount of the contrasting color to produce the desired effect.

A little experimentation and a little ingenuity with these procedures can produce effects that will be almost exactly like those occurring in natural marble. This tile can be installed on a floor and makes a most attractive synthetic marble surface.

Marbelized tile will have a much lower plant cost than terrazzo-type tile because of deletion of the grinding process. This tile is manufactured to actual finished thickness, so material costs are much lower. There is no waste material at all, unless the manufacturer wishes to grind off 0.002 in. or so to improve the overall appearance. The finished cost will be roughly one-third less than that given for the terrazzo-type tile.

Industrial Floor Tile

Any of the methods discussed above may be used also to manufacture heavy-duty floor tile for industrial floors.

This tile requires no grinding whatever; it is decorative as well as being able to withstand the punishment that might be given by fork-lift trucks and other heavy equipment traveling constantly over it. This tile requires no sealer of any kind simply because none of the fillers or other materials are porous.

This material would be highly suitable for use in such an environment as a meat-packing plant, where standards of sanitation demand a floor that is completely nonporous for ease in cleaning.

A typical formulation for this type of tile would be the following:

1.	Flexible isophthalic resin	7.0 lb
2.	Monomer (one or more)	2.5
3.	Catalyst	0.1
4.	Internal mold release	0.1
5.	Pigment	0.5
6.	Crushed quartz, No. 00	50.0
7.	Aluminum oxide or corrundum, 100 mesh	40.0
8.	Silica, 200 mesh	10.0
		110.2 lb

Other abrasion-resisting fillers and aggregates can also be used in this formulation. There are many available. The major concern, however, is to utilize materials which are as low in cost as possible. Such materials as tungsten carbide, boron carbide, and others of this type are more expensive. Aluminum oxide, corundum, or its man-made substitute, carborundum, and the silica and quartz components will give a material that is sufficiently wear resistant for almost any foreseeable environment.

This tile can be manufactured at any thickness, but 0.125 in. is a fairly acceptable thickness for such installations and will be sufficient for almost unlimited years of wear. Costs can vary, according to the fillers and aggregates used, but plant cost can be well under 22 cents per sq ft.

Conductive Floor Tile

Another type of floor covering that can be easily manufactured on the same basis as those already discussed is semiconductive floor tile. There is considerable demand for such tile for such environments as operating-room floors, and other areas where static electricity can present major hazards. Many laboratories, chemical plants, explosives plants, and refineries must install this type of floor covering in areas where a small spark caused by static electricity could cause a serious explosion.

The National Fire Prevention Association has published a guide for specifications for this type of installation. (Bulletin No. 56, published in 1956, goes into detail on such materials.) Every state has some regulations governing materials used in such localities, and many major cities implement these regulations with variations of their own. Most adhere fairly well to the specifications laid down by the National Fire Prevention Association bulletin, however.

This bulletin specifies that in order to meet standards set forth in Article 252 a floor shall have a path of moderate electrical conductivity between all persons and equipment making contact with the floor to prevent the accumulation of dangerous electrostatic charges. It states that no point on a nonconductive element in the surface of the floor shall be more than $\frac{1}{4}$ in. from a conductive element of the surface. Moreover, a floor must have a resistance of less than 1 million ohms as measured between two electrodes spaced 3 ft apart at any points on the floor. Also, the resistance of the floor must be more than 25,000 ohms as measured between a ground connection and an electrode 3 ft apart at any two points on the floor. This provides a rather wide range in specification, and a formulator will have no trouble finding fillers, pigments, and other ingredients to accomplish the desired purpose.

The polyester resin is a good nonconductor. In fact, polyester resins have extremely high dielectric strength and are used as insulating materials in many applications. Most of the fillers and aggregates mentioned in prior formulations for floor tile are also nonconductive. The resin cannot be changed into a conductor, so conductivity must be accomplished through the other materials.

All the metallic pigments are conductors to some degree. The iron oxides, chrome oxides, and other metallics are most useful in such a formulation. Carbon black is an excellent conductor. Aluminum oxides, titanium dioxides, zirconium dioxides, and many others will prove of value. Some of the larger aggregates also can be used. Aluminum oxide, carborundum, and a few of the others have some degree of conductivity. There are several sources of hard, crushed anthracite available which would be an asset to such a formulation. Acetylene black is perhaps the most conductive of readily available materials. Metallic lathe shavings can be used as aggregate, and some rather attractive patterns can be fashioned in this way.

It does not take as great an amount of conductive materials as one might suppose to accomplish the minimum standards set forth in the above specifications. Careful consideration of colors and patterns must be decided upon, and then materials must be selected that will meet or surpass the standards.

A great variety of colors and patterns are not necessary to meet the demands of the market. Flooring of this nature is only a small part of the market, but however small, it is worthwhile considering. To be able to offer a complete line of floor tile for every possible installation is a very good marketing aid for a manufacturer.

Medium-pattern Terrazzo-type Floor Tile

Since the terrazzo patterns discussed previously have been essentially small patterns, with chips of $\frac{1}{4}$ in. and possibly of $\frac{3}{8}$ in. under one method set forth, somewhat different methods and techniques must be used to obtain larger patterns.

Larger patterns are highly desirable in the market and are very expensive in manufactured terrazzo because of the amount of grinding necessary.

In discussing medium patterns of terrazzo-type tile, No. 2, No. 3, and No. 4 stones will be contemplated. These, of course, may be blended in any color combinations if desired.

A mix quite similar to that recommended for the small-pattern terrazzo-type tile would be used, only substituting larger aggregates.

Any of the methods already discussed in this chapter may be considered to produce the blanks. These blanks, because of the size of the stones involved, must be either $\frac{9}{16}$ in. or $\frac{5}{8}$ in. in thickness. Obviously, it would be far too great a cost to grind blanks of this thickness down to 0.125 in. or 0.140 in. If only about 0.100 in. were removed, too little of the pattern would be revealed, and the tile would have absolutely no flexibility whatever.

The cost of medium-pattern terrazzo tile would be very high because of the great amount of materials in a tile of this thickness. Freight rates for transporting this tile would be very high because of the heavier weight.

For the sake of time and space, let us consider the manufacture of this tile by the compression-molding method only.

Consider a plant setup like that shown in Diagram 1, and add a large diamond saw to the production line. If production warrants, add two or more such saws. A saw with a diameter of 32 to 34 in. is sufficient to cut 12×12 in. blanks, depending on the size of the mandrel and collars on the saw. Vacuum-cup holding devices can be made to hold the blank from both sides and to hold the two parts after the saw has cut through. Such an operation can be somewhat automated by building a conveyor belt to carry the blanks into the saw, with the blanks standing vertically to match the blade.

A diamond saw gives a surprisingly smooth cut, so when the two parts come out of the sawing operation, they will need very little grind-

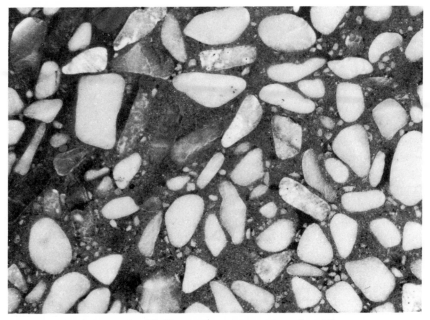

PHOTO 4. *Medium-pattern, terrazzo-type floor tile.*

ing. The thickness of the diamond blade can be such that the blank can be cut perfectly into two parts, leaving almost no grinding to do.

In this way, two tiles result from each blank, with even less waste material than when manufacturing small-pattern tile. Costs can be surprisingly low, even considering that extra labor is involved in the sawing operation. Plant cost, boxed ready to ship, will be in the vicinity of 27 cents per sq ft, depending very much on the amount of ingenuity and technique used in engineering the blank-handling facility.

Medium-pattern terrazzo tile may be manufactured also by the method for manufacturing large-pattern tile, described below, but costs would be somewhat higher because of a larger loss of materials during process.

Large-pattern Venetian-type Floor Tile

Beautiful terrazzo-pattern floor tile, sometimes referred to as "Venetian" tile, can be manufactured from polyester resins. These patterns can be made with stones of 6-in. size marble.

A plant to manufacture this tile may be set up as shown in Diagram 3. A pressure-casting process must be used; it is very likely that no other method will soon be devised where tile of this type can be manufactured at comparable costs. Diamond saws would be added to the production line.

The molds would consist of undivided metal boxes, $12 \times 12 \times 48$ in. or more in length. These dimensions would have to allow for shrinkage, probably around 0.040 in. in the 12-in. dimension.

The mold would be filled, vibrated, and placed in the autoclave at 200 to 300°F at pressures of around 100 psi. Upon curing, this large billet of material would be placed in the automatic carriage of the diamond saw, and would be slabbed up in tile almost to final dimension. A final 0.010 in. or so would be removed by grinding.

This type of tile will have a very wide market due to its unique beauty. In terrazzo, such tile sells for as much as $3.50 per sq ft laid in place. The plant cost of this tile can be as low as $0.45 per sq ft completely finished and boxed.

A formulation for this tile would be quite similar to that for small-pattern terrazzo-type tile, with the exception that very large stones would be used instead of small chips. The percentage of resin will decrease somewhat as the size of the stones increases, and of course the particular marble stones that are used will effect resin requirements. A softer, more porous stone will take slightly more resin than dense stone.

The choice of stone to be used in this formulation becomes of foremost importance. With so large a pattern exposed, the stone must have beautiful veining or variegations in order to be desirable. Such stone is available in Vermont and in Alabama and Georgia. Mexican marble is most

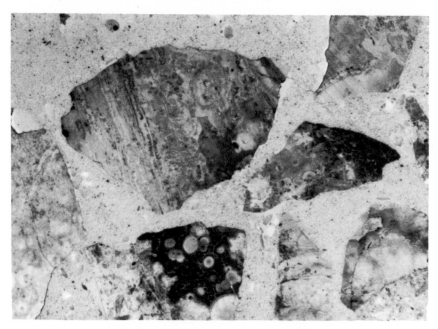

PHOTO 5. *Large-pattern terrazzo-type tile (Venetian).*

desirous for this use, and in particular the one referred to as onyx. This stone is not an onyx at all, but is really a calcium silicate; however, it is durable enough for this purpose, and its colors and veining are spectacular. Spanish, Portuguese, and Italian marbles are also very desirable for this tile.

Costs of these imported marbles are surprisingly low because stones of this sizing either are considered waste marble or must be crushed into smaller chips for use in terrazzo. Shipping costs are of primary concern. An Italian marble of this size can be imported for around $35.00 per ton, which makes it completely feasible to use it in tile of this nature. Actually, the additional cost of imported marble in these large sizes is compensated for by the lesser percentages of resin consumed in the formulation.

Tile with such large stones will have much less flexibility than tile made with the same resins and smaller stones.

Engineering Properties of Polyester Terrazzo-type Tile

Tests were made on six different samples, with six different formulations, all very similar to those given earlier for small-pattern terrazzo-type tile.

Property	ASTM Method Used	Data
Specific gravity	D792	1.68–1.76
Thermal conductivity	C177	0.12–0.15
Coefficient linear expansion	D697	0.00009
Refractive index	D542	1.42–1.66
Specific heat Btu/(lb)(hr)		0.46–0.52
Water absorption, 24 hr	D570 (sealed)	0.02–0.09
Modulus of elasticity	D638	3.1×10^5
Tensile strength × 1,000 psi	D638	3.1–3.6
Elongation, %	D638	2.1–3.4
Hardness, rockwell	D785	M65, 98–105
Impact strength	D256	2.2–3.5
Flexural modulus	D790	$2.5–2.9 \times 10^5$
Flexural strength × 1,000 psi	D790	3.3–3.6
Compressive strength × 1,000 psi	D695	28–33
Flammability	D635	Essentially nonburning
Dielectric strength, volts/mil	D149	440–490
Heat distortion, °F, 264 psi		220–240
K factor		0.66–0.80
Coefficient of friction	Wet level	0.23
(Rubber on unsealed tile)	Dry level	0.26
Taber abrasion, wt loss	D-1044-54	63–65

Chemical resistance will not be discussed extensively here. The polyester matrix of course will have excellent chemical resistance, but the exposed marble chips will have poor resistance to acids and will stain very badly unless a good chemical-resistant sealer coat is applied. The chemical resistance of the terrazzo-type tile as a whole is dependent on this sealer. (Formulations which are recommended for sealer coatings on this type of tile are given at the end of this chapter.) The marbelized type of tile and industrial tile will have excellent chemical resistance because of the types of fillers and aggregates used in them. No sealer coat of any kind would be necessary on these types of tile.

Properties such as flexural modulus may be changed drastically by using a more flexible or more rigid resin, or, as suggested earlier, by increasing or decreasing the resin percentage in the compound.

Tests on the coefficient of friction were run on unsealed tile. The sealer coat can change these figures greatly, so it is important to keep this in mind in choosing a sealer coat for such tile.

Such properties as flammability may be changed by adding such materials as diammonium phosphate and antimony trioxide to the formulation. Rather small percentages of these will make the tile completely nonburning.

The information given in Chap. 11 supplies the formulator with complete data for controlling the total properties of the end product through choice of the most advantageous ingredients going into the formulation.

A manufacturer who is contemplating the advantages, disadvantages, costs, and other factors involved in grinding and diamond-sawing operations will find the following comparisons helpful.

Costs: Diamond Sawing vs. Grinding. A formulation such as that given for the small-pattern terrazzo-type tile will be very close to $8.40 per cu ft. This cost will include all materials, labor, utilities, equipment write-off, etc. This gives a compound cost of $0.0007 per 0.001 in. in thickness of tile 12 × 12 in.

In calculating grinding and sawing costs, all labor, power, equipment write-off over a 5-yr period, etc., are figured. Grinding medium, diamond blades, etc., are included in costs.

Cost

1. For small-pattern tile, using No. 1 chips
   Manufacture blank ¼-in. thickness, 0.250 in.
   Grind to 0.140-in. thickness
   Material lost in grinding, 0.110 in............................ $0.0770
   Cost of grinding... 0.0495
   Material in tile, 0.140 in..................................... 0.0980
                                                                   ‾‾‾‾‾‾‾
                                                                  $0.2245

2. For a slightly larger pattern, using No. 2 chips
   Manufacture blank ⅜-in. thickness, 0.375 in.
   Grind to 0.140-in. thickness

Material lost in grinding, 0.235 in	$0.1645
Cost of grinding	0.1057
Material in tile, 0.140 in	0.0980
	$0.3682

3. For medium patterns, using Nos. 2, 3, and 4 chips
   Manufacture blank 9/16 in. thickness, 0.562 in.
   Saw down middle with diamond saw

Material lost in saw cut 0.250 in	$0.1750
Cost of saw cut	0.0800

   Grind each of two tiles 0.016 in., total 0.032 in.

Material lost in grinding, 0.032 in	0.0224
Cost of grinding	0.0144
Material in the two tiles 0.098 × 2 in	0.1960
Cost two tiles	$0.4878
Cost per tile	0.2439

4. For large-pattern tile, using stones up to 6 in.
   Pressure cast in billets 12 × 12 × 48 in. or longer
   Saw into slabs 0.156 in. thickness
   Grind to 0.140-in. thickness

Total material lost per tile 0.266 in	$0.1862
Cost of saw cut	0.0800
Cost of grinding 0.016 in. from each tile	0.0070
Material in each tile	0.0980
	$0.3712

These costs do not reflect the cost of rejects, inspection, and boxing; nor do they include the application of a sealer coat.

These will be very accurate processing costs on a high-production line and fairly well-automated equipment. There are many possibilities of reducing these costs. Perhaps newer grinding techniques can be developed. Possibly diamond-saw blades can be developed that are less than the 0.250 in. in thickness specified here. Some newer developments are being studied in such equipment as wire saws and blade saws which could be a tremendous boost to this type of manufacturing. Wire saws and blade saws are so much more adaptable to the "gang" type of cutting tool, where multiple heads work off the same equipment. Diamond saws are rather limited where the thickness of the cut slab is as low as contemplated here because of the space taken up between the blades by the collars.

A possibility of utilizing one saw, fitted with multiple diamond blades

$\frac{9}{16}$ in. apart, and yet another single-blade saw to saw these slabs into two tiles may very well be the answer.

Whatever equipment and techniques a manufacturer may devise, improvements may always be made. This is the difference between successful and unsuccessful business. Constant improvement means lower costs and keeps the manufacturer ahead of his competitors.

Many other types of floor-covering materials may be manufactured from polyester resins by a wide variety of processing methods and techniques. To date, very little has been done in research and development on this type of product. A few processes and products will be set forth here, about which there is already some knowledge available.

Nonground Polyester Terrazzo-type Tile

This tile would be a rather new concept in flooring materials. It would not need an adhesive for installation, but would be set into the freshly poured concrete slab of a building under construction. No flexibility would be required, so lower cost, rigid resins can be used.

This process would involve equipment such as shown in Diagram 2, without the grinding equipment, and the equipment shown in Diagram 4, with the exception that two aggregate spreaders would be used instead of one.

It would consist of a large quantity of open molds, mounted on a continuous conveyor belt. The molds would pass under the liquid components first, and a thin layer (about 0.030 in.) of polyester resin, catalyst, and mold-release mixture would be deposited into the molds. This is a clear resin. Now the molds pass under the large aggregate spreader, where No. 1 chips, or even a mixture of No. 1 and No. 2 chips, blended into proper color combinations, would be spread into the clear resin. Vibration would cause these chips to instantly settle to the bottom of the mold, displacing the resin. Now the molds continue under the filler-materials spreader. The filler materials would be preblended together with the desired dry powdered pigment. This blend would now be spread evenly into the molds in the proper amount, and the vibration would cause it to settle into the resin. As this material settled into the molds, its higher specific gravity and the vibration would thoroughly wet it out, displacing any air bubbles in so doing.

The result will be that roughly half of each marble chip would extend above the resin-filler combination. This is the back of the tile.

The conveyor continues through the oven, and the cured tile is removed at the opposite end. The back of the tile will be a very rough surface. The face of the tile will be a smooth, finished surface, very similar in appearance in every way to ground terrazzo. It is a finished tile, and does not need a sealer.

These tiles must be packaged face to face, as the rough back would most likely scratch the front surface. Also, a box of these tile is considerably heavier and thicker than the same number of ground tiles. Apart from this, there are no dissimilarities.

The tile is laid, as mentioned, at the same time a concrete slab is poured. The rough back with the exposed marble chips will give an

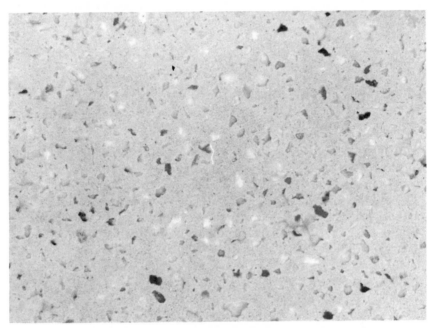

PHOTO 6. *Nonground terrazzo-type floor tile.*

excellent permanent bond to the concrete. Some labor is saved because the concrete needs only screeding and no throweling. Further labor and cost is saved because the labor and material involved with adhesives is eliminated.

This tile will give a most satisfactory floor since the polyester can be chosen to fit the needs of the environment and does not need to be flexible. All fillers and aggregates are completely enclosed in resin. Since no grinding is required, many kinds of fillers and aggregates may be used that could not be used in a ground tile.

Silicas, quartz, serpentine, chert, slate, orthoclase, and many other hard, abrasion-resistant stones and fillers may be employed. Many of these are available in beautiful colors.

When these kinds of stones are crushed, their cleavage is such that two or more sides are almost perfectly flat. The vibration will cause them to end up with one of these sides down.

This process has many advantages and disadvantages. A disadvantage would be higher resin content than ground tile. This tile will be approximately 20% resin by weight, so the cost will be reflected in the finished tile. Packaging this presents somewhat more of a problem than thin, flat tile, the pattern is not quite as pronounced as that in ground tile.

There are many advantages to this process. No grinding is necessary and no sealer coat is required. No adhesive is required for laying. Equipment requirements necessitate a minimum of capital investment for large-scale production.

Nonground terrazzo tile is a manufactured tile which is well worth looking into as a high-volume marketable product.

Calendered Tile, Using B-Staged Synthetic Chips

A polyester floor tile may be manufactured on a production line quite similar to that of many vinyl and vinyl-asbestos floor-covering manufacturers, as well as linoleum manufacturers.

Web calendering is probably the most widely used method of producing floor-covering materials today. While initial investment is quite large, the rates of production, and the low cost per sq ft make such an investment worthwhile. This process will produce a polyester tile with excellent properties and good flexibility at very low cost. The tile will be able to compete very well with vinyl-asbestos tile in price, yet will be much more durable and maintenance-free.

The basic production line would consist of an equipment setup similar to the one shown in Diagram 5. The scrim material can be made of a variety of materials; fiberglass, cotton, asbestos, and even some of the synthetic fibers make excellent scrim. The scrim would unwind, pass through a dip vat to pick up a quantity of matrix material, pass through two rollers of variable spacing to control thickness, and then onto a continuous conveyor belt of either silicone rubber or fluorocarbon.

The saturated scrim would pass first under the station where the B-staged chips are deposited on the surface, and then through the calender, which would imbed the chips to the desired depth into the matrix. The chips may be raised above the surface slightly to leave a textured finish, or they may be flush with the surface of the matrix for an overall smooth surface. This is accomplished by adjusting of the rolls in the calender.

The belt would continue into the oven, where the material would be cured. After emerging from the oven, the material would be cut up into squares of the desired size. The edges would be trimmed, and all waste material would be conveyored away. All cutting and trimming may be done completely automatically at the same speed of the conveyor belt.

The belt should be about 52 in. in width in order to manufacture a solid sheet of material slightly over 48 in. in width. This belt, traveling at 15 ft per min, would produce approximately 28,000 sq ft of tile per working shift. The 48-in. sheet may be cut up into 12 × 12 in., 24 × 24 in., or 48 × 48 in. pieces.

Production of the B-staged chips is the most critical part of such an operation. Actually, two separate production lines are required to

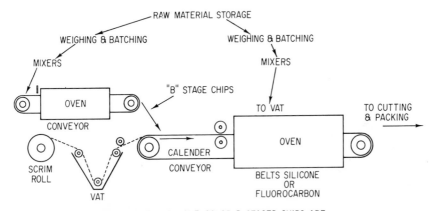

WHEN MORE THAN ONE COLOR B STAGED CHIPS ARE
NEEDED, ADDITIONAL CHIP LINES WILL HAVE TO BE INSTALLED.

DIAGRAM 5. *Calendered floor tile, using B-staged chips.*

produce chips in two separate colors in the quantities needed for this production schedule.

These two production lines are very similar to the main line, except that the belt of the conveyor would in fact be the molds which shape and size the chips. These belts must be custom made; a plant should have them made up in a number of sizes so that the marble patterns may be small, medium, and large. To make these belts, natural marble chips are positioned properly on the surface of a long smooth form. Side forms of an appropriate height should be installed, and a good-quality silicone-rubber compound poured over the stones and allowed to cure. After stripping from the form, this rubber belt can be installed on the conveyor system, and the ends bonded together with the same material to form a continuous belt. The indentations of the belt will match the shapes and sizes of natural marble chips.

A mixed formulation would be deposited on this belt. The excess is screeded off; this will leave each indentation filled. The belt will pass through an oven to B stage, or partially cure, the chips.

The end of the *B*-staging production line would be placed directly over the end of the main production line, so as the *B*-stage conveyor turns over the roller at its end, the chips fall directly into the waiting matrix below.

This system is mainly limited to two colors of chips; too much equipment would be required to produce more colors. The matrix, of course, can be any desired color, so with any two colors of chips a three-color material can be produced.

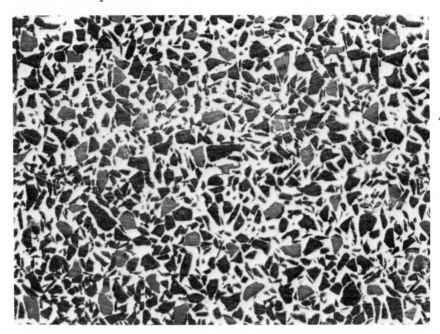

PHOTO 7.   *Calendered floor tile with B-staged chips.*

These *B*-staged chips will look so much like real marble chips that only close examination will be able to tell the difference. The mix used will be marbelized, so the chips will have veining like natural marble, and their shape will be that of natural marble. A good formulator will be able to match real marble colors quite closely.

A *B*-staging process such as this one is no different than any normal polyester mix. It will be a normal molding compound, with the exception that it will contain a dual catalyst system. One catalyst will *B*-stage the material in a moderate-temperature oven on the chip production line; the second catalyst will finish curing it on the higher-temperature oven on the main production line. (These catalysts will be discussed at length in Chap. 11.)

This production line will give a floor tile of excellent quality. Since there are no grinding operations necessary, very hard fillers may be used. Silicas, quartz, and such fillers are much more durable and chemical resistant than marble chips. This tile will actually outwear a tile using natural marble chips as a major ingredient, and of course maintenance of such a floor will be very minimal to keep it in top condition.

A formulation for the matrix would be as follows:

1. Flexible isophthalic polyester resin........................ 12.00 lb
2. Monomer (one or more)................................. 4.00
3. Silica, 100 mesh....................................... 50.00
4. Silica, 200 mesh....................................... 25.00
5. *T*-Butyl peroctoate..................................... 0.16
6. Internal mold release.................................. 0.16
7. China clay... 6.00
8. Pigment... 2.68
                                                        _____
                                                        100.00 lb

This mix will be a very viscous liquid that will pick up very well on the scrim as it passes through the tank. The rollers will take off any excess material and leave the impregnated scrim at the desired thickness as it goes onto the conveyor belt.

A typical mix for the *B*-staged chips would be the following:

1. Flexible isophthalic polyester resin..................... 8.00 lb
2. Monomer (one or more)................................. 2.50
3. Hydroheptyl peroxide.................................. 0.08
4. *T*-Butyl peroxide...................................... 0.08
5. Dimethyl analine (add after or before catalysts)............ 0.01
6. Lauroyl mercaptan (add with dimethyl analine)............ 0.25
7. Internal mold release.................................. 0.10
8. Silica, 100 mesh....................................... 50.00
9. Silica, 200 mesh....................................... 25.00
10. Barytes, No. 1 bleached............................... 10.00
11. China clay... 2.00
12. Pigment... 1.98
                                                        _____
                                                        100.00 lb

A marbelizing mix may be added at the moment this mix is ready. The marbelizing formulation would be the same as that given before for compression-molded marbelized tile.

The oven temperature for *B*-staging this mix would be held between 185 and 195°F. The cycle time will be almost exactly ½ min, so the *B*-staging conveyor can be very short. The oven temperature on the main production line would be held at 300°F, so the cure cycle will coincide exactly with the B-staging cycle.

Mixers for both the matrix and the chips should be of the continuous type, so production will be smooth and uninterrupted.

This type of process can be highly automated, with very little labor involved. The tile can be manufactured at almost any thickness for meeting competition. It will be an excellent quality tile at any thickness, from 0.070 in. on up to 0.125 in.

The production line may be changed from one thickness to another with very little down time. Only the belts on the B-staging line would have to be changed, and the rollers on the matrix adjusted, and the calender adjusted. The same applies to changing from a textured to a smooth tile—only the calender would have to be adjusted. To switch from small pattern to either medium or large pattern, only the belts on the B-stage line would have to be changed.

The basic production line is very versatile, and although the investment is quite large, profits can compensate the investor.

Materials Cost for Production of Calendered Tile with B-staged Chips:

Belt, 48-in. width, speed, 15 ft per min; production, 60 sq ft per min. Possible production, 28,000 sq ft per shift; probable production, about 25,000 sq ft.

Matrix at $0.095 per lb

Tile at 0.100 in. thickness	Cost (sq ft)	Cost (sq ft)	Tile at 0.0625 in.
5 oz per tile	$0.0295	$0.0236	4 oz per tile
19 lb per min			15 lb per min
9,020 lb per shift			7,200 lb per shift

Scrim, at $0.018 per sq ft

1 oz per sq ft	$0.018 sq ft	1 oz per sq ft

B-staged chips, at $0.057 per lb

13 oz per sq ft	$0.0455	$0.024	7 oz per sq ft
49 lb per min			27 lb per min
23,420 lb per shift			13,000 lb per shift

Tile at 0.100 in. thickness would have a material cost of $0.0930 per sq ft.
Tile at 0.0625-in. thickness would have a material cost of $0.0656 per sq ft.

A process such as the one given above will have very low labor costs. Equipment depreciation will be considerable, but due to the volume involved, this should be very low per tile. Power requirements are high, but again very little per sq ft.

Plant equipment for such a production line would cost at least $500,000. Buildings, installations, and raw-materials storage can add roughly this much more.

Several other floor-covering materials may be manufactured by calendering. Most of these would be rolled goods, similar to linoleum, but of much higher quality. If desired, these materials may be cut up into squares as tile.

Rolled, Linoleum Types of Floor Coverings

This process would entail an equipment arrangement quite like the major production line shown in Diagram 5. A suitable membrane material would be selected, which could be a fiberglass surface-matting, sometimes called veil mat, or a closely woven cloth, such as rayon, cotton, or other fiber.

The design is printed onto the membrane by the silk-screen or cylinder processes, using a printing ink that will not "run" during further processing.

The design can be almost any acceptable pattern, including terrazzo, marble, brick, wood grains, parkett, or possibly even designs unknown in today's flooring market. Any design can be economically printed on a suitable membrane with the technology of today's printing industry. Designs can be in multicolors and can be exactly like the real product.

The roll of membrane would unwind, pass through the dip tank, where it would pick up a suitable quantity of clear resin, and then onto the smooth-surfaced silicone rubber or fluorocarbon conveyor belt. It would pass through a short oven to gel, and upon emerging from this stage would have a coating of suitable thickness flow-coated on the upper surface. Then it would pass through a calender to adjust final thickness and through a second short oven for curing. The final stage would consist of trimming the edges, and it would be ready to roll.

At the time of this writing there are no polyesters on the market that would be suitable for such an end product. There has been no need for such a resin as yet, so no resin manufacturer has developed one.

Raw materials are readily available, and intermediates are on the market which are suitable for the manufacture of such a resin. A demand for a resin such as this will present no problems to a major resin manufacturer. (In Chap. 11 will be found suitable starting formulations for a resin of this type, together with suggested raw materials and intermediates.)

It will be doubtful if anyone can formulate a polyester resin with abrasion resistance equal to that of a polyurethane, but it is possible that in the future someone will develop a polyester with some as yet unknown intermediates with superior properties in this respect.

Many variations of the process described here may be used, and many techniques can be developed as production is in progress. Many different effects may be obtained, such as depth, or three-dimensional effects in a pattern.

Since floor-covering materials constitute a very large percentage of the cost of any construction, this is the field where polyesters must make major progress. It is a very wide field, and architects, builders, and owners are not at all happy with the selection from which they must choose today.

The biggest single objection to today's floor-covering materials is that they require entirely too much maintenance. In this regard, the polyester resins can gain a major portion of the flooring market. The products which have been described here require a very minimum of maintenance, and the wear and tear of normal use will not deteriorate these materials for many, many years.

Adhesives

Tiles such as those discussed require special adhesives. These adhesives may be plant-applied or applied to the substrate in the field. Adhesives must be applied in a ribbed form by notched trowel in the field, or by a special extruder head in the plant.

Plant-applied adhesives are perhaps the most economical because much labor and time is saved in the field. Workmen merely wet the adhesive with a proper solvent, and lay the tile.

Actually, two separate adhesive systems should be considered. A much lower cost adhesive may be used above grade, while below and at grade a very good quality adhesive must be used. Moisture and hydrostatic pressures will lift a tile if a very good quality is not used. This has always been a major problem with vinyl and vinyl-asbestos tile and yard goods.

A good starting formulation for field-applied adhesives above grade is as follows:

1. Emulsion: natural rubber, polyvinyl acetate, SBR rubber, neoprene, or polyisobutylene rubber........................... 30.0 lb
2. Emulsion: refined wood rosin................................ 30.0
3. Chlorinated biphenyl or polyphenyl......................... 15.0
4. Asbestos shorts.. 25.0
                                                 100.0 lb

The above weights are based on solids. Water is the required diluent. Water also serves to clean tools and excess adhesive off the surfaces of the tile.

A starting formulation for field-applied adhesive for use at and below grade is the following:

1. High-viscosity, chlorinated rubber, or chlorinated polypropylene 40.0 lb
2. Refined wood rosin.. 20.0
3. Chlorinated biphenyl or polyphenyl........................ 10.0
4. Asbestos shorts... 15.0
5. Silica, 325 mesh... 15.0

                                                            100.0 lb

The above is based on solids, and a solvent will be necessary. Many solvents may be used; toluol, xylol, some hexane, ketones, and chlorinated solvents are all adequate. If a fire hazard from solvents is a consideration, then by all means choose from the chlorinated solvents.

Both of the adhesives described above are one-component adhesives and are easy to apply by notched trowel. Two-component adhesives, such as the epoxies, are excellent, but they present too many problems in the field. Workmen are likely to misjudge the proper amount of mixing or the proper proportion of ingredients. The two-component adhesives have a limited pot life, whereas these one-component adhesives do not have this limitation.

To the above formulations must be added such materials as stabilizers, viscosity-control additives, and if desired, pigments.

Emulsion-based adhesives are unlikely to give good service at or below grade. Some manufacturers of adhesives are working toward this end, but to this writer's knowledge, tests under hydrostatic pressures for long periods of time have been rather disappointing as yet.

For adhesives to be applied to the back of the tile in the plant, a hot-melt adhesive should be considered. It will be advantageous because of the cost of solvents, and because of fire hazards involved.

The equipment would be a hot-melt extruder, with ribbed head, or possibly a simple hot-melt pot; the material is flow-coated in ribs on the back of the tile.

A starting formulation for such an adhesive would be as follows:

1. Amorphous polypropylene................................. 30.0 lb
2. Polyisobutylene rubber, medium viscosity.................. 30.0
3. Polybutene, high viscosity............................... 15.0
4. Chlorinated polyphenyl................................... 5.0
5. Refined wood rosin....................................... 5.0
6. Asbestos shorts.. 15.0

                                                            100.0 lb

Of course, pigments may be added if desired—also, some curing agents, flow-control additives, and antioxidants, etc.

An adhesive such as this may be applied at the plant site in the production line, just before the boxing sequence. This material will be dry as soon as it reaches room temperature.

In the field, workmen would merely wet the adhesive surface with a suitable solvent, such as hexane, and lay the tile in place. The speed of evaporation of the solvent may be adjusted to suit the laying speed and solvency of the adhesive so that a very tacky surface will result at the moment of laying. This is of utmost importance so that the tile will remain in place, regardless of the irregularity of the substrate.

Applicators of such tile differ as to the preferred thickness of the ribbing of the adhesive. Cost of the adhesive must be considered, and optimum bond to the substrate also must be obtained. The fact that no substrate is perfect must be a consideration. A good starting point for the ribbing would be about 0.040 to 0.050 in. Test rooms can be laid at these thicknesses, and results may indicate slightly more or less than these amounts.

Many variations of the above adhesives may be considered. There are multiple materials from which to formulate such adhesives. Cost and bond are the two prime factors to be considered. Ease of application is also of importance, but slightly secondary. A list of manufacturers of these materials may be found in the Appendix.

Accelerated testing of adhesives is recommended before any actual installations are considered. A very good method of testing these materials is with a series of 12×12 in. concrete blocks, 2 in. or more in thickness. A hose connection is bonded in place at one end of each block with a good, two-component epoxy. The tile is applied to one side of the block with the adhesive to be tested. The other five sides of the block are thoroughly sealed with the epoxy and allowed to stand for 48 hr. The hose connection is hooked up to a water-filled pressure vessel, to which some 5 to 10 psi air pressure is applied.

A 21-day test is recommended for the adhesives which are to be used at or below grade. A 7-day test is sufficient for any adhesive to be used above grade. If the tile has not lifted in this length of time, the adhesive should be considered adequate.

For use in northern regions, and for exterior environments in particular, freeze-thaw tests should be run on the adhesives. An ordinary home deepfreeze is adequate for this use. The adhesives above which give good results on the hydrostatic tests may be used as they are on the concrete blocks. After the hydrostatic tests are finished, the blocks will be thoroughly saturated with water. These blocks should be placed in the deepfreeze for 24 hr, thawed for 12 hr, and replaced for 12 hr

CHART 1. ADHESIVES FOR POLYESTER FLOOR TILE

L—low   X—not recommended
M—medium   O—not known
H—high
P—poor
F—fair
G—good
E—excellent

Adhesive	Cost	Ease of application	Tack	Water resistance	Solvent resistance	Alkali resistance	Acid resistance	Oxidation resistance	Low-temp. flexibility	High-temp. properties	Flammability	Tensile strength	Concrete	Wood	Existing terrazzo	Existing vinyl tile	Existing vinyl-asbestos	Existing linoleum	Existing asphalt tile	Existing rubber tile	Above grade	At and below grade
Solvent-based:																						
Chlorinated rubber	H	G	E	E	P	F	E	F	G	G	L	M	G	G	G	F	G	O	O	F	G	G
Chlorinated polypropylene	H	G	E	E	P	E	E	G	G	O	L	M	G	G	G	F	G	O	O	F	G	G
Polystyrene	M	F	G	E	G	G	G	G	P	P	H	M	G	G	G	P	F	O	X	X	F	F
Amorphous polypropylene	L	G	G	F	P	P	F	P	F	P	M	L	F	F	F	F	F	F	F	X	F	P
Butyl rubber	M	G	G	G	P	G	G	G	F	F	M	M	F	F	F	X	F	F	X	X	F	P
Neoprene rubber	M	G	G	F	F	G	G	F	F	F	M	M	F	F	F	X	F	F	X	X	F	P
NBR rubber	M	G	G	F	F	G	G	G	F	F	H	M	F	F	F	X	F	F	X	X	F	P
SBR rubber	L	G	G	G	P	G	G	G	F	F	M	M	O	F	O	X	F	F	X	X	F	F
Reclaimed rubber	M	G	F	F	P	F	F	F	P	P	H	M	F	F	F	X	F	F	X	X	O	F
Polyisobutylene	L	F	G	P	P	G	G	G	O	F	H	L	G	G	G	F	F	F	X	X	F	X
Asphalt-based	L	G	F	P	P	F	G	G	P	P	M	L	G	G	G	X	F	F	G	X	O	O
Coal tar-based	M	G	F	P	P	G	G	G	P	P	M	M	G	G	G	X	F	F	G	X	F	P
Polyvinyl chloride	M	G	F	P	P	G	G	F	F	F	M	M	F	F	F	F	F	F	X	X	F	P
Polyvinyl acetate	M	G	F	P	P	G	G	F	F	F	M	M	F	F	F	F	F	F	X	X	F	X
Emulsion adhesives:																						
SBR rubber	M	E	G	F	F	G	G	G	F	F	M	M	G	G	G	X	G	G	X	X	G	P
NBR rubber	M	E	G	P	F	G	G	G	F	F	M	M	G	G	G	X	G	G	X	X	G	P
Neoprene rubber	M	E	G	P	F	G	G	F	F	F	M	M	F	F	F	X	F	F	X	X	F	X
Acrylic elastomer	H	E	G	F	G	F	F	G	F	F	L	M	F	F	F	X	F	F	X	F	F	X
Chlorinated rubber	M	E	E	G	P	F	E	F	G	G	M	M	G	G	G	F	G	G	F	F	E	G
Polyisobutylene	M	E	G	G	P	G	G	G	G	F	M	M	G	G	G	X	G	G	F	X	O	G
Polyvinyl acetate	M	E	F	P	F	G	G	F	F	F	M	M	F	F	F	F	F	F	X	F	F	X
Hot melt, plant applied:																						
Polyamide	H	F	F	G	E	G	F	F	P	F	M	M	G	G	G	F	G	G	X	F	G	F
Amorphous polypropylene/ Polyisobutylene/polybutene	M	G	G	G	P	F	G	G	G	P	M	M	G	G	G	F	G	G	X	X	G	G

41

in the water-pressure test. This cycle should be repeated at least six times. If in this time an adhesive is still holding the tile firmly in place, it should be an adequate adhesive for almost any substrate.

Rigid adhesives should never be considered for tile of this type. Normal expansion and contraction of a substrate will cause them to fail in time. Since the tile will have a coefficient very close to that of the substrate, an adhesive will only have to be pliable enough to withstand whatever stresses are involved, plus at least a 100% additional safety factor. This is no problem with such adhesives as suggested here.

The quality of the adhesive is equally as important as the quality of the tile iteslf. This must not be overlooked.

Sealers and Wear Coatings

As a sealer coat is required for some of the tile discussed in this chapter, it becomes also a vital part of any floor-tile manufacture to be contemplated.

There are many ways to approach this phase of the process. The approach that is most appealing is to apply merely a very thin sealer coat which will adequately close the pores of the marble chips and make the floor suitable for normal waxing. This can be accomplished easily at very low cost by flow-coating 1 to 2 mils of an acrylic lacquer, or a cellulose-acetate-butyrate lacquer.

The above method solves the sealing problem adequately and gives a tile with a very nice appearance. It leaves a lot to be desired, however. The wear resistance of these materials is very low, and chemical and stain resistance leave much to be desired.

In order for the manufacturer of a polyester tile to turn out a top-quality product, the top coating should be more than merely a sealer. It should be a tough, wear-resistant material that will not need waxing or polishing to maintain its finish. It should have good chemical and stain resistance. If possible, it should be able to withstand scorching from cigarettes and matches. This is a lot to expect from a single-coating material, and such a material is not easily formulated. All known coating materials fail in one or more of the required properties.

A good starting formulation for a sealer coating would be as follows:

1. Polyacrylate, 40% solids in MEK........................... 40.0 lb
2. ½-sec butyrate, 25% solids in acetone...................... 30.0
3. Tricresyl phosphate.. 5.0
4. Chlorinated polyphenyl.................................... 5.0
5. Solvent: ketones, toluol, or chlorinated.................. 20.0
                                                            _____
                                                            100.0 lb

CHART 2. COATINGS FOR POLYESTER FLOOR TILE

Legend: L–low M–medium H–high P–poor F–fair G–good E–excellent X–not recommended O–not known

Sealer coats

Coating	Cost	Curing speed	Color, gardner	Ultraviolet resistance	Infrared resistance	Oxidation resistance	Abrasion resistance	Flexibility	Bond to tile	Water-spot resistance	Acid resistance	Alkali resistance	Alcohol resistance	Alip. solvent resist.	Arom. solvent resist.	Iodine resistance	Liq. shoe polish resist.	Blood resistance	Heat resistance	Cigarette-burn resist.	Coef. of friction	How it takes:	Liquid floor waxes	Paste floor waxes
Urethane, moisture cure	M	F	2	F	F	G	E	E	G	G	G	G	G	M	F	F	F	G	P	P	M		F	G
Urethane, blocked	M	F	3	F	F	G	E	E	G	G	G	G	G	M	F	F	F	G	P	P	M		F	G
Urethane, 2 component	M	F	2	F	F	G	E	E	G	G	G	G	G	M	F	F	F	G	P	P	M		F	G
Oxirane polyester	M	P	1	G	G	G	F	F	F	G	E	G	G	M	G	F	G	G	F	F	L		G	G
Melamine	H	P	—	G	G	G	G	P	G	G	F	F	G	M	F	F	G	G	G	F	L		G	G
Polyamide, solvent solution	M	G	5	P	P	E	G	G	F	G	G	F	P	M	F	G	P	G	F	F	M		P	F
Acrylic/butyrate	H	G	1	E	E	F	P	F	G	F	F	F	P	M	P	F	F	P	P	P	M		G	G
Chlorinated polypropylene	H	G	1	G	G	E	G	G	G	F	F	F	F	M	F	P	P	P	F	G	M		F	G
Diallyl phthalate, sol.	H	F	1	E	E	F	G	F	G	G	F	F	F	M	F	G	F	G	G	G	M		G	G
Polycarbonate, solution	H	E	1	E	E	F	F	F	G	E	E	E	E	M	E	G	E	G	G	G	M		G	G

For wear coat

Coating	Cost	Curing speed	Color, gardner	Ultraviolet resistance	Infrared resistance	Oxidation resistance	Abrasion resistance	Flexibility	Bond to tile	Water-spot resistance	Acid resistance	Alkali resistance	Alcohol resistance	Alip. solvent resist.	Arom. solvent resist.	Iodine resistance	Liq. shoe polish resist.	Blood resistance	Heat resistance	Cigarette-burn resist.	Coef. of friction	How it takes:	Liquid floor waxes	Paste floor waxes
Urethane, moisture cure	M	F	2	F	F	G	E	E	G	G	G	G	G	M	F	F	F	G	P	P	M	NOT TO BE WAXED		
Urethane, blocked	M	F	3	F	F	G	E	E	G	G	G	G	G	M	F	F	F	G	P	P	M			
Urethane, 2 component	M	F	2	F	F	G	E	E	G	G	G	G	G	M	F	F	F	G	P	P	M			
Oxirane polyester	M	P	1	G	G	G	F	F	F	G	E	G	G	M	G	F	G	G	F	F	L			
Melamine	H	P	—	G	G	G	G	P	G	G	F	F	G	M	F	F	G	G	G	F	L			
Polyamide, solution	M	G	5	P	P	E	G	G	F	G	G	F	P	M	F	G	P	G	F	F	M			
Acrylic/butyrate	H	G	1	E	E	F	P	F	G	F	F	F	P	M	P	F	F	P	P	P	M			
Chlorinated polypropylene	H	G	1	G	G	E	G	G	G	F	F	F	F	M	F	P	P	P	F	G	M			
Diallyl phthalate, sol.	H	F	1	E	E	F	G	F	G	G	F	F	F	M	F	G	F	G	G	G	M			
Polycarbonate, solution	H	E	1	E	E	F	F	F	G	E	E	E	E	M	E	G	E	G	G	G	M			

43

A starting formulation for a combination sealer-wear coat would consist of the following:

1. Polycarbonate, ground powdered polymer.................... 30.0 lb
2. Methylene chloride....................................... 45.0
3. Perchloroethylene.. 20.0
4. Chlorinated biphenyl..................................... 5.0

    100.0 lb

Another starting formulation for a sealer-wear coat would be the following:

1. Diallyl phthalate polymer, 50% in MEK.................... 75.0
2. Diallyl phthalate monomer............................... 5.0
3. Triallyl chlorendate monomer............................ 5.0
4. Chlorinated biphenyl.................................... 5.0
5. Benzoyl peroxide.. 1.0
6. Solvent: toluol, ketone, or chlorinated................. 9.0

    100.0 lb

These coatings may be applied by multiple spray-gun setups, but flow-coating lends itself better to automated production in most cases.

Chart 2 gives comparisons of properties of such coatings, and the manufacturer may choose which might best fit his needs.

Three

FLOORING MATERIALS MANUFACTURED IN PLACE

Many types of beautiful, long-wearing flooring materials may be formulated, mixed, applied, and finished at the job site. Polyester resin is
most adaptable to this type of work. Any personnel accustomed to working with terrazzo flooring will be adept at this work since the same
procedures are followed to a large extent.

These floors may be laid over existing concrete, wood, and many
types of existing flooring materials. Over unfinished floors no pretreat-
ments of any kind will be necessary, but over some types of existing
floor-covering materials, special cleaning methods and primers may have
to be used. Test-patching a small 12 × 12 in. part of such a floor is
an accepted method of determining bond.

The flooring described herein may even be laid over old ceramic
tile, with proper cleaning, preparation, and a specially formulated primer.

New concrete and wood floors present no problem whatever. On old
substrates, or over existing floor-covering materials, wax is perhaps the
most prevalent problem. Wax must be thoroughly cleaned off, using

solvents, ammonia solutions, and quantities of rinsing water. All surfaces must be allowed to dry.

Existing cracks of any appreciable size in a floor must be patched, and with wood floors all boards must be firmly nailed down. For patching cracks, glass fiber in narrow rolls is available. The 2-in. width is usually sufficient for this work. It may be random mat, or woven cloth but it should be light in weight and the thickness should be minimal.

The polyester resin suitable for this type of work is usually a resilient orthophthalic resin. An isophthalic resin is also quite suited to this work and will give a better bond to many types of substrates than the orthophthalic. For these uses, the resin should be purchased with the proper monomers and with suitable promoters already added. A number of resin manufacturers have resins for this purpose as a standard product. Most of these resins have a dual monomer system, approximately two-thirds styrene and one-third methyl methacrylate. This enables the resin to be used on the exterior as well as on the interior. The inhibitor should be hydroquinone. The promoter, sometimes referred to as the accelerator, can be either dimethyl analine or diethyl analine, for use with a benzoyl peroxide catalyst, or it may be cobalt napthenate or cobalt octoate, for use with methyl ethyl ketone peroxide catalyst. Many prefer a dual promoter system made up of both dimethyl analine and cobalt octoate, so either of the two catalysts may be used in the field.

Many variations of the promoter and catalyst systems are available to give good room-temperature cures in this type of work. The catalyst manufacturers (listed in the Appendix) have many excellent new developments for this type of work. Gel and cure time can be adjusted to the needs of the formulator, and work can progress at any temperature from 20°F to temperatures of the hottest summer weather.

There are many facets to formulating the very best finished product. The data available in Chap. 11 will supply the formulator with all the necessary information regarding the choice of proper resins, promoters, catalysts, fillers, pigments, aggregates, and additives to obtain a top-quality end product for any given environment.

Terrazzo-type Flooring

This is perhaps the most popular flooring material that can be formulated, applied, and finished at the job site. When finished, it looks almost exactly like terrazzo, yet is much more durable and maintenance-free.

The procedure for applying terrazzo-type flooring is quite similar to the process for terrazzo. For the sake of space, application over a new concrete substrate will be discussed. Details of variations in procedure over other types of substrates are given at the end of the chapter.

A new concrete floor should be at least 21 days old before any work is begun. It is imperative to determine that no oil or wax-type curing agents were used on the concrete by the builder. This is not likely today, as most building specifications clearly eliminate this type of curing agent on any concrete that is to be covered with flooring materials.

The concrete must be dry and swept clean of all loose dirt; any paint dropped on the floor must be cleaned off either with solvents or by a small hand grinding wheel.

Among technical people there is some disagreement about the next step. There are those who insist that a light acid wash is required to neutralize the alkalinity of the surface. This writer is not among this group for a number of reasons. First, this step adds considerable expense and a delay in work of several days because, after the neutralizing wash, the floor must be rinsed and allowed to dry thoroughly. Secondly, when the floor is neutralized, the surface of the concrete is somewhat weakened in the bond between the cement and aggregates; this could cause a failure of the flooring material through no fault of the polyester material itself.

If a concrete slab has been steel-troweled to an extremely dense surface (which is unlikely because the builder is aware that this is undesirable), or if an excess of cement was used on the surface, leaving a thin "glaze," then an appropriate step would be to run a coarse wire brush over the surface with a power grinder to roughen up the surface slightly.

The next step in the process is to apply a primer coat. Here again, the technical people disagree. Those against using a primer will argue that it is a waste of time and material. They say, and rightly so, that the formulation will have enough excess resin to gain sufficient penetration and bond into the concrete.

This writer will offer two reasons for using the prime coat, which accomplish two completely different purposes. First, a primer helps minimize pinholing. Small air or gas bubbles, referred to as pinholes, are one of the difficulties encountered in this type of work. Air will be trapped in the mix as it is formulated. Some of this will come out as the mix is spread and cured, and some will not. Some of the pinholes are caused by moisture in the fillers and aggregates, creating a slight reaction between the alkaline fillers and the acidity of the resins and catalysts. Not all the pinholes can be attributed to these causes, however, as a very large percentage of these bubbles will work their way out of the poured mix before gel occurs.

If the mix is poured out onto an unprimed floor, some of the resin must work itself, by gravity alone, into the concrete pores. As this resin displaces the air in these pores, the air works its way upward through the mix. This air, coming from underneath the polyester mix, does not have time to work its way out of the mix before gel occurs. The result is a host of tiny air bubbles just under the surface of the cured material, which are exposed when the grinding and finishing operations begin.

A coat of primer resin eliminates this part of the pinholing problem. A coating some 2 to 3 mils in thickness is sufficient. This should consist of a resin-catalyst mix, with no fillers. Because of the low viscosity, this mix would get much better penetration and bond to the substrate than would a very viscous topping mix. By the time the topping operation begins, the resin will have reached its maximum penetration and in so doing will have displaced all the air bubbles.

The second, and even more important reason for using a primer is slightly more complex: Shrinkage during the cure of such a material is a major problem. The larger the area to which it is applied, the greater the problem. A formulation such as the one set forth herein for this use will have a linear shrinkage of approximately 0.15 to 0.2%. At 0.2% this means a shrinkage of 0.024 in. per linear ft, or 0.240 in. in 10 ft. This being about ¼ in., so in a room with 20-ft dimensions, the shrinkage would be a total of roughly ½ in. Shrinkage may not seem to be a problem to the unexperienced, but it really is. During the curing of the material, very high stresses are set up by this shrinkage, which can cause the topping to crack and lift. This occurs in monolithic flooring, which does not have the benefit of dividers or contrast strips. Many owners and architects prefer the monolithic, seamless type of finished floors. Others prefer that the flooring be divided into 3- or 4-ft squares between aluminum, brass, or even plastic divider strips. In the latter flooring, shrinkage presents few problems.

With large monolithic applications, the primer coat is the answer to the shrinkage problem. The primer is formulated for a very slow cure, so the topping actually cures before the primer. In this way, almost all the stresses are eliminated because the ¼-in. topping can actually move the small amount necessary when shrinking without undue stress.

The primer resin preferably should be a very flexible isophthalic resin, of the type referred to as "putty" resins, which are used sometimes as automobile-body-patching and caulking compounds. This resin should be promoted with roughly half the normal amount of accelerator. The amount of catalyst must never be reduced, as incomplete cure will result. The reduction of promoter will merely delay the cure. This type of polyester resin will give excellent bond and penetration into the substrate.

The primer coat may be applied by brush, trowel, spray gun, roller, or squeegee. On large areas, two-component spray equipment is by far the most economical. This equipment is available in either conventional or airless models from a number of suppliers (see the Appendix).

With two-component spray equipment, one pot holds a mix of resin and promoter, and the second pot holds a mix of resin and catalyst. The two components are mixed in the gun chamber just before the mix goes onto the substrate. Such mixes can be formulated to last for days, with no cleaning of equipment necessary and no lost material due to overmixing quantities. The equipment soon pays for itself in the material saved alone.

When the resin has been applied in the proper thicknesses, most of it will penetrate into the concrete. Workmen who apply the topping may prefer to wear spiked shoes to avoid walking in the primer. Spikes such as those used on golf shoes are ideal, as they have large, rounded points and are not too uncomfortable.

The topping operation may begin immediately after the primer has been applied, with a waiting period of no more than 10 min. In this time the resin will have penetrated to its maximum depth and displaced the air present. If the application is to be a monolithic floor, no further preparations are necessary. If divider or contrast strips are to be used, these must be laid before the primer is applied.

Divider strips must be bonded firmly in place before the topping procedure so as not to be moved from position. The best method is to lay these a day ahead of the primer and topping. The substrate should be measured and marked off in squares of the desired size. All marking must be done with either ink-type markers, colored chalk, or graphite pencils. Wax-type crayons must never be used.

The edges of the metal strips that are to go next to the concrete should be roughed up with coarse sandpaper. The strips may be $\frac{1}{4} \times \frac{1}{4}$ in. or $\frac{1}{4} \times \frac{3}{8}$ in. or more, but the $\frac{1}{4}$-in. dimension must always be the thickness of the poured topping. In this way, the strips serve as forms to which the material is easily screeded.

Adhesive is applied to the roughed-up side of the strips, and they are placed according to the marked-off floor. A good adhesive formulation for the strips would be the following:

1. Liquid, unmodified epoxy, 175–200 epoxide eq.................. 1.0 lb
2. Polyamide, 290–320 amine value.......................... 0.5
3. Thixatroping agent (such as silica aerogel)..................... 0.1
                                                          ⎯⎯⎯
                                                          1.6 lb

A small amount of adhesive will coat one side of a lot of divider strips. This formulation must be used within 2 hr after mixing at an ambient temperature of 75°F, so in a small area one-half of the above amount or less may be desirable. Small kits can be prepared beforehand, so in the field no measuring or weighing is necessary.

Once the epoxy gels, subsequent work may begin. The primer can be applied, and topping operations may be carried out.

As stated before, the application of the topping is quite similar to that of terrazzo. The mixer itself will be a portable-type, known as a mortar mixer, and may be fitted with either an electric motor or a gasoline engine. The bowl should preferably be made of stainless steel. This type of bowl is readily available, and its use will prevent many hours of cleaning to prevent color pickup from the bowl. A good size for this mixer is between 3 and 5 cu ft. A few equipment manufacturers can supply these mixers with a water-jacketed bowl, with immersion-type heating elements installed. These are most advantageous for use in winter months, where raising the temperature of the mix facilitates troweling and screeding.

All materials to be used should be prepackaged at the plant site in proper weights and amounts to prevent doing this time-consuming operation in the field. Human error is much more likely to occur in the field than at the plant, where proper weighing and batching equipment can be installed.

The liquid components can be packaged in mixer-sized batches, or they may go to the field in drums. Since they are easy to handle, proper-sized cans can be used to draw off enough of the resins and catalyst with good accuracy.

The large aggregates must be packaged separately from the fillers. These marble chips may be prepackaged in the proper color combinations, or they may be packaged as to size and color, allowing a wider range of color combinations to be formulated in the field.

The filler materials should all be mixed together and packaged at the plant site in mix-size, moisture-proof bags. All fillers and aggregates must be closely controlled as to moisture content. The maximum allowable should be 0.02%. A typical formulation for this material is as follows:

1. Resilient or flexible resin, promoted........................ 22.00 lb
2. Catalyst.. 0.22
3. Pigment, as desired, but approx.......................... 1.00
4. Marble chips, No. 1 (any color combination)............... 65.00
5. Marble chips, No. 0 (any color combination)............... 20.00
6. 40–200-mesh ground limestone............................ 15.00
7. China clay (aluminum silicate).......................... 5.00
8. Barytes, No. 1 bleached................................. 5.00

                                                          133.22 lb

Depending on the specific gravities of different materials used, this will come out very close to 1 cu ft. Multiply by the size of mixer to be used.

This mix will be of such consistency that it may be poured. It will flow well, and is easily troweled and screeded. Its thixotropy is such that the aggregates will not settle out rapidly, giving adequate time to work with the material.

The sequence of the mixing operation is of minor importance, but slightly less air will be entrained into the mix by always adding the liquid components last.

A mix such as this must be used up within the time allowed by the catalyst system. There is no problem in formulating for a 2-hr pot life, which is more than enough. Care must be taken to clean the mixer properly after each batch, as this material is most difficult to remove after gelling.

The material may be placed into position on the floor by workmen using wheelbarrows, 5-gal buckets, or other means. On very large areas, pumping equipment such as used with concrete may be used to great advantage. A crew of four men, without mechanical means to transport the material from the mixer to the application point, can easily lay 2,500 to 3,000 sq ft per 8-hr shift. This will include primer, divider strips, and topping, but will not include the grinding operation.

The material is now allowed to stand for 24 hr at 75°F or above. More time should be allowed at lower temperatures.

Grinding equipment will consist of normal terrazzo grinding machines, and the process for grinding is the same as that for terrazzo. Approximately 0.100 in. should be removed from the polyester material to get adequate exposure of the pattern.

Either two or three grinding steps may be used, always ending up with stones of the finer mesh grit. The first step may be using No. 40- or No. 60-mesh stones, removing at least 95% of the total with these. The second step may be with No. 220 stones and the third with No. 400 stones for an excellent finish, or these two steps may be combined, using No. 320 stones. It all depends on the type of finish desired.

Quantities of water are used, and many applicators may wish to use fine silica, aluminum oxide, etc., along with the first grind to aid in the grinding. Techniques may vary slightly in order to produce flooring at minimal costs.

The material will not reach its maximum cure for approximately 7 days, but after the grinding will take any normal wear and use. A slight styrene odor may be present during the grinding, but if it is still present after 72 hr will indicate improper cure of the material.

Many techniques and variations of techniques may be developed to speed up operations and to give better quality floors. Mechanical equipment to handle the mix from the mixer to location, vibrating screeds to better compact the material and eliminate air bubbles, and new and better grinding procedures can all aid in reducing overall costs.

During the grinding operation, the floor can be inspected for pinholes.

If they are present in any quantity, the floor will have to be grouted. This should take place between the second grind and final grinds. Grouting is the most disagreeable step in finishing the floor and must be eliminated if at all possible. A small resin-promoter-catalyst mix must be color matched to the surface, and a thixotroping agent added to give body. China clay is adequate for this purpose.

Using a steel trowel, this mix is applied to the surface, with all surplus wiped away. One pound of this mix will cover a very large room. It is allowed to gel, and then the final grinding may be done.

PHOTO 8.   *Manufactured-in-place polyester floor tile, Beta Industries, Inc.*

The grouting may seem like a very simple operation, but it is much more than that. Before it may be done, the floor must be allowed to dry. After it is applied, it must be allowed to gel. This is time lost in the overall process. It may not be too important on a large job, where the men can go on to another section of flooring while waiting, but on small jobs much effort and time are wasted. The number of trips the men will have to make to the job can mean the difference between profit and loss.

Terrazzo-type flooring is quite competitive in price with terrazzo and is a much better flooring; however, the only way it will be able to completely eliminate terrazzo will be by developing a means of doing away with the grouting phase of the process.

The primer coating does its part and eliminates at least 30% of the air bubbles. A good vibrating screed can do away with another 15 to

20%. Also, mixing techniques may be developed that will eliminate a great percentage of the air bubbles.

The most difficult job is to remove carbon dioxide from the mix to eliminate that portion of pinholes which is caused by this gas formation instead of by air bubbles. There appear to be only two ways to accomplish this. The first would be by deleting all calcium carbonate from the mix. This would be impossible because the marble chips have no substitute that could be used. The 40- to 200-mesh limestone can be replaced, using a filler such as talc. Since most of the alkaline reaction comes from the finer calcium carbonate materials, this is the first logical step.

The second method of preventing these gas bubbles would be by eliminating all moisture from the mix. There cannot be a reaction of this kind without some moisture present. The only solution to this problem is for the suppliers of these fillers and aggregates to set up proper drying equipment for processing these materials to produce a moisture content of as near zero as possible. Once these materials are properly dried, they should be packaged in moisture-proof, polyethylene-lined bags.

A number of suppliers of these materials now offer them at 0.1% or less moisture content, but for this casting operation, as well as for many types of manufactured tile, this is entirely too much water. The moisture content of these materials can be reduced to 0.01% with drying equipment available today. If the flooring industry demands that these materials be dry, even though they may cost a fraction more, the suppliers will install the proper equipment. (See a complete discussion of the effects of moisture on polyester formulations in Chap. 11. The effects are many, and all affect the properties of the end product detrimentally.)

Terrazzo-type flooring must have a sealer coat, which is the last phase of the process. Several of the sealers or wear coats described in Chap. 2 will be entirely suitable for this room-temperature cure. These may be sprayed on, or some of them may be brushed or squeegeed on successfully.

Marbelized Flooring

This type of floor covering is low in cost because it does not require grinding. For best appearance, however, a fine-grind should be done to remove 2 to 4 mils of the surface. The cost of such a grind is very low and the added appearance it gives will be well worth the small expense.

The process is identical to that of applying the terrazzo-type flooring, with the exception of the grinding stage. The floor is primed, and divider strips are placed if desired. Since this material is placed at thicknesses of about 0.125 in. instead of 0.250 in. for the terrazzo-type floor, any divider strips to be used will have to be this dimension.

A formulation for this marbelized tile will be as follows:

1. Resilient or flexible polyester, promoted.................... 26.00 lb
2. Catalyst... 0.26
3. Pigment (may vary)..................................... 2.00
4. Marble chips, any color, Nos. 00 or 000.................... 65.00
5. Silica, 100 mesh.. 20.00
6. 40–200-mesh ground limestone............................ 15.00
7. Barytes, No. 1 bleached................................. 5.00

133.26 lb

This mix will be almost exactly 1 cu ft. It may be multiplied by the size of the mixer to be used. The liquid components must always be premixed together and then added to the dry fillers. When well mixed, one or more marbelizing colors are added, such as the following formulation:

1. Resin, such as the above, promoted........................ 1.00 lb
2. Catalyst... 0.01
3. Pigment... 0.20
4. 40–200-mesh ground limestone............................ 2.00
5. China clay... 2.00

5.21 lb

This formulation will give a very viscous mix because of the high quantity of clay. It must be viscous in order to prevent excess blending into the large mix. In this way, the marbelizing colors will remain more intact, giving the desired effect. This amount will be sufficient for roughly 4 cu ft of the large batch. The formulator will probably wish to add two such colors.

The procedure for mixing this small amount of contrasting color into the large batch is to place it into the mixer in a thin stringy form and turn the mixer some five to eight revolutions at the same time. This will give a quantity of the color, or colors, throughout the batch.

The procedures for placing this material on the floor and the desired effects are varied. The principal objective is to handle the material as little as possible to avoid overmixing of the veining colors into the matrix. Any screeding or troweling must be done with care.

Since this mix is rather low in viscosity and thixotropy, it is readily pourable. The objective is for the workmen to pour the material out onto the substrate in as nearly its final position as possible. A flat-edged container is ideal for this pouring, or a special pouring spout can be devised to fit on any container to be used to move the material from the mixer to the location.

The material may be poured out in swirls and other forms so the final product will look quite like natural marble. A little practice and ingenuity can produce very beautiful floors.

Final leveling may be done with very careful screeding or troweling. A good tool to build for this use is a vibrating trowel. It can have a plane surface of approximately 12×24 in. or more, with an electric vibrator built into the back. In this way, leveling may be done with minimum lateral movement of the material.

An ultrasonic type of vibrator may do a better job than a normal machine.

Very beautiful floors can be designed with this type of material. If divider strips are used, the floor may be checkerboarded, with alternating squares of different colors of synthetic marble. Divider strips may be laid off in such a design that contrasting strips, designs, emblems, etc. will add to the beauty of the finished floor.

As stated, this floor does not require grinding, but a single pass of the grinder, with No. 320-, or No. 400-mesh grinding wheels will greatly enhance the appearance of the finished product. Three to five mils removed with the grinder will be sufficient.

If desired, a sealer or wear coat, such as those described in Chap. 2, may be applied.

Industrial Floors

For industrial floors, where extremely heavy traffic can be expected, a floor covering of a slightly different type should be used. This would be a material that would withstand the rigors of fork-lift trucks and other heavy equipment. It would withstand heavy objects being dropped on the floor, and it would take any amount of abrasion that might be inherent to the environment.

The substrate would be prepared in the same manner as described for the other types of manufactured-in-place floors.

A formulation such as the following would be used:

1. Resilient isophthalic resin, promoted	15.00 lb
2. Catalyst	0.15
3. Pigment	2.00
4. Quartz, crushed, No. 00	55.00
5. Aluminum oxide, alundum or corborundum, 20–50 mesh	40.00
6. Silica, 100 mesh	25.00
7. Silica, 200 mesh	5.00
	142.15 lb

This formulation will give almost exactly 1 cu ft of mix. It is slightly heavier than some of the other formulations because of the specific gravity of some of the components.

All mixing will be done exactly as in previous formulations. The material will be a highly viscous mix, but because of the type of fillers and aggregates will screed and trowel out very easily.

A ⅛-in. topping of this material will withstand very heavy abuse, but on the floors of some types of plants it may be desirable to apply it to ¼-in. in thickness. If it is to be applied over ⅛-in., then the largest-sized aggregate, the No. 00 quartz, should be larger. At ¼ in. this aggregate should be No. 0 or No. 1. The aluminum oxide may be sized upward also, but the remaining fillers should remain the same.

This floor will be decorative as well as enduring. Almost no abuse can destroy it.

Should it be desired that an area of floor have a completely nonskid finish, the following procedure would be used: When the floor is finished in sections, loose aluminum oxide, as listed above, is hand-scattered over the surface in a very thin layer, perhaps covering as much as ½ of the surface. Because of the density of this material, it will sink down into the matrix until only the top shows.

The above procedure will give an added decorative finish to the floor; it will have extra abrasion resistance and will be nonskid under any conditions.

Flooring That Withstands Strong Chemicals

Flooring for any specific environment may be formulated from polyester resins, with few exceptions.

One of the notable exceptions would be a surface where large quantities of chlorinated solvents would be spilled, or where quantities of very strong caustic compounds may come in contact with the surface. A few oxidizing acids will also seriously attack polyester resins. (See Chart 3 for details on applications.)

In formulating flooring for specific end uses, the poured-in-place method is much more practical than manufactured tile. A tile manufacturer simply is not set up to turn out a few thousand square feet of custom-made tile. Also, the joints of manufactured tile might be attacked, and the chemical may penetrate to the concrete and destroying it.

With the monolithic application, there are no areas for the chemical to enter. An example of such a floor would be in an annodizing plant where quantities of such chemicals as chromic acid would frequently be spilled onto the floor. Such an acid would destroy concrete very

CHART 3. FORMULATING FOR SEVERE ENVIRONMENT

Legend:
P—poor
F—fair
G—good
E—excellent
D—discolors, no attack
X—detrimental
V—asset

	Abrasion resistance	Hardness (Barcol)	Compressive strength	Impact strength	Coef. of friction	Sulfuric acid 10%	Hydrochloric 10%	Nitric 10%	Glacial acetic 20%	Phosphoric 20%	Citric 20%	Hydrofluric 30%	Chromic 20%	Uric 20%	Chlorox 10%	Sodium hydroxide 10%	Ammonium hydroxide 10%	Sodium chloride 10%	Dist. water pH 8.3	Carbon tet. 100%	Toluol 100%	Isopropyl alcohol 100%	Acetone 100%	Gasoline 86 octane	Motor oil 30 wt.	Animal blood
Polyester resin:																										
Rigid orthophthalic	F	G	E	F		E	E	P	P	E	E	E	E	E	F	F	F	E	F	P	G	G	F	E	G	E
Rigid isophthalic	F	F	E	G		E	E	D	F	E	E	E	E	E	G	G	G	E	F	P	G	G	F	E	G	E
Rigid bisphenol A	F	E	G	G		F	F	P	P	G	G	F	P	F	E	E	E	E	E	P	G	G	F	E	G	F
Rigid bisphenol B	F	G	G	P		F	F	P	P	G	G	F	P	F	E	E	E	E	E	P	G	G	F	E	G	F
Chlorinated, HET-based	F	G	E	F		G	G	D	P	G	G	F	F	F	G	G	G	E	G	P	F	G	F	E	F	G
Chlorinated, chlorophthalic	F	G	E	G		E	E	D	P	G	G	G	F	F	G	G	G	E	G	P	F	G	F	E	F	G
Pigment, filler, aggregates:																										
TiO₂, rutile	X	X	X	X	X	X	X	X	X	X	X	X	X	X	X	X	X	X	X		_No Effect_ →					X
Lead carbonate (white lead)	X	X	X	X	X	V	V	V	V	V	V	V	V	X	X	X	X	X	V							V
Iron oxides	V	V	V	V	V	X	X	X	X	X	X	X	X	X	X	X	V	V	V							X
Chrome oxides	V	V	V	V	V	V	V	V	V	V	V	X	V	V	V	V	V	V	V							V
Phthalocyanines	X	X	X	X	X	V	V	V	V	V	V	V	V	X	V	V	V	V	V							V
Cadmium	V	V	V	V	V	V	V	V	V	V	V	V	V	V	V	V	V	V	V							V
Carbon black	V	V	V	V	V	V	V	V	V	V	V	V	V	V	V	V	V	V	V							V
Zirconium dioxide	V	V	V	V	V	V	V	V	V	V	V	V	V	V	V	V	V	V	V							V
Silica	V	V	V	V	V	V	V	V	V	V	V	X	V	V	V	V	V	V	V							V
Quartz (silica)	V	V	V	V	V	V	V	V	V	V	V	X	V	V	V	V	V	V	V							V
Aluminum oxide	V	V	V	V	V	V	V	V	V	V	V	V	V	V	V	V	V	V	V							V
Carborundum	X	X	X	X	X	V	V	V	V	V	V	X	V	X	V	V	V	V	V							X
China clay	X	X	X	X	X	X	X	X	X	X	X	X	X	X	X	X	X	X	X							X
Barium sulfate (barytes)	V	V	V	V	V	X	X	X	X	X	X	X	X	V	V	V	V	V	V							V
Calcium carbonate	X	X	X	X	X	X	X	X	X	X	X	X	X	X	X	X	X	X	X							X
Zirconium silicate	V	V	V	V	V	V	V	V	V	V	V	V	V	V	V	V	V	V	V							V
Glass flake	V	V	V	V	V	V	V	V	V	V	V	X	V	V	V	V	V	V	V							V
Mica	X	X	X	X	X	X	X	X	X	X	X	X	X	X	X	X	X	X	X							X

rapidly. Even an epoxy floor topping would be destroyed in a few months.

A formulation for a flooring of this nature would have to take into consideration not only the particular resin used, but also the fillers and aggregates. Every component going into the formulation, including the pigments, must be able to withstand the particular environment.

Thus, out of necessity, the formulation must exclude such ingredients as calcium carbonates, metallic pigments such as iron oxide, talc, clay, and barium sulfate, and barytes. Quartz is silica, and silica will withstand all acids, with the exception of hydrofluoric acid. Therefore, in any acid environment the fillers must consist of quartz and silica, except where hydrofluoric acid is a consideration.

A formulation for a highly acid environment would be the following:

1. Rigid isophthalic polyester, promoted...................... 15.00 lb
2. Catalyst.. 0.15
3. Pigment (chrome oxide or phthalocyanine)................. 2.00
4. Crushed quartz, No. 00................................ 55.00
5. Silica, 20–40 mesh..................................... 30.00
6. Silica, 100 mesh....................................... 25.00
7. Silica, 200 mesh....................................... 5.00

$$\overline{}$$
132.15 lb

The above formulation will give a mix for approximately 1 cu ft.

Note the change to a rigid resin for a highly acid environment. Without exception, the resins of very high modulus have better chemical resistance than the resilient, or flexible, resins.

Since the resin itself will withstand hydrofluoric acid very well, if a clear coating of this polyester is applied at a thickness of some 0.010 in., this floor could be used in a laboratory or plant where hydrofluoric acid is likely to be spilled.

In another location where a strong alkali might be present, the type of resin used in the formulation must be changed. With alkalies, the bisphenol polyester gives very good service. A few of the chlorinated polyesters will also withstand alkalies well.

Flooring for Meat-processing, Poultry, and Seafood Plants

Flooring materials which are to be used in meat-processing plants have long been a major problem. Poultry and seafood plants present the same problem to a large degree.

Animal bloodstains are extremely difficult to remove from most surfaces. Sanitary conditions required by federal, state, and local laws are almost impossible to maintain with normal floor covering materials. Concrete, vinyl, vinyl absestos, linoleum, and others simply cannot be cleaned adequately. Many packing houses use ceramic tile, which stands up very well, but when wet is too likely to cause workers' accidents from slipping. In addition, it is a great problem to keep the grouted joints in a proper sanitary condition.

Polyester resin stands up very well under these conditions, and a monolithic flooring of this type easily meets sanitary requirements. There are no joints, and the floor is completely nonabsorbent. The ease of keeping it in proper condition is a major advantage in this type of industry. It is also a most excellent flooring material for many other types of food-processing industries where sanitary requirements are very strict.

A good formulation for this type of floor would be the following:

1. Rigid isophthalic polyester, promoted...................... 16.00 lb
2. Catalyst.. 0.16
3. Pigment (iron oxide, chrome oxide, cadmium)............... 2.00
4. Quartz, crushed, No. 00................................. 55.00
5. Silica, 100 mesh.. 25.00
6. Barytes, No. 1 bleached................................. 5.00
7. Silica, 20–40 mesh...................................... 30.00

133.16 lb

The above formulation will produce approximately 1 cu ft of material. The mix will be a rather liquid one and will flow, screed, and level very nicely.

The floor produced will be a decorative surface, very durable, and will be very easy to maintain in sanitary condition. The normal detergents used for cleaning floors will not attack this material. Animal blood, vegetables, and other foodstuffs found in processing plants will not stain, discolor, or attack this flooring.

It can be applied by the same methods used for the other floors discussed in this chapter. Proper substrate preparation, a primer with low promoter content, will be applied so the topping will cure before the primer, avoiding the stresses set up by shrinkage. The thickness of the topping should be about 0.125 in., and it may be ground about 0.005 in. with a fine set of stones if desired.

Semiconductive Flooring

Many industries working with chemicals, explosives, and other highly inflammable materials must have a flooring material that has enough electrical resistivity to prevent electrostatic sparks that could cause much loss of property and human lives through major explosions. (Specifications for such a flooring material are set forth by the National Fire Prevention Association in Bulletin No. 56. These specifications are stated in Chap. 2.)

Laboratories, operating rooms in hospitals, and many other locations are good markets for this type of flooring material. In some cases, it may be more practical to lay the manufactured semiconductive floor tile described in the preceding chapter, but in many areas it may be preferable to apply a manufactured-in-place material. Particularly in new structures, where time is not a factor, the in-place material will be more economical and will have the advantage of being monolithic. In occupied buildings, however, manufactured tile is best because it may be installed and the floor used the same day, whereas the monolithic system will tie up the floor for at least 2 or 3 days.

The formulation of this material may be quite varied, as stated in the preceding chapter. As many fillers, aggregates, and pigments as possible are chosen for their electrical conductivity. Since the resins are completely nonconductive, these materials must furnish the conductivity. Metallic pigments and fillers are ideal.

Protective Toppings for Bridges and Causeways

Polyester compounds have many applications as toppings for concrete, both old and new. Concrete bridges and causeways are fine situations where such materials can be serviceable.

After many years of use, concrete roadway surfaces begin to pit, spall, crack, and deteriorate in general. Water gets into these openings, and the presence of moisture and air sets up corrosion on the reinforcing steel. Once the steel begins to oxidize, spalling is increased very rapidly. As the steel oxidizes, the structural strength of the entire span weakens, and unless repair measures are taken at once, the life of a bridge or causeway is limited.

This is particularly true in many cases where bridges and causeways are constructed over or near the sea. The addition of the element salt to the oxidation process accelerates the destruction of the structure. Repair work, when delayed too long, will be of no value because the advanced degree of oxidation of the steel will cause any new concrete to spall in a very short time. Concrete is porous, and some moisture and air will keep the oxidation process going to some extent.

In recent years, engineers are turning to organic polymers for patching and topping these structures. The topping is designed, not only to make the surface air- and waterproof, but to give a surfacing that will withstand wear and tear to a degree that is far superior to concrete.

Many types of such materials have been tried, including polyvinyls, neoprenes, epoxies, and polyesters. So far, the epoxy toppings and the polyester materials have given outstandingly the best service.

The epoxy compounds are much more expensive than polyester. The two are comparable in many ways in mechanical properties. Epoxy has a slightly higher bond strength to the concrete and a slightly higher tensile strength because of better bond to the aggregates used.

In outdoor exposure, however, polyester is proving far superior to epoxy. Views differ as to their worth, however, and of course the weatherability of each compound depends very much on its individual formulation.

Toppings of this type must have some flexibility, resilience, and elongation in order to withstand the constant contraction and expansion of bridges and causeways. The lower the amount of water absorption, the better protection the topping will give.

Because of the nature of epoxies, flexibility, resilience, and elongation must come from the curing system used and from either reactive or nonreactive diluents.

These materials will produce the desired results in the above properties, but other properties are changed too drastically in a negative way. When a compound must be formulated for ambient-temperature curing, as a topping must be, epoxies just will not stand up in outdoor exposures as well as polyesters.

The process for repairing and retopping a bridge or causeway structure would be as follows:

1. Clear away all loose and spalling concrete. Notch out any existing cracks. Air tools are ideal for this work.

2. Clean thoroughly any reinforcing steel exposed. Sandblasting is preferable, but power brushes may be able to do an adequate job.

3. Apply a cleaning solution to all oil, grease, and other foreign matter that have accumulated on the surface through the years. Solvents and caustics may both be necessary.

4. All surfaces must be as dry as possible.

5. Apply a good flexible isophthalic polyester to all surfaces, including interior of cracks, steel, and parts to be patched. This primer should be promoted so as to cure very slowly.

6. Using narrow strips of glass cloth and a polyester such as the primer above, patch all cracks, being sure that the glass cloth reaches 3 in. or more on each side of the crack.

7. Patch all holes, spalled areas, and pits of more than $\frac{1}{2}$ in. in depth with a compound such as the formulation for the topping below.

8. Apply the topping to a thickness of about $\frac{1}{4}$ in. for best results. This is poured onto the surface and screeded and troweled into final position. If a rough surface is desired, this may be accomplished in

various ways: The surface may be "broomed" as the compound begins to gel; it may be cross-troweled with a notched trowel; or aggregates may be scattered into the surface.

A good formulation for this topping would be the following:

1. Isophthalic polyester, promoted.......................... 20.00 lb
2. Catalyst... 0.20
3. Pigment, as desired, but about........................... 2.00
4. Quartz, crushed No. 1.................................. 60.00
5. Quartz, crushed No. 00................................. 20.00
6. Aluminum oxide, or carborundum, 20–50 mesh.............. 20.00
7. Silica, 100 mesh....................................... 10.00
8. Silica, 200 mesh....................................... 5.00

$$\overline{137.20 \text{ lb}}$$

The polyester resin should have a flexural modulus of about 250,000 to 300,000 psi. This will place it between a flexible and a resilient category. Flexible and resilient resins may be mixed, if desired, to achieve this as long as both are isophthalic resins.

The resin must have at least a dual monomer system in order to possess maximum weathering properties. About $\frac{2}{3}$ of the monomer may be styrene and $\frac{1}{3}$ methyl methacrylate. One-third each of styrene, diallyl phthalate, and methyl methacrylate will give even better service in such an environment. This will give a very complex polymer with a highly cross-linked structure. The more complex the cured polymer, the better the durability in exterior exposure.

The fillers and aggregates must be as dry as possible, and since there are no calcium carbonates present, the allowable moisture content may be as high as 0.1%. This is an absolute maximum and should be kept as low as possible.

The mix above will be almost exactly 1 cu ft and is to be multiplied by the size of the mixer to be used. On large areas, very large mixers are often best. Care must be taken that laying crews can handle the mix adequately during its pot life. Special laying equipment can be built, which is quite similar to concrete paving machines. Such mechanization will pay dividends when large areas are to be done.

In such large areas, expansion joints must be considered. Since a concrete structure such as a bridge will have expansion joints designed into it, these will be adequate. The coefficient of the topping compound will be very close to that of the concrete itself.

The treatment of these expansion joints is of great importance to the total job. The finished joint must be the same width as that already in the structure. It must be a permanent joint that will not deteriorate under such severe environmental conditions.

When the topping is laid, ¼-in. thick strips of appropriate width should be laid directly in place over the existing expansion joints of the structure. These may be metal or wood strips, or they may be strips of rubber. A good external release must be applied to these strips so they may be easily removed. Polyvinyl alcohol or a good paste carnuba wax are adequate for this purpose.

After the topping has gelled and partially cured, these strips are re-moved. A good polyurethane elastomer is an excellent material with which to fill these joints. It will obtain a good bond to all surfaces contacted and will be very durable. Another material suitable for these joints is silicone elastomer. The silicone compound has the disadvantages of being much higher in cost and of requiring the application of a special primer in order to get bond to the surfaces involved.

Either material should be formulated so as to have good weathering properties and elasticity of at least 500%. This will take care of all expansion and contraction adequately and will give a good seal to the joint at all times.

This type of repair and topping of a concrete bridge or causeway will restore it for many years of use. If it is done in time—before the damage to the steel is excessive—it can save many millions of dollars of taxpayers' money.

Reinforcement of Airport Runways

Another large market for the materials described above is their use on the runways and landing strips of major airports. Each year, larger and larger aircraft are being developed. The ends of runways where these huge planes touch down are becoming very problematic for the industry.

These areas of runways are designed with as much as 16 in. of highly reinforced concrete, which just does not stand up to the tremendous forces imposed by the landing of large aircraft. The shock of the impact of the planes and the terrific friction of the tires setting down literally tear the concrete apart. Special concrete has been developed for such purposes, but, particularly in military installations where huge bombers constantly land, these areas must be replaced as often as every 6 months.

The cost of replacing such quantities of concrete is very high. First, the remaining concrete must be removed, then steel must be cut and removed, and then the whole strip replaced. Of even more concern is the time required, during which the runway cannot be used. In time of emergency, this could be very serious indeed.

The solution to this problem is a thick topping of a polyester compound that will withstand these conditions. This will have to be applied on the runway before it is used in order to have maximum protection. The new concrete runway would be aged at least 21 days, and the following material would be applied.

1. A polyester primer, as described earlier, promoted so as to cure very slowly. In this case, it should not gel for at least 72 hr and should reach full cure not less than 1 week later. This primer will be almost entirely absorbed into the substrate, displacing the air bubbles out through the primer.

2. A layer of medium-weight fiberglass cloth is now applied. This is done with the same type of resin as above, promoted to cure at about the same rate. A layer of resin, approximately 0.030 in., is applied over the primer. The glass cloth is now rolled out into this resin.

3. The topping is now applied, at a thickness of about ⅜ in.

The formula for this topping would be the following:

1. Isophthalic polyester (flexural modulus 300,000 psi) . . . . 16.00 lb
2. Catalyst. 0.16
3. Pigment (if desired) 2.00
4. Quartz, crushed No. 2 . . . . 60.00
5. Quartz, crushed No. 1 . . . . 25.00
6. Quartz, crushed No. 00 . . . . 15.00
7. Silica, 100 mesh 10.00
8. Silica, 200 mesh 5.00
                                                                         ——————
                                                                         133.16 lb

The above formulation will be approximately 1 cu ft of mix and may be multiplied by the size of the mixer used.

The material should be screeded and troweled to the desired smoothness and allowed to cure for 7 days before the runway is used. The exotherm heat caused by a topping of this thickness will be sufficient to cure the lesser-promoted polyester underneath.

This topping will be approximately six times as strong as the best concrete yet devised. Its compressive strength, tensile strength, impact strength, and tear strength will be impressive.

Such an application is not low in cost, but the cost will be amortized very rapidly when compared to the cost of completely replacing large sections of runways plus the down time involved.

Here, again, very large machinery may be used, such as concrete laying machines.

There are numerous variations of such toppings for bridges, causeways, runways, sidewalks, and many other structures. A good use would be on structures in northern regions, where in winter months much money is spent keeping areas clear of ice and snow.

Polyester Toppings with Integral Heating Systems

Airfields are particularly difficult to keep free of ice and snow during storms because they are very large areas. Therefore, many workmen and fleets of heavy equipment are necessary during the critical months. This expense must be sustained whether there is immediate need or not. When needed, these men and equipment must be on hand and ready to clear the runways. Since they work only about $\frac{1}{10}$ of the actual time during these months, the expense per sq ft of ice and snow cleared away is very large.

A topping such as that for landing areas and bridges may be applied to an entire runway. The thickness would be such that it could afford maximum strength at the ends of the runways, and it could be much thinner, without the fiberglass reinforcement, throughout the majority of the area.

Electrical heating elements would be imbedded directly into the polyester topping. These could be thermostatically controlled in such a manner that power would be used only when snow and ice were present on the runways.

Power requirements would be quite high during the use of the system, but costs would be nil during the majority of the time, when the system would be off.

The capital investment for the installation of such a system would approximate $2.50 per sq ft. This would include the polyester topping, heating elements, and the entire electrical system. The cost of electricity during actual operating hours would be $0.003 per sq ft per hr.

Careful study will reveal that the capital investment and the cost per sq ft of operating this system would be far less than the cost of maintaining many men and heavy equipment on duty during the entire winter months, plus the very sizeable capital investment required by the equipment purchase.

This same system may be used on bridges, overpasses, and areas of freeways where icing conditions prevail during the winter months. Much cost and many human lives could very probably be saved in this manner.

City sidewalks in heavily congested downtown areas could be treated in this same way. The cost to city governments and store- and office-building owners can be easily amortized in a very short time.

The applications set forth here are just a few, and many more very useful applications may be found. It will be the responsibility of every segment of the polyester industry to find new and better markets for these products. This writer is convinced that the market is limited only by the ingenuity, knowledge, and ability of the people involved in this great industry.

Monolithic Seamless Flooring

During the past 5 years, many types of manufactured-in-place seamless floor-covering materials have been researched. A number of these are already on the market, while others are still in the developmental stages.

Some of these are of the spray-up type, others may be applied by trowel, brush, roller, or squeegee. Most of them are based on polyurethane materials of the moisture-cured variety. Because of the low-solid content of these materials (usually 40 to 50%), it takes many applications to build up a flooring to the desired thickness. The added hazards presented by the high solvent content makes them entirely unsuitable for application in many areas.

Most of these materials consist of a pigmented base coat on the substrate into which loose "chips" are scattered to give a decorative pattern. Then multiple coats of the clear urethane are applied over the top.

The chips may be a great variety of materials, ranging from gold and silver colored flakes to thin sheets of compounded vinyl film which is broken into chip-sized pieces for scattering into the base coat.

From the multitude of intermediates available today, polyester resins can be developed that would be suitable for this type of flooring material.

Hydroxyl-terminated polyesters are now used in many instances as the curing agent in many of the better urethane coatings. But the polyester that would be used as a coating for such a flooring material must be an entirely different type of material. Its cured properties would have to be very close to those of a cured polyurethane in order to have the qualities necessary for this use.

Of primary importance is abrasion resistance. In the past polyesters have not been noted for this property. They have been used in many areas where resistance to abrasion was a primary objective, but always in a highly filled state; that is, the fillers and aggregates have furnished the abrasion resistance, and the polyester resin has been merely a binding medium.

For seamless flooring applications, where a clear top coating is necessary, the polymer will have to be very different. Resin manufacturers will have to take a completely new look at intermediates and raw materials for such a polyester. The data available in Chap. 11 examine closely such intermediates as polybutadiene, for use as a substitute for glycols, and such acids as digallic, for use in place of the more conventional acids and anhydrides.

Polyesters can be developed with the necessary properties. It is a matter of research and development. Much work is now being done

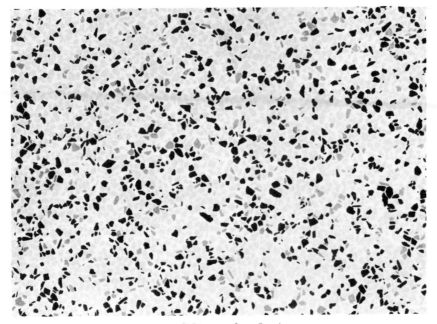

PHOTO 9. *Monolithic seamless flooring, spray-up.*

along these lines, and an increasing demand for such a resin will speed this work along.

An abrasion-resistant polyester would be much more advantageous than the urethane now used. Cost would be comparable, or slightly lower, for the polyester. The polyester would be applied as a 100% solids material, with no solvents involved. An additional advantage is that polyester can be formulated to cure under almost any ambient conditions, while urethane is somewhat limited in this respect. The most important advantage of polyester would be that it can be applied to any thickness in a single application, without the air and gas bubbles which are so prevalent in the polyurethanes.

The toxicity to workmen who apply a polyester is almost nonexistant, whereas the polyurethanes, formulated from diisocyanates, still present some problems.

Polyesters may be formulated to withstand ultraviolet and infrared light and oxidation much more easily than urethanes because of basic molecular differences.

This type of floor covering presents a very large market. It can compete in price with the most economical of present flooring materials. New designs, new methods of application, and new polyester polymers can make this flooring material a most attractive new product for the industry.

Four

WALL PRODUCTS

There are many types of wall materials for which polyester resins are ideal. Some of these may be ideally suited to exterior use, others may be formulated especially for interiors, and many of them may be suitable both exterior and interior applications.

Modular panels are becoming increasingly a very large part of the construction industry. These panels are premanufactured in the plant and shipped to the job site ready to install. In most cases both the interior and exterior are finished, and the interior has been filled with a foam type of insulation material. The panels are manufactured to proper sizes, with suitable installation fittings, so that in the field a very minimum of work is required.

The latest trends include all piping, electrical conduits and wiring, terminal boxes, and all other necessary accessories already installed. Provisions for windows and doors are made. Premanufactured baseboards and other complementing materials are made to match.

This type of construction fits in very well with the general rise in the cost of building. Work done in the plant is always better and lower in cost than work in the field. By premanufacturing all possible units, costs can be held in line and in many cases actually lowered.

Not only are these materials utilized on new construction projects, but in many instances they have even a wider market for remodeling old buildings.

The next few years will witness a massive effort to clean up America's slums and ghettos. Already, in many of the large cities, this work has begun. Ways, means, and materials for this work is in its infancy, and the manufacturer who can develop materials with which to speed and cut down the cost of such work will be in on the ground floor of perhaps the largest segment of the building-materials market.

Some of the nation's large construction companies and some of its best architects are devoting full time to this effort. The consensus of opinion at the moment seems to be that the best way to carry out remodeling goals is to utilize the basic structures already existing wherever possible and practical.

Using these skeleton structures will entail new wall materials, both interior and exterior, flooring made up in large panels ready to install, and ceiling materials also made up in large panels.

In many buildings where good building standards were carried out and dimensions are close enough, entire rooms can be premanufactured and assembled at the plant and transported to the job site, ready to set in place. Unfortunately, not all buildings which are to be remodeled will meet these standards.

The types of wall materials discussed in this chapter will be ideal for both new construction and the remodeling of old structures.

Synthetic Ceramic-tile Panels: Semigloss Finish

Real ceramic tile is a luxury item in the building-materials market. It is expensive, and labor requirements to install it are extremely high. Only homes and apartments in the medium- to high-price range can afford these luxuries.

Ceramic tile is one of the most desirable of building materials because of its beauty, durability, and ease of maintenance. It is also very practical and available in colors to match almost any bathroom or kitchen fixture.

Synthetic ceramic tiles have been made for some time. Some of these are made up in 4×8 ft panels, and others are confined to 4×4 in. squares. The small, square tiles have been made mostly from polystyrene plastic. They are well made and have properties which make them reasonably good building materials. However, they are installed piece by piece, so labor costs are still high.

Most of the synthetic panels that have been marketed to any extent have been "painted on" synthetic tiles. Most use pressboard, which is flow-coated or spray-coated with the pigmented base color. The material moves on to a hydraulic press, where the upper plate is fitted with ribs to match the gout joints. These ribs are roller-coated with the synthetic grout color, usually white. The press closes, and the pressboard is indented to simulate the appearance of laid ceramic tile at the same time as this indentation is coated.

This material is low in cost and therefore is attractive to a certain segment of the market. However, it is still merely painted hardboard, and its durability is limited. Hardboard is very susceptible to termites and water rot. Particularly in steamy bathrooms, its life is very limited. It is readily flammable, so will add to any fire hazards in a building.

For the most part, the coating materials have been alkyds, which have very limited resistance to the alkaline cleaning compounds used in such areas. The gloss is soon impaired, and appearance is soon less than satisfactory.

A few synthetic ceramic tiles have been produced, using good-quality coating materials. One manufacturer uses polyester resins; another uses an epoxy. They still are just coating, however, and the finish is about 0.006 in. in thickness. Since the hardboard backing is limited in strength, the finish can be only as high in impact strength as the backing. Blows of moderate force will dent and break the coated surface.

A much better quality synthetic ceramic tile can be made in the following fashion: The basic production line will be a continuous conveyor belt, with part of the entire conveyor enclosed in an oven. The molds will be mounted across the conveyor, or the 8-ft dimension of the belt and the 4-ft dimension (lengthwise) of the conveyor. The molds are hinged to the conveyor at each end, and in the center to the conveyor chain. In this way, they will go around the end of the conveyor with no problems. Diagram 6 gives a typical equipment setup for this type of production.

Each mold will consist of multiple small cavities, 4×4 in., with ribs extending some 0.030 to 0.040 in. above the small pans. These ribs will constitute the indentations in the finished panel, simulating the grout.

The first step in the production line is to coat these ribs with a white polyester formulation to a thickness of about 0.005 in. This is done automatically by a reverse-roller coater as the mold reaches this station. This mix will be a very viscous formulation, with fast gel, so the subsequent operations will not damage this coating on the peaks of the ribs. The coating then passes under a set of infrared lights at the second station for gelling.

At the third station, the tile mix is flowed into the mold to the level

of the ribs. Here the mold is vibrated moderately to assist in leveling
out the mix in the cavities.

The molds then pass through the oven for cure, and, upon emerging
from the oven at the other end, the backing is applied. The backing
material may be a good-quality hardboard, or it may be a low grade
of plywood. The conveyor belt which carries the plywood to this station
should be mounted directly above the main production line. The adhesive should be applied to the top side of the backing material, and,

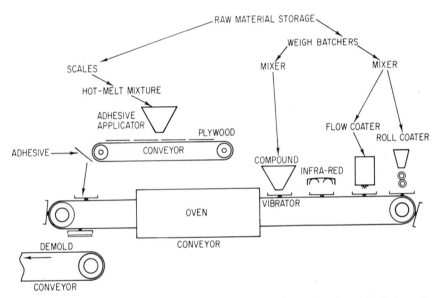

DIAGRAM 6. *Production line for synthetic ceramic tile, and other 4 x 8 ft wall
panels.*

on reaching the end of the conveyor, should be turned as it is lowered
onto the synthetic tile mix below, with the adhesive side down.

The entire panel is demolded as the mold turns upside down when
it rounds the end of the conveyor. The panel falls onto a third conveyor,
which will carry it out to be stacked and packaged.

The entire operation, from the time the ribs are coated to the time
the part is demolded, can be as low as 3 min. Production can be very
high, and for a production line such as this, with 20 molds mounted,
should run to well over 5,000 sq ft per hr.

Almost every phase of such a production line may be automated,
with very little labor involved. The equipment necessary for such a
production line include readily available conveyor systems, an oven,

mixers, a flow-coater, a roller-coater, and a hot-melt adhesive applicator. The Appendix lists this equipment and gives suppliers.

A formulation for the rib-coating material will be as follows:

1. Hexahydrophthalic resilient polyester-monomer............. 100.0 lb
2. Dimethyl analine (mix well before adding catalyst)........... 0.3
3. t-Butyl peroctoate....................................... 1.5
4. Titanium dioxide (rutile)............................... 10.0
5. Colloidal silica.. 7.0
6. China clay.. 20.0

138.8 lb

A formulation such as this will have a mixed pot life of at least 4 hr at 75°F, but will gel under infrared lights in a few seconds. The viscosity will be a smooth, creamy liquid, suitable for roller coating. The thixotropy will be such that it will not run, smear, or flow. It will stay exactly where the roller-coater places it, on top of the ribbing.

This mix will be formulated in a high-shear dissolver-type mixer, added in the sequence shown above. Care must be taken not to overmix, as friction heat can gel the mix. If there is any trouble blending in the particular colloidal silica used, it may be added second, before the promoter and catalyst. In this way, it may be mixed far longer, without the danger of gel. If any heat buildup is evident in the mix, let it cool to ambient temperature before adding the other ingredients.

The formulation for the synthetic ceramic compound would be as follows:

1. Hexahydrophthalic resilient polyester-monomer............. 20.00 lb
2. Dimethyl analine (mix well before adding catalyst)........... 0.04
3. t-Butyl peroctoate....................................... 0.30
4. Silica, 100 mesh.. 75.00
5. Silica, 200 mesh.. 25.00
6. Barytes, No. 1 bleached................................. 10.00
7. Pigment... 5.00

135.34 lb

This compound should be mixed in a heavy-duty mixer of the double-arm type. The liquid components and pigments should be premixed before adding them to the dry fillers in the large mixer.

The consistency will be a heavy, flowable paste, suitable to handle in a pressure flow-coater system. It will level out into the molds with very little vibration.

The conveyor will now carry the molds through the oven, curing the tile and synthetic grout coating. The backing material will be deposited upon the mold, adhesive side down.

The material in the mold will have a temperature of around 300°F as it emerges from the oven. This heat will remelt the hot-melt adhesive that has cooled somewhat, and a firm bond will be formed. A very light pressure by a roller, some 2 to 3 psi, will be sufficient to press the backing into place.

The formulation for the hot-melt adhesive will be the following:

1. Amorphous polypropylene............................... 100.0 lb
2. Semirefined wood rosin (MP 250)......................... 20.0
3. Chlorinated biphenyl plasticizer........................... 10.0

130.0 lb

The above will be a very low-cost adhesive—about 14 cents per lb when buying raw materials in large lots. Its melting point will be about 200°F, and it will flow nicely in the adhesive applicator at 250°F.

This adhesive should be applied in very thin ribs to achieve best results. When it is applied to the hot material in the mold, it will remelt sufficiently to flow out into a solid, flexible membrane between the ceramic tile and the backing material.

There will be no shrinkage to cause warping of the panels. Also, this adhesive will be waterproof and practically nonflammable.

Any of the above formulations may be made completely nonflammable by the addition of 5% diammonium phosphate and 5% antimony trioxide, which will add less than 2% to the cost of an average mix.

The cost of the above synthetic ceramic panels will be approximately 9 cents per sq ft, not including the backing material. This backing material will add 4 to 6 cents per ft, depending on the material used, thickness, etc.

These costs will include all labor, materials, equipment write-off, power, and plant costs. They may vary slightly, depending on the degree of automation and the ingenuity shown in setting up the equipment.

This tile will have a semigloss finish, depending largely on the degree of polish on the mold faces. It will be very hard and scratch resistant and will be suitable for bathrooms, kitchens, and other areas where semigloss, heat- and chemical-resistant panels are desirable.

For the same panels, but with a very high gloss finish, the process would be exactly the same, except that one more station would be added to the production line. This station would flow-coat a gel coat onto the mold surface, either before or after the rib-coating station. If the gel coat is applied after the rib coat, the finished panel will have a nice contrast; the tile part would be high gloss, and the grout joint would be semigloss. If the gel-coat is applied before the rib coat, then the whole surface will have a high-gloss finish.

With the addition of the gel coat, the tile would have less abrasion resistance, but it would be quite suitable for wall areas. The semigloss material would be better for areas such as kitchen work areas where hot pots and pans would be likely to be set down.

The gel coat can be formulated with a heat-resistant polyester, which will take up to 500°F, such as a resin based in part on HET acid.

However, in time a work surface would become scratched and lose its appearance because of abrasion.

A formulation for a gel coat suitable for wall surfaces would be the following:

1. Hexahydrophthalic rigid polyester resin-monomer. . . . . 100.00 lb
2. Dimethyl analine (mix before adding catalyst). 0.04
3. t-Butyl peroctoate. 1.20
4. Cellulose acetate butyrate (½ sec) 2.50
                                                                                        ─────────
                                                                                        103.74 lb

A gel-coat resin such as this should come from the resin manufacturer with the ½-sec butyrate already in the resin-monomer system. It dissolves into the resin during the cooling stage of the manufacturing process. Whichever of the above formulations go next to the mold—whether it be the gel coat or the rib coating and the tile mix—must have an internal mold release added to the formulation. This internal-mold-release compound must be tested thoroughly. It will not affect the bond between the gel coat and the tile mix because it will be passed to the face and back of the material next to the mold. The polyester material above it will exude a portion on up to the surface next to the hot-melt adhesive, and with certain mold-release compounds this bond can be impaired. Tests on several of the mold-release compounds from companies listed in the Appendix show several that will not impair this bond.

There are many suitable external mold releases on the market that will do a good job if applied to the face of the mold, and that give many good, clean releases per application. But, wherever possible, an internal mold release must be used, as the cost is much less.

Molds such as these will have to be custom-made. They should be made of a good, hardened steel, to be chrome-plated, or they may be made of stainless steel. They may be designed so the face of the tile may have rounded or beveled edges. Such molds may also be made of cast iron and plated. Aluminum is not recommended because it is too soft and will soon become scratched and worn, giving panels with an inferior finish.

The appearance of the panels depends entirely on the finish on the molds. They should have a 5-μ polish and should be repolished each 7 to 9 days of use to keep producing panels of similar appearance.

Now, on this same production line, by much the same process, many other types of wall products may be produced merely by changing the molds on the conveyor.

Synthetic Brick Panels

Under this heading will be included dimension stone, sandstone, and other synthetic stone-facing materials where molds must be designed to show a grout line around the individual "stones."

The process will be exactly like the one used to produce the synthetic ceramic tile. The only differences will occur in the design of the molds and the finish on the molds; also, in these materials a gel coat is never used. These panels should always be finished with little or no gloss.

Mold design and finish is of utmost importance with these materials in order to achieve complete authenticity. If these cavities are designed properly, the finished panels will be exactly like natural stone or brick.

Cast-iron molds are ideal for this use. This material may be cast in the foundry over an actual panel-sized prototype set up with actual stone or brick itself. The rough texture of the cast iron will simulate very nearly the surface characteristics of the prototype.

Other mold materials are entirely feasible for short runs of a few weeks. Castable silicone elastomers may be used as liners for smooth-surfaced steel molds. These would be open pans such as described later in this chapter for smooth panels, with wood-grain, marbelized, and granite finishes.

The silicone rubber would be poured over a prototype set up in natural stone or brick, with the outside of the rubber fitting the open molds. In this way, changing the type of panel to be manufactured would take but a few minutes.

It must be emphasized, however, that these silicone mold liners would be temporary. Their usable life span depends largely on the types of resins used. With some resins, they will give up to 250 good parts, and with other resins no more than 50 good-quality parts can be expected. In general, with rigid resins, their life span is longer than it is with flexible or resilient resins.

Another way to make temporary mold liners is to use phenolic resin, epoxy-phenolic resin, or a very high heat-resistant epoxy. These will be rigid molds. The natural stone, brick, or other prototype is coated with a proper external mold release—in these materials usually a silicone release. The above materials are catalyzed and poured over the prototype. Heat lamps may be applied until the material has partially cured, and then it may be stripped from the prototype and placed in the oven for curing. The entire part may be placed in the oven at once for curing, but because of the weight involved, this is usually not practical. Properly formulated mold liners of this type will give good service for up to 500 parts.

A manufacturer may wish to begin production with these temporary mold liners. In this way, he can turn out limited runs of a number of finished products to feel out the market for them, without tremendous tooling costs.

PHOTO 10. *Synthetic brick panels.*

A single prototype of each of the products discussed here can be laid up by a good mason on heavily reinforced plywood. This arrangement will allow the prototype to be moved with a fork-lift truck when necessary. A form should be built around it to the proper height for pouring any of the tooling resins mentioned.

The prototype must be sealed. One or two coats of a good catalyzed epoxy are applied and cured. Using the silicone rubber, no mold release will be required, but using the other tooling resins, a light coat of the recommended mold-release material will be necessary.

These prototypes will be permanent. If handled properly, they may be used thousands of times. Many sets of mold liners may be taken from them.

Polyester resin is not recommended as a tooling resin in this particular-application since high-temperature curing is required in this process. Polyester tooling works very well as temporary tooling for polyester products when ambient-cure or moderately low temperatures are to be used. With temperatures above 250°F, the monomer in the polyester formulation will attack the polyester tooling, whereas the phenolics, epoxy-phenolics, and certain straight epoxies are unaffected.

Temporary tooling must be carefully evaluated against permanent tooling. When all costs, including labor, materials, etc., are taken into consideration, permanent tooling is by far cheaper. Also, parts are better quality and will not vary from day to day as to finish, gloss, and general appearance.

Temporary tooling is of real value only in short runs for proving out a product. Once the market for the product is established and processing methods and techniques are fully developed, the manufacturer who is cost-conscious will change immediately to permanent-tooling materials.

The formulations to be used in these types of panels will be roughly the same as those used in ceramic tile panels. The coating for the ribs will be exactly the same, except in some few cases the mix will not be white. Particularly when the production line is producing white brick panels, the grout color would usually be black.

The compound to be used for the actual synthetic brick, dimension stone, sandstone or other type of simulated stone would vary slightly, according to the actual type of panel being produced. Even the type of temporary mold liners may affect the formulation to some degree.

If a production run is contemplated with silicone-rubber liners, then by all means an acrylic polyester should be used. This polyester resin is based in part on acrylic acid and uses a large percentage of acrylic or methacrylate monomer. Such a resin will give many more good-quality panels per mold than any other polyester.

With steel molds, the choice of the resin is not important; however, the possible exterior environments in which the panels will be used must be kept in mind.

When using temporary phenolic, epoxy-phenolic, or epoxy mold liners, almost any resin, with the exception of isophthalic resin, may be used. A formulation with isophthalic polyester does not release well from such molds.

The percentage of resin should be lowered somewhat in order to get proper appearance on these panels and to cut costs. In the stone patterns little, if any, pigment will be used in the formulation. Fillers will vary greatly to achieve authenticity of the panels.

To avoid the great number of variables in actual mold material, formulations will be given which would be proper for use in steel or cast-iron molds.

Brick mix

1. Orthophthalic polyester-monomers........................ 18.000 lb
2. Dimethyl analine (mix well before adding catalyst).......... 0.036
3. *t*-Butyl peroctoate....................................... 0.210
4. Pigment, any color to simulate color of brick.............. 2.000
5. Silica, 20–50 mesh...................................... 75.000
6. Silica, 100 mesh.. 25.000
7. Silica 200 mesh... 15.000

135.246 lb

Note that larger fillers are used in this instance than in the ceramic compound. This is possible because this material will be thicker than the ceramic mix in order to have an authentic brick appearance. The thicker a compound is to be poured, the larger the aggregates and fillers possible.

Dimension-stone mix (black stone)

1. Orthophthalic polyester-monomers........................ 18.000 lb
2. Dimethyl analine (mix before adding catalyst).............. 0.036
3. *t*-Butyl peroctoate....................................... 0.210
4. Pigment, carbon black................................... 1.000
5. Marble chips, No. 00, black marble....................... 80.000
6. Silica, 100 mesh.. 25.000
7. Silica, 200 mesh.. 15.000

139.246 lb

Note the change to colored aggregate; this saves on pigment. Also, the larger-sized aggregates may be used because the size of the dimension stone and the thickness to be poured will permit this. In addition, note the slightly higher filler-to-resin ratio permitted by the use of slightly larger aggregates. Cost is lowered in this manner.

Sandstone mix

1. Orthophthalic polyester-monomers .... 18.000 lb
2. Dimethyl analine (mix before adding catalyst).............. 0.036
3. *t*-Butyl peroctoate....................................... 0.210
4. Granite, crushed, No. 00................................ 80.000
5. Granite, crushed, No. 0000.............................. 25.000
6. Silica, 200 mesh.. 15.000

138.246 lb

Note the lack of pigment in this compound. In order to get an authentic sandstone appearance, color must be derived from the aggregates and fillers. Granite is ideal for this because it is multicolored. The finished appearance of this mix will be almost identical to that of natural sandstone.

Any natural stone can be matched perfectly with a polyester compound by choosing proper fillers, aggregates, and, when necessary, pigments.

Authenticity is a combination of well-designed molds and good matching in color, gloss, and other appearances. A careful study of the natural material being matched will reveal such small details as tiny specks of different colors imbedded in the surface. There is no problem in obtaining fillers and aggregates in any color to match perfectly these effects.

Many times it is most advisable to use ground marble dust instead of pigments. It is obtainable in practically every color from the marble-chip suppliers listed in the Appendix. This material is very low in cost, and the color shades will more closely match natural marble and stone colors. Care must be taken, however, in matching these colors. The ground marble dust will give colors far darker than anticipated, when wet out with the resin. Quantities much less than the formulator would imagine will be necessary.

Travertine and Terra Cotta

These two types of panels are set apart from others in this chapter for several reasons. These will be full-sized 4×8 ft panels, with no grout lines, yet they will not be smooth-surfaced materials such as discussed later under marble, granite, and wood grain.

Each product takes separate molds, whether they be the temporary or permanent molds. Of course, the only way to achieve complete authenticity is to take the molds from the natural stone. This is reasonably easy to do with terra cotta because it has no indentations, holes, etc., as does travertine. The latter has many undercuts in the natural stone which presents a problem when casting molds. However, this is overcome by using silicone-rubber temporary molds; this highly flexible material will stretch and pull out of these undercuts, whereas the rigid materials and cast iron will not.

Possibly a good way to attack this problem would be to set up a prototype in a good, heat-resisting plaster. Since the great majority of the face of travertine is smooth, polished material, the prototype can be cast face down on plate glass, allowed to partially cure, and then turned face-side up. The holes, indentations, etc., to match the natural travertine would then be handworked into the surface before the plaster fully cured. Care could be taken to avoid any undercuts, leaving all the imperfections slightly beveled for easy release. When fully cured, this material may be sealed or treated much as the natural stone would be prior to the mold-casting procedure. Plasters are available today that will allow cast-iron molds to be taken from them.

A good mold maker could probably take polished steel plate and weld the surface in such a manner that it would very closely simulate the imperfections in travertine. This would be an ideal method of building the molds and much more economical. Permanent molds could be made possibly for less cost than even temporary tooling by the other method. Also, each of the molds to be built would be slightly different, adding to the authenticity of the finished product.

A number of means of building these molds should be considered before proceeding. There are many good mold and die makers in the business, who know the simplest and most economical way to make dies and molds for a given product. They should be shown a full-sized slab of the material to be copied. After careful study, recommendations and alternate methods of building the molds can be discussed.

Authenticity is of utmost importance because if the synthetic material does not match the natural product in every way, then its market value is very low.

Rustic Stone Panels

There is much being done in construction materials today in rustic panels. These are panels in which small stones are partially imbedded into concrete, leaving the surface rough. These materials are most complementary to many types of buildings. Materials such as these can be made up very economically with polyester resin in 4×8 ft panels, which weigh a small fraction of the concrete version.

They will be made on the same type of production line as shown for the synthetic ceramic tile, except for a few changes in equipment setup. Here, there will be no need for a rib-coater, but there will be an aggregate-spreader added to the production line just before the conveyor enters the oven.

These panels, instead of being produced face down, as are the others discussed, will be made face up. The backing material, whether it be a good grade of hardboard, plywood, or asbestos-cement board, will be placed into the mold at the start of the production line, with the adhesive side up.

The second station in this production will be where the matrix formulation is flowed out into the mold and vibrated so that it is level. The thickness may vary, according to the size of stones to be used. For

No. 1 stones, the thickness should be about 0.030 in., and for No. 2 stones, about 0.040 in.

A formulation for this matrix would be as follows:

1. Orthophthalic polyester/monomer.......................... 100.0 lb
2. Dimethyl analine (mix before adding catalyst).............. 0.2
3. *t*-Butyl peroctoate.. 1.1
4. Silica, 100 mesh.. 400.0
5. Silica, 200 mesh.. 100.0
6. Pigment, as desired, but approximately.................... 8.0
                                                             ――――――
                                                             609.3 lb

This will be a very liquid, flowable mix, which will level out in the molds very easily.

The mold now passes under the aggregate-spreader, where the desired amount of rough stone is spread into it. A very small amount of vibration will cause the stone to sink into the bottom of the mold, displacing the matrix and leaving something over half of the stones exposed above the surface.

The amount of stones deposited on the surface of the matrix may vary according to the effect desired. The amount will be close to 1.5 lb per sq ft when using No. 1 stones, and nearly 2.1 lb per sq ft when using No. 2 stones.

Any excess stone that do not get down into the matrix will be easy to remove after the panel goes on through the oven and is removed from the mold to be stacked. These loose stones will fall off and may go back into the aggregate-spreader for reuse.

Such panels as these are not limited to Nos. 1 and 2 stones. They may be made up with much larger stones, but of course cost, shipping weight, etc., will go up considerably.

These stones may be marble chips, crushed granite, white or tinted quartz, or rounded river gravel. Many beautiful designs can be devised in these panels by changing or even mixing the stones to be used.

These panels will not warp because of the elasticity of the adhesive. As the polyester compound cures, it can shrink without causing any stresses to the backing material. The bond will be excellent between the polyester matrix and the adhesive. The oven heat and the exotherm heat will melt the adhesive sufficiently for it to adhere well.

Synthetic Marble and Synthetic Granite Panels

There are two completely different ways to make these materials. The first method to be discussed will be poured-material with backing.

The same production line as previously outlined will be used, with the same equipment setup as for ceramic tile, except that the rib-coater will not be used. The molds will be open, smooth-surfaced steel, finished to a 5-μ polish. The mold surface must be kept in this condition to produce high-quality finishes on the product.

The process for both marble and granite panels will require a gel coat. That given earlier in this chapter for high-gloss ceramic tile will be ideal for this use.

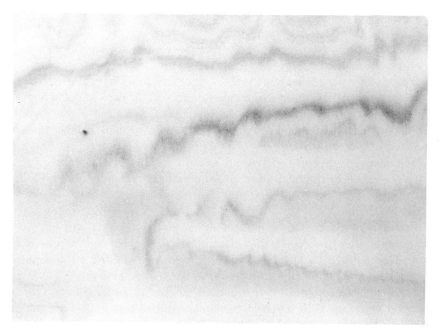

PHOTO 11.   *Synthetic marble wall panels.*

Following the gel coat, the marbelized mix will be placed in the molds by pouring, and will be vibrated so that it levels out in the cavity. The thickness of the material should be approximately 0.040 in.

Formulation for the marble mix

1. Orthophthalic polyester, resilient-monomers................ 20.00 lb
2. Dimethyl analine (mix before adding catalyst)............... 0.04
3. *t*-Butyl peroctoate.. 0.25
4. Pigment... 3.00
5. Silica, 100 mesh.. 80.00
6. Silica, 200 mesh.. 30.00

133.29 lb

The above would be marbelized with one or more colors.

Formulation for the marbelizing mix

1. Orthophthalic resin-monomers............................. 1.000 lb
2. Dimethyl analine (mix before adding catalyst).............. 0.002
3. *t*-Butyl peroctoate....................................... 0.010
4. Colloidal silica.. 0.500
5. Pigment... 0.200
6. China clay 1.000
                                                            ─────────
                                                            2.712 lb

This veining mix will be sufficient for approximately 3 cu ft of the matrix. If more than one veining color are to be used, then use about this amount of each veining color for 6 cu ft of matrix.

This veining mix will be very thixotropic and will not blend too much into the matrix if it is mixed in properly. With the matrix compound in the large double-arm mixer, the veining color or colors are added as the mixer turns about 6 to 8 revolutions. This will streak the entire mix appropriately.

Formulation for the granite mix

1. Orthophthalic polyester, resilient-monomers................ 20.00 lb
2. Dimethyl analine (mix well before adding catalyst).......... 0.04
3. *t*-Butyl peroctoate....................................... 0.25
4. Granite, crushed, No. 00.................................. 75.00
5. Silica, 100 mesh... 20.00
6. Silica, 200 mesh... 15.00
                                                            ─────────
                                                            130.29 lb

Note the lack of pigment in this mix. The combination of crushed natural granite and the silicas will give an authentic appearance of natural, rather fine-grained granite.

Crushed granite materials are available from many sources and are available in red, gray, pink, and a slightly green color. Any of these may be used.

The placing of the backing material on both the marble and the granite is done as previously outlined for the ceramic panels.

Synthetic Marble and Synthetic Granite Slabs

These materials are made very much like those above, with the exception that no backing material is required. The slabs are made up at a thickness of about ⅜ in. and therefore do not require backing.

Synthetic marble and granite slabs are preferable for commercial buildings, etc., where extremely hard wear and tear may be expected. They are usually fastened to the building walls with an epoxy adhesive. Multistory buildings may have the entire exterior covered with this material.

Since this material does not have a backing, it is advisable to make it up in 2 × 4 ft slabs. This is a convenient size for workmen to handle, and much less breakage will occur during handling, shipping, and installing.

The molds that are used for making the panels may be used to cast this material in 4 × 8 ft slabs. Then these may be sawed up after leaving the conveyor, or divider strips may be placed in the large molds, dividing them into four sections. This latter method is most convenient and economical.

For the marble slabs, the same compound and the mixing methods used for the thinner panels would be used, except that more material would go into the molds.

For the granite slabs, either the same mix as for the granite panels may be used, giving a rather fine-grained effect, or much larger crushed granite may be used in the mix, giving a coarse-grained slab. The coarse-grained granite is more desirable for very large buildings.

These materials, particularly the granite, can be installed on a building for a fraction of the cost of natural stone. Granite is one of the most desirable of building materials, but it is just too expensive. It is roughly double the cost of marble because of its hardness. Granite is almost pure silica, so the cutting, grinding, and polishing costs are very high.

Synthetic granite and marble made in this way will be inexpensive enough so that most buildings can afford the beauty and prestige of such a facing. Only an expert, examining these materials at close range, can possibly tell that they are not natural stone.

Slabs of marble similar to this are now being produced in several plants in the United States, but the price is very close to that of natural marble. Production problems include: lack of mass production procedures and the fact that manufacturers are making the present material much too thick.

Most of these small plants are job-shop operations. They take an order for one building and produce it in individual molds at room temperatures. The set of molds is tied up for at least 4 hr, while the workmen wait. Everything is done fairly much by hand labor, so naturally costs are very high.

Most of these materials are now produced anywhere from ½ to ¾ in. Entirely too much compound is used, and therefore shipping weights and installation costs are extremely high on such a heavy material.

The only way a product such as this can possibly find a very wide market is by lowering costs. The only solution is mass production, with proper automation to reduce labor costs. There is no need to custom-produce special colors for buildings. A manufacturer can produce synthetic marble in six colors, and granite in four, and satisfy demands completely.

In production such as previously outlined, where around 5,000 sq ft per hr can be produced, costs will go down to about 28 cents per sq ft in the ⅜-in. thickness. Adding overhead, profits, distributors, and other costs, it can still go on a building installed for well under $1.50 per sq ft.

This market can be very large, and a manufacturer of polyester products would be wise to look into it carefully. When this material is available in large quantities at reasonable prices, builders and architects will use it.

Marble and Wood-grain Panels

There are many types of paneling on the market today which simulate wood grain and marble. They are either high-pressure laminates, which are very expensive, or they are printed-type panels, where plywood or hardboard is primed with a base coat, and then a design is printed directly into the base coat. Then a clear top coating is applied, usually a melamine, and the whole is baked. Particularly in wood grain, millions of sq ft are sold each month. It is reasonable in cost, and the quality is excellent for interior use.

There are also other ways of producing these panels, not only in wood grain and marble, but in many other decorative designs.

A material quite similar to the high-pressure laminates may be produced on a production line such as previously discussed in this chapter. It may be produced with a very low pressure, such as that applied by a calender, or with no pressure at all.

Printed alpha-cellulose overlays, sometimes called saturating papers, are available in large rolls at any width desired. The manufacturers of these materials are listed in the Appendix. Some manufacturers have hundreds of designs from which to choose. These same patterns are used by the high-pressure laminating industry to manufacture their materials. The only difference is that they use much heavier weights of the paper than are contemplated here.

These printed papers are available in weights ranging from what is referred to as 29 lb to over 100 lb. (These weights refer to that number of pounds per 3,000 sq ft.) At low pressures, or at no pressure at all, the very lightest weights of these materials must be used.

On the production line, the face of the mold will receive a gel coat, such as that recommended for the ceramic panels. The printed paper will be immersed in this gel coat, pass through the oven for curing, and receive the plywood or hardboard backing, just as most of the other panels described in this chapter. Just enough pressure should be applied to ensure that the surface of the adhesive is in contact with all surfaces of the printed laminate.

The gel coat should be entirely clear, and the adhesive on the hardboard or plywood should be colored to form the background color. The entire operation would be very economical, and the quality would be equal to, or superior than that of, the printed-on variety now on the market.

These very light-weight papers are completely transparent when wet out with polyester, so the fibers do not show at all. Nothing stands out except the printed design and the background color.

These printed papers are very low in cost. On a wood grain, where there is only one color printed on, they cost about 1 cent per sq ft when buying in large quantities. On a marble design, where there are as many as three colors, they sell for about 2½ cents per sq ft.

These panels can be made up in wood grain and marble at very low costs, possibly selling for even less than the printed-on type now so widely marketed. They are much more authentic-looking than a design which is printed onto a base coat on the backing. In most cases printing procedures are much the same as when printing overlay paper, but it is more difficult to print a stiff, hard surface than a soft, pliable paper.

A manufacturer with this type of production line will find this is a method of producing panels well worth looking into. The quantities of this type of material being sold are very high.

Concrete Block, Clay Block, Cinder Block, and Brick Facings

There are several companies producing block and brick facings today. These are made by a wide variety of processes, and almost all of them are made with polyester resins. Some of them are of excellent quality and are produced in large quantities, so prices are reasonable.

There seems to be very little selection of colors and patterns in these facing materials. A great number of them are made in a salt-and-pepper pattern; others are made in a terrazzo pattern. The salt-and-pepper pattern is usually done with a white background, with very small black aggregate in it to give the speckled effect.

These are nonground facings and are low in cost. (The terrazzo pattern is more expensive because this facing must be ground.) They make very attractive building blocks, and actually there is more demand for them than the processors can supply. There is a need for much larger production of these block facings, at lower costs, and in many different patterns.

Building blocks are mainly used in southern and west coast areas, where climatic conditions permit their use. In the colder climates, they

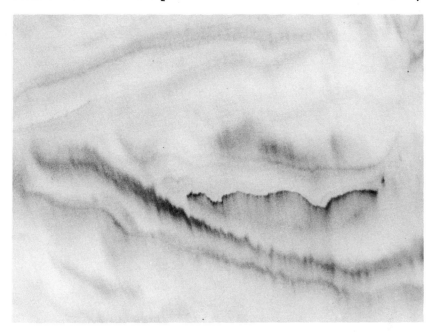

PHOTO 12.   *Concrete block facing, marbelized.*

are used extensively for interior wall construction, while in the warmer climates they are often used for an entire structure.

Because of the excessive weight of blocks and bricks, they are seldom transported for long distances. Usually they are manufactured within a hundred miles or so from where they will be used. Because of this transportation problem, either the facings must be applied at the manufacturing plant where they are made, or the facings can be manufactured separately and bonded to the block at the block plant or at the construction site.

Since plant work is lower in cost than labor performed in the field, this seems to leave two choices: all facings are manufactured and applied at the block plant, or the facings are manufactured in another plant and then bonded to the block in the block plant.

Undoubtedly, the former route is most economical. Several block manufacturers have installed some kind of production line to do this work simply because of the demand for faced block. Those already in the business would like very much to get out of it. They say they are block manufacturers, and the facing part of the business does not pay profits. The business of facing materials *would* pay profits if a proper production line were set up to do this work with very low labor costs and high output.

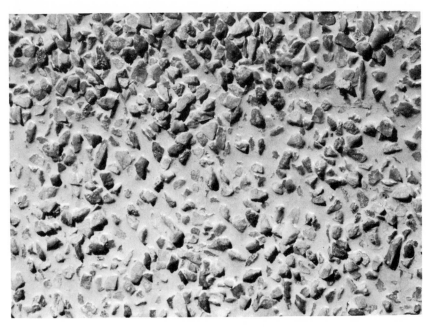

PHOTO 13. *Concrete block facing, rustic.*

Block can be faced in two ways: The facing can extend out from the block itself, half the thickness of a normal mortar joint, so when the blocks are laid the facings meet flush and the mortar does not show; or, the facing material can end flush with the edges of the block, so the mortar joint will show.

The first method is very bad in one way: The extending portion of the facing is often damaged in handling and shipping. The percentage of loss is fairly high, so this method should be avoided whenever possible in plant-applied facings.

Another means of attacking this problem could be for a polyester-product manufacturer to produce these oversized facings, with a suitable adhesive on the backs; workmen could then easily apply the facings to the blocks after a wall is erected.

These facings may be made up very thin, the adhesive applied to the backs, and packaged with a release paper between the individual facings.

A production line such as used to produce the items discussed previously in this chapter can easily be used to produce these facings.

High-gloss facings may be desired, in which case a gel coat would be necessary. For semigloss facings no gel coat would be required.

They would be produced by much the same methods used in paneling, with the exceptions that there no backing would be required, and the molds would have to be divided into the proper sizes.

The compounds used would be quite like those given earlier. Patterns could be solid colors, speckled, salt-and-pepper effects, marbelized, or a number of different designs. The facings could have smooth or textured surfaces, depending on the mold material used.

There are a number of metal-goods manufacturers who can supply steel with hammered finish, sandblasted finish, and a variety of other surfaces. Some of these would produce very desirable finishes on block facings.

The finished thicknesses of the facings could be from 0.020 to 0.050 in. in all patterns with the exception of the terrazzo patterns. It would not be practical to manufacture terrazzo patterns with this type of production line without adding all the grinding equipment that would be necessary.

On emerging from the oven, the back sides of the facings would have the adhesive applied. A waterproof, durable adhesive is necessary as the majority of these facings would be used on the exteriors of buildings.

A formulation for such an adhesive would be as follows:

1. Chlorinated natural rubber	15.0 lb
2. Toluol or xylol	25.0
3. Liquid, refined wood rosin	5.0
4. Chlorinated biphenyl	5.0
5. Polybutene, medium viscosity	5.0
6. Silica, 325 mesh	40.0
7. China clay	5.0
	100.0 lb

The adhesive would be applied to the back of the facing by an extruder with a notched head to achieve a ribbed effect.

This adhesive would have a very high tack. The release paper would have to be applied at once to prevent the escape of the solvent. These facings would be ready to box, probably in packages of 25 to 50.

At the job site, the paper would be stripped off and the facings bonded to the block wall by a contact type of adhesive that would instantly bond to the surface. The adhesive would be impervious to water, and even in climates with much rainfall and humidity would not lose its bond. Such an adhesive may be immersed in water for long periods of time, and still the bond will be retained.

Although this solution to the block and brick facing problem may not be ideal, it seems to be the best route to take. Damage during handling, shipping, and application will practically be eliminated. Cost of transportation of these light facings will present no great problem, so they may be shipped all over the country from a single plant.

The market is ripe for these materials. They are not being used in quantity, however, simply because they are not available at costs conducive to large-scale use.

Modular Panels

Perhaps the greatest single building-material market to be explored is that of modular panels. Already it has become a major industry. Plants are being installed all over the country to meet the demands for such panels. Some plants produce the complete panel, including both faces and the insulating material in the void between, and then finish one or both sides of the panel. Other plants merely assemble the modular panels from materials purchased from other manufacturers. Some of these perform the finishing operation, and others purchase the side paneling prefinished.

A number of these companies do not use foamed cores, but use paper honeycomb materials instead. These are lower in cost, but thermal-insulation values suffer somewhat. Also, the paper materials are subject to termites, dampness, and fire.

Some prefer to use pressed hardboard for the "skins," as they are sometimes referred to, while others prefer plywood. A number of the foamed cores are made of sheet polystyrene foam, while some are made of sheet polyurethane foam. More recently, the trend has been to foam the urethane in place between the already assembled "skins."

Modular panels are not used for structural support. They are used as fill-in walls and partitions. Many times they are so designed as to be movable. This is of particular interest in office buildings, where the room-size requirements of one tenant would not coincide with the needs of another.

This writer feels that modular panels can be produced in a different manner, using polyester resins, which would cut the cost by a very large percentage. A completely different approach would be used.

By the method proposed, the entire panel would be produced and finished in a single production line. Diagram 8 shows such a production line. Here the complete unit would be produced and finished in a series of steps whereby the panel would be an integral laminate, with each step bonded firmly to the others.

Basically, there would be two production lines, one mounted directly above the other. The upper line would be somewhat shorter and would produce the skin for one side of the modular panel. The bottom line would produce the second skin and would complete the panel.

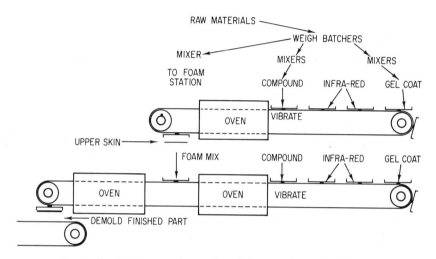

DIAGRAM 7. *Production line for integral modular panels. Both skins and foam are made of polyester compounds.*

At station 1 the deep, open molds would receive a gel coat some 4 to 5 mils thick. The molds would progress to station 2 for gelling under infrared lamps. At station 3 the gel coat would be treated with the background design or color. This may be wood grain, marble, solid color, or any decorative design discussed earlier in this chapter. One side of the finished modular panel might be wood grain, while the other side might be a solid color, a marble pattern, or a ceramic-tile pattern. The upper station 3 may be producing the wood grain design, while the lower station 3 may be producing the marble or other pattern.

This background would be applied to a thickness of from 0.015 to 0.030 in. as desired, giving the entire skin, including the gel coat, a total thickness of 0.020 to 0.035 in. or more if desired.

Each mold would pass on through its respective oven to station 4. At this station, the lower mold would receive a layer of polyester compound containing the blowing, or foaming, agent. The skin from the upper station 4 would be placed, face-side up, directly onto the foaming core mix, constituting the upper mold, to contain the foam as it rises in the mold.

Then, the entire lower conveyor would carry the panel on into the next oven, where the foam would rise and cure, bonding the entire part into an integral modular panel.

At station 5 the panel would be finished, and at station 6 the panel would drop out onto a third conveyor, which would carry it on to be packaged and shipped. No trimming or finishing operations would be required.

If desired, some of the molds could be designed in shapes to allow for windows and doors, or window and door openings could be cut in the panels in the field with an abrasive-blade saw. Such accessories as fastening devices should be installed before packaging. Metal clips or other fasteners may be countersunk into the foamed core with a good epoxy adhesive.

If the manufactuer wishes, the production line may be further enlarged to include the installation of electrical conduits and outlets and other necessary equipment. These may be properly placed into the molds before the gel-coat operation, so when the finished panel comes off the production line, they will be a part of the entire panel.

Another approach would be to place silicone-rubber blanks in the position where these electrical installations are later to be made. These blanks may be easily pulled from the panel after production is completed, leaving the properly placed ducts for electrical conduits and outlets.

Each of these methods should be carefully considered. Each has merit, and end cost would be the deciding factor. By either method, no cutting, drilling, or other work would be necessary in the field.

The skins or exteriors of the panels may be made by any of the processes discussed earlier in this chapter. The desired pattern may .be any of those mentioned, and the pattern may be achieved by any of the methods. Wood-grain, marble, and many other patterns may be done by the printed-overlay-paper method. Marble, sandstone, ceramic tile, brick, or any of the other synthetic finishes may be used. There will be little or no difference in production speed if the two sides of the panel are completely different. The two production lines for producing these skins must be synchronized in speed so that the two parts meet at station 4. This will create no unusual problem, regardless of any differences in the patterns to be produced on the two sides.

The formulations will be the same as those given earlier for each respective type of finish. The gel coat may remain the same, unless special finishes are desired. A matte finish is perhaps the most difficult of any possible finishes in polyester, but even this may be accomplished with proper additives. (Chapter 11 will discuss this at more length.)

The foamed core of the panel will be the most critical part of production. Formulations will have to be very exact, and the proper amounts will have to go into the molds in order to maintain exact thicknesses in the finished panels. The thickness may be 4 or 5 in., or any other desired thickness, limited only by the depth of the molds. This thickness will depend entirely on the amount of foaming polyester formulation deposited in the mold between the two skins.

Foamed polyester has never made any progress among foamed plastics. The accepted blown plastics include polystyrene, polyurethane, and epoxy. Recently progress has been made with foamed polyethylene. Blown polyvinyls have long been used, but have many limitations for such an application as ridgid thermal insulation.

Polystyrene is the lowest in cost of the accepted blown plastics. Its major limitation is the difficulty of obtaining a nonflammable compound. Polyurethane may be made as strong and as rigid as desired, but is prone to pick up moisture from the air too readily. Epoxy foams have been the best to date, and cost has been their major drawback. Foamed polyethylene shows much promise: it is low in cost, nonabsorptive, and has other good features.

Many researchers have recognized for years that the properties of polyesters make them ideal for semirigid and rigid foams. They have been used extensively as curing agents or hydrogen donors with diisocyanates to produce the best-quality polyurethane foams available. These polyesters are somewhat different from straight polyester foaming material. They are generally saturated polyesters, containing no monomers. They react with the diisocyanates through the hydroxyls in the polyester and the NCO of the diisocyanate.

Considered here, however, is an unsaturated polyester, containing its proper quantities of monomers and cured by peroxide catalysts. This has been a subject of much research over the years. Varying degrees of success have been reported, but little or no such material is actually being produced today.

The major problem has been the lack of exact controls on the catalyst system. It has been too difficult to find a catalyst that would gel a formulation at the exact instant that the blowing agent reached its maximum expansion. The result has been poor cell formation and "fallen" foams, comparable to what happens to a cake in the oven when someone slams the oven door.

Blowing agents are available that are suitable for foaming polyesters at a rather wide temperature range, from 200 to over 400°F. The factors that must be considered include not just the temperature of the oven, but also the exotherm temperature of the resin itself, which is of utmost importance.

Polyester resins can have peak exotherm temperatures of from 250 to well over 400°F, depending on the intermediates and amounts of intermediates used in the manufacture of the particular resin. Even the catalyst system can have some effect on the peak exotherm temperature. Also, monomers and promoters can affect exotherm temperatures to some degree. Furthermore, the thermal conductivity of the mold material or of the skins surrounding the core mix can have a bearing on the maximum exotherm temperature reached. Even very minute amounts of moisture in the resin or fillers and the acid number of the resin can affect the exotherm in one manner or another.

Thus, in order to manufacture a high-quality unsaturated polyester foam, all the above factors must be closely coordinated. The temperature at which the blowing agent reaches its maximum expansion must match the peak exotherm temperature of the resin, and this must very closely coincide with the oven temperature and the temperature at which the catalyst system gels the foam.

It may seem that there are too many controls to coordinate, and of course in the field this would be true. These polyesters very probably can never be foamed in place in the field as can the epoxies and polyurethanes. But in a manufacturing plant such as contemplated here there should be no unsurmountable problems.

At the plant, there can be very close controls for every phase of the operation. Compound temperature, mold temperature, temperature of the skins when they come in contact with the foaming compound, and the temperature on the oven can all be very closely controlled.

The resin manufacturer can produce a resin that will reach an exact peak exotherm temperature, and the catalyst system and blowing agent can be matched to that with little difficulty.

A good starting formulation for the foam core will be the following:

1. Rigid orthophthalic polyester-monomer, formulated for a peak exotherm of 300°F.. 100.00 lb
2. Dinitrosopentamethylenetetramine (blowing agent)......... 6.00
3. Phthalic anhydride (activator for blowing agent)........... 0.20
4. t-Butyl perbenzoate (catalyst)........................... 0.75
5. Dimethylhexane diperbenzoate (co-catalyst).............. 0.25
6. Dimethylanaline (promoter) add after mixing above........ 0.05
7. Colloidal silica (thixotroping agent)..................... 5.00
8. Diammonium phosphate (fire retarder).................... 5.00
9. Antimony trioxide (fire retarder)........................ 5.00
10. Pigment, if desired..................................... 3.00

_____

125.25 lb

A number of other blowing agents may be used, with a suitable activator. Azodicarbonamide, oxybisbenzene sulfonyl hydrazine, and other dinitroso compounds may be used to achieve the required blowing temperature.

The above would be mixed on a high-speed, high-shear type mixer for as short a time as possible to attain a homogeneous mix. Overmixing will build up too much heat in the compound.

The foamed material will have a density of approximately 2 lb per cu ft and a K factor of 0.19 to 0.20.

It will be an extremely rigid panel, with considerably more structural strength than a similar panel made with polystyrene or polyurethane foam because of its integral manufacture. All three parts will be firmly bonded into one single product.

The cell structure of the foam will be excellent because of the combinations of mold and skins forming the containing cavity for its formation. Over 95% of the cells will be closed, giving the panel a very low thermal conductivity. Compressive strengths of the completed panel will be impressive in both directions.

The panel will be very fire resistant, particularly if the flame-retarder additives are also used in the manufacture of the skins.

The completed weight of the panel will be considerably lower than that of a panel made with wood, metal, or hardboard components.

This product can be the basis for a very large industry. The capital investment required will be considerable, but this is a product with an already established market that is growing steadily. It may be produced and marketed very competitively with present modular panels.

Many of the products discussed in this chapter will need either an internal or an external mold release. Due to the wide variety of possible materials that might be used in the design of the molds themselves, the writer has excluded mold-release materials from formulations. The companies which manufacture such materials are listed in the Appendix. A number of compounds will be found to give good, fast release of products from any type of mold material that is used.

Five

BUILDING ACCESSORIES

In the construction industry, very few materials have remained constant over the past hundred years. These materials have been changed and improved vastly during this period.

Bathroom Fixtures: Tubs, Commodes, Lavatories

A notable exception has been bathroom fixtures. Today, we are installing pretty much the same tubs, commodes, and lavatories that were in use well before the turn of this century. Styles and shapes have changed and colors have been added, but basically they are the same fixtures our grandparents used.

The bathroom of the home, office, or school is perhaps the largest problem that confronts architects, builders, owners, and decorators. Largely, the problem is just ignored. Installations are made with the only fixtures available; the people who must live with these fixtures daily may not like them, but they learn to tolerate them simply because there is nothing else on the market with which they may be replaced.

The fixtures of a bathroom constitute a rather large percentage of building costs. The cost of these items is high because of the process required to manufacture porcelain and ceramic materials. The percentage of rejects during manufacture further raises the cost. Breakage during handling, shipping, and installation is high. After installed and in use, these materials are still very prone to chipping and breakage. Certain household commodities will stain them, and these stains are hard, if not impossible, to remove.

Basically, these bathroom fixtures are good; their manufacturers have improved the quality somewhat and have changed basic styles to make them more functional. There is much room for improvement, however, particularly in making them more decorative to the home, office, or school.

Polyester compounds can be formulated for the manufacture of these fixtures. Chemical resistance will be entirely comparable, rejects can be cut down considerably, breakage during manufacture, handling, shipping, and installation can be drastically reduced, and the hazards encountered during daily use can be minimized.

Polyester bathroom fixtures may be manufactured in beautiful designs and patterns, and color choice would not be limited in any way. Every home could afford a marble bathroom set, as costs would be lower than present materials. Decorators could accomplish miracles in the bathroom, which is usually a rather drab portion of the home. Architects would at last have a choice in specifying bathroom fixtures.

The setting up of a manufacturing plant for these polyester bathroom fixtures will be a sizable investment. In order to compete adequately, they will have to be mass produced just as the currently available fixtures are.

Proper tooling will be the largest single cost of setting up such a plant, and it can vary widely, depending on the number of styles, shapes, and models to be placed on the market.

Professional tool and die makers must be employed to do this work. The shapes and undercuts involved, particularly in the manufacture of the commodes, present problems that only a professional can cope with.

Men who are presently employed in making molds and dies for this type of work are not plentiful, and considerable work must be done in selecting the proper mold material. During the manufacture of prototypes, several materials should be tried to see which will prove best in actual production.

A number of books have been published concerning mold and die manufacture. Since tooling is the most important factor to be considered, books about this subject should be studied carefully. New materials and techniques in tooling have recently come to light, which are well worth consideration.

First, consider flexible tooling versus fixed, rigid tooling. With any end product that can be manufactured without undercuts, permanent metal tooling should definitely be used. Some undercut parts may be manufactured with such tooling, where inserts and withdrawal sections can be built in.

All flexible tooling, whether it be silicone rubber, fluorocarbons, urethane elastomers, or other polymeric substance, is temporary tooling, with a limited useful life. These are fine to use in research and development work and to manufacture a limited number of products, but they should be avoided in actual production work whenever possible.

Some of the new heat-resistant glasses and ceramics may very well be considered for tooling. They can be polished to a very fine finish, and will give excellent-quality parts.

Plastics tooling, such as polyester, epoxy, phenolic, and epoxy-phenolic will give good quality parts, but, again, is limited in productive use and so is temporary.

Cast-iron, cast-aluminum, and lead-based alloys are probably the best substances for permanent tooling for this type of product. Cast iron may be chrome-plated with an excellent surface, and such tooling has an almost unlimited usable life.

Throw-away tooling materials may also be considered. These are finding many uses in the production of plastics parts. Mostly they consist of polyethylene, ABS, or polyallomer sheet material of rather light gauge, vacuum-formed to make molds and dies. The major drawback of these materials is their limited heat resistance; thus, a production line set up to use these types of molds would be very limited as to working temperatures. They are practical, however, where casting is done at ambient or low temperatures and the exotherm of the compound to be processed is reasonably low. These types of molds are used three or four times, and then thrown away.

Bathtubs, shower pans, lavatories, and toilet tanks present no major die problems. The commode itself, however, is entirely another matter. To make tooling for the shapes and forms of present models would be a nightmare. The first step must be to design another type of commode form so that making tooling for it will be simpler.

Redesigning the commode should present no major obstacles. The consumer will have no trouble adjusting to another shape. Its basic design has not changed much in a century, so perhaps it is time to change it anyway. The food or underpart of the commode will require the most change. There is no reason why it should be its present shape, and no one should object to a change that would alter this portion. Smooth, clean, straight lines should be preferred to the present curves and undercuts.

It may very well be worthwhile to consider making the commode in two parts—top and bottom—separately, and later joining them together. This could solve quite a few problems, with a minimum of redesigning.

The male portion of the die for the water duct would almost necessarily be silicone rubber, which would give the required flexibility for removal after curing. Very likely all other mold and die components could be of the rigid, permanent type.

Since there would be at least four parts per bathroom set—lavatory, tub, commode, water tank, and top to the tank—for large-scale production it will be necessary to set up four separate production lines. If the commode were to be made in two parts, this would add another line. Shower pans would add still another line. This does not mean that every piece of equipment in the plant would have to be duplicated this many times. Only the molds, conveyors, and ovens would be multiple. The same mixers and the same weighing and batching equipment could serve all the production lines at once since the same compound would be used in all simultaneously. Possibly the gel-coating equipment would have to be multiple, depending on the production-line setup.

Diagram 8 shows a suggested production line for these bathroom fixtures. This basic setup can be varied widely to accomplish the same end result.

The following formulations would be the type to be used in such an end product:

Gel coat

1. Tetrachlorophthalic rigid polyester	100.00 lb
2. Dimethyl analine (mix well before adding catalyst)	0.20
3. t-Butyl peroctoate	1.00
4. Cellulose acetate butyrate (½ sec)	3.00
	104.20 lb

The cellulose acetate butyrate should be added to the resin by the resin manufacturer. This is a very effective thixotroping agent, to be used in polyester gel coats to prevent "crawl" and running on vertical, horizontal, or other surfaces.

This gel coat should be sprayed on all surfaces of the dies both male and female, to a thickness of about 5 mils. The result will be a product with an extremely high gloss and excellent chemical resistance to acids and alkalies. Abrasion resistance will be good, and the surface will be very difficult to chip and scratch. Stain resistance to iodine, etc., will be excellent.

Molding compound

1. Hexahydrophthalic resilient polyester...................... 20.00 lb
2. Dimethyl analine (mix well before adding catalyst)........... 0.04
3. *t*-Butyl peroctoate....................................... 0.25
4. Pigment... 5.00
5. Silica, 100 mesh... 80.00
6. Silica, 200 mesh... 25.00
7. Barytes, No. 1 bleached................................. 5.00

135.29 lb

This mix will be approximately 1 cu ft and may be multiplied by the size of the final mixer. All liquid components will be premixed in

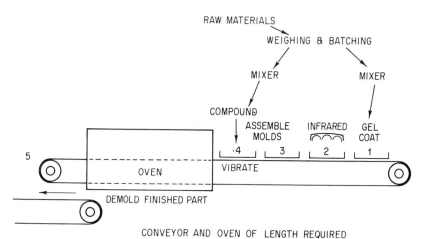

DIAGRAM 8. *Production line for bathroom fixtures, etc.*

a high-speed dissolver-type mixer and added to the fillers in the final mixer.

If the fixtures being manufactured are to be synthetic marble then the following veining mix should be used:

1. Hexahydrophthalic rigid polyester......................... 1.000 lb
2. Dimethyl analine (mix before adding catalyst).............. 0.002
3. *t*-Butyl peroctoate...................................... 0.010
4. Cellulose acetate butyrate (in resin)...................... 0.030
5. Pigment, any color....................................... 0.300
6. Colloidal silica... 0.100
7. China clay.. 0.400

1.842 lb

One or more of these veining colors may be added, but a total of about 1 lb per cu ft of the compound will give about the right amount of veining. They should be blended in as discussed in previous chapters.

The veining mix will be extremely thixotropic, so it will not blend in too much into the compound and will not smear and smudge as it is poured into these rather deep molds.

At station 1, the male and the female molds would be gel-coated with the clear coating. This would probably be done best by spray because of the contours involved. At station 2, the male would be assembled into the female. At station 3, the infrared oven would gel the gel coat. The parts would go on to station 4, where the molding compound would be poured into the molds. This mix will be liquid enough so that it will require minimum vibration. Care must be taken that no air pockets remain unfilled. The conveyor will then take the parts through the oven for curing and on to station 5, where they will be removed from the molds by air pressure. The molds, both male and female, will have quick-disconnect air fittings installed at several places around them. A quick blast of air will easily remove a part from its mold.

The part will be finished, with no subsequent operations necessary. It may be placed on a second conveyor to be carried to the packaging section.

These fixtures may be made up in white or any solid color, the marbelized design above, or they may be made up in a multitude of other patterns and designs. The marble pattern will probably be the most popular of all.

A second method of production that should at least be considered for making these fixtures is the pressure-casting process, also known as the autoclave process. This method, while possibly somewhat slower, would produce slightly better products. This process is first discussed in Chap. 2. In making bathroom fixtures the process would be quite similar, with the exception of a difference in the molds.

Since this product is gel-coated, there is no problem of pores or pinholes showing on the surface. The casting process discussed herein will produce a part that looks quite as good as the autoclave process. However, any pores and pinholes within a part will detract somewhat from the strength of the part. So a pressure-cast part will be slightly stronger than a cast product.

Other methods of producing these products include compression-molding, injection-molding, bag-molding, and plunger-molding. With any of these processes, there are problems to be solved, and advantages and disadvantages. The size of the parts, particularly the bathtub, will present some very large problems, and these dies would be extremely expensive. Of the alternate methods offered, the injection-molding method would possibly offer more advantages for long-term production than any of the others.

Shower Pans and Shower Stalls

These two items would be produced in a manner similar to the other bathroom fixtures. The shower pans could be considered a part of such a production line. The shower stalls would be somewhat different, however, in that they would have to be made in four parts, one with the opening for the door.

The method and the pattern or color could be exactly like the bathroom fixtures so that everything in the room would match.

Vanity Tops, Bar Tops, Kitchen Tops, and Table Tops

Vanity tops for bathrooms may be produced by a number of processes, but such a production line as outlined above would be very good. Tops may be made up into two separate parts, or the lavatory may be built right into the vanity top, all in one piece.

Here, again, the molds are the most important part of the operation. Vanity tops may be produced in small quantities with aluminum, phenolic high-pressure laminate, or with epoxy or polyester molds. Aluminum scratches very easily, so is unsuitable for long production runs. Too much polishing would be necessary. Plastic tooling would be very limited in its useful life.

For long runs, stainless steel or mild steel with chrome plate, polished to a 5-μ finish, are the only kind of permanent molds to use. Any good metal shop can make these, with the curvatures necessary for the returns, sideboards, and whatever final design is decided upon. See Diagram 9 for a suggested design for the vanity-top mold, with or without the built-in lavatory.

A smaller manufacturer may wish to produce these products in smaller quantities. If so, the investment of having a metal shop produce the male and female molds for the lavatory may be too great. These will have to be drawn, so tooling costs will be quite high. When a large number are to be made up, the tooling charge is easily distributed; but for a few sets of molds, this charge would be quite high.

Good-quality parts may be manufactured in short runs with plastic tooling. A good prototype lavatory of normal porcelain may be purchased. Care should be taken that no undercuts exist in it. Temporary polyester molds, both male and female, may be taken from this lavatory.

Polish the lavatory with two coats of a good, hard carnauba wax, buffing between each coat. Apply a gel coat by spray (such as described earlier in this chapter) to a thickness of 10 mils. Allow to gel, and apply another coat of the same material, pigmented, to a thickness of about 30 mils. Hand-roll out fiberglass random matting well into this, and allow to cure.

Only one mold may be taken at a time from the one lavatory. It may then be turned over, and the other mold may be taken in the

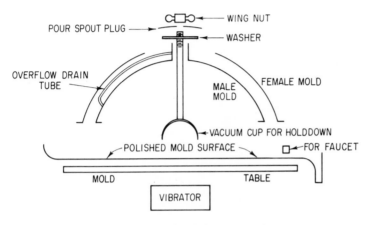

THE LENGTH AND WIDTH OF THE VANITY TOP MOLD MAY
BE AS DESIRED, USUALLY STANDARD

DIAGRAM 9. *Mold arrangement for casting vanity tops with integral lavatory.*

same manner. If desired, two porcelain lavatories may be purchased so that a pair of molds may be made at the same time.

After the polyester molds partially cure, strip them from the lavatory and place them in an oven to cure for 30 min at 250°F. Then they may be trimmed around the edges with a coarse file, and this edge may be sanded.

The holes for the drain and for the overflow must be kept open; they may be prepared as shown in Diagram 9. A silicone-rubber gasket is bonded to the edge of the male mold so that no resin can get under it and between it and the top of the vanity-top mold. A vacuum-cup arrangement (as shown) or an external-clamp arrangement will hold the male mold in position while the part is poured.

The first step is to carefully wax and polish the exterior of the male mold and the interior of the female mold with two coats of a good carnuaba wax. Internal mold releases do not work well with polyester tooling. If the face of the vanity top mold is highly polished chrome plate or stainless steel, no mold release will be necessary, but a very light coating of a good prepared external mold release may be applied if desired.

The male mold is fixed firmly in place, as are the small vacuum-faced silicone plugs for the faucet holes. The entire surfaces of the vanity-top mold, the male mold, and the interior of the female mold are all sprayed with about 5 mils of the gel coat mentioned earlier. When this has

PHOTO 14. *Polyester vanity top.*

gelled, the marble compound is poured over the entire surface and vibrated into place. No compound is poured over the male mold at this point. Now, the female mold is lowered into place. The lips extruding from its lower part will keep it from sinking down into the marble mix. The pour plug is removed from the female, and the space between male and female is filled. The pour plug is replaced, and the last portion of compound is poured in. (No vibrating must be done while the lavatory part is being filled, as this will cause the colors to streak and smear.)

All formulations may be quite similar to those for other bathroom fixtures given earlier. In this use, even much higher filler contents are possible. Mixes as high as 9 parts fillers by weight to 1 part resin are entirely feasible by using a good amount of larger aggregates in the mix. The maximum size of the aggregate will be determined by the thickness of the product. Aggregates up to size No. 0 quartz may be used if the part is ¼-in. thick or more. Usually, parts are made about ½-in. thick, so sizes No. 1 or even No. 2 quartz may be used.

A formulation for these products might be the following:

1. Orthophthalic resilient polyester........................ 13.000 lb
2. Dimethyl analine (mix before adding catalyst)............. 0.026
3. *t*-Butyl peroctoate....................................... 0.140
4. Pigment, any color....................................... 1.000
5. Quartz, No. 1... 80.000
6. Quartz, No. 00.. 20.000
7. Silica, 100 mesh.. 10.000
8. Silica, 200 mesh.. 5.000
9. Barytes, No. 1 bleached................................. 5.000

$$\overline{134.166 \text{ lb}}$$

This gives a molding compound that is only 10% resin. It will be sufficiently fluid so that it will flow out into the vanity-top mold without any great amount of vibration. No vibration will be necessary to fill the lavatory molds. If vibration seems to be necessary, then it must be very little.

The formulation above would be marbelized with a veining mix like the formulation given earlier in this chapter.

These formulations would be suitable for heat cure at temperatures of above 200°F. Should lower-temperature cures be desired, a benzoyl peroxide should be substituted for the *t*-butyl peroctoate.

Kitchen-cabinet tops, with or without the sink built-in, will be made in exactly the same manner. The same mold used for the vanity tops may be used, or a different shape may be desired. For the sink, whether it be a double or single, temporary male and female molds may be made by the same method described for making the lavatory molds. A proper porcelain prototype would be purchased, and then polyester molds would be taken from it.

These polyester molds will give good parts for up to 100 uses if properly cared for. They should be waxed and polished after every 5 to 8 parts taken from them.

Many other areas of the house may also use these materials. The breakfast bar, tables, even large dining-room tables will be beautiful with this material for a top. Desks, work tables, sewing cabinets, and many other pieces of furniture in the average house will be complemented with such material installed on the top.

In commercial buildings, there are thousands of uses for this synthetic marble material. At bank counters marble tops are almost a tradition. In stores of all kinds these materials will prove most useful, beautiful, and durable. In bars and lounges they will add a great amount of decor. No amount of alcohol spilled on the surface can affect the finish. Glasses or bottles that are dropped will not mar the surface. Synthetic marble will take a great amount of hard use and still remain beautiful.

Many other building accessories are very easy to make with polyester resins. These are the relatively small items, to which little thought is given. The percentage of total construction cost for these items is very small, but a plant can manufacture them and ship these materials all over the country. On a nation-wide basis, the market is indeed very large.

Baseboards, Feature Strips, and Dividing Strips

These items are relatively easy to make in either terrazzo or marble patterns.

They may be manufactured by a small industry, with limited capital, or on a large scale by a manufacturer producing one of the types of floor tile discussed in Chaps. 1 and 2.

Here, again, the molds are the principal elements involved. The shaped molds for casting the baseboards will be relatively inexpensive. Any good metal shop can shape and weld these molds from a heavy-gauge sheet metal.

The surface should be highly polished so that either marble or terrazzo patterns may be made. The terrazzo pattern will have to be ground, whereas the marble will not.

The molds should be $\frac{1}{4}$ in. deep so they will accomodate the terrazzo, which will have to be placed at this thickness. When the same molds are used for making the marble pattern, they will be only half-filled.

The formulas given in Chap. 2 for the poured-in-place terrazzo compound, or for the marbelized pattern, will be ideal for this use. The marble pattern will require a gel coat, whereas the terrazzo pattern (to be ground) will not.

The radius of the mold is of utmost importance. It must be shaped to an exact radius so it may be ground easily. A number of manufacturers (listed in the appendix) make diamond-grinder heads to fit any radius.

These molds should be made some 3 or 4 ft long for ease in handling and grinding.

The process for filling the molds will be to place the material in the cavity and vibrate it sufficiently for it to level out. The parts may be cured at room temperature or they may be oven cured. For production in large quantities, curing must be done by heat so that the molds may be reused rapidly. For the larger manufacturer with a production line, these molds would be fastened to the normal production line.

These parts may be compression-molded as well. For a manufacture who is compression-molding floor tile, the only extra expenditure would be for a set of dies.

Other parts that are so much a necessity are feature strips and dividing strips. These may be made exactly like baseboards in either terrazzo or marble patterns. The only added expenditures are the molds or dies.

When laying either terrazzo or marbelized flooring, either premanufactured or manufactured-in-place tile, there is always a need for these parts. Contrasting divider strips may be used to mark off the floor in squares, and the feature strips, either 4 or 6 in. wide, are often used around walls, sometimes set out from the wall about 12 in. Many different effects are easily designed with a supply of these materials. They are used very little simply because they are not available.

Stair Treads and Risers

These two items go along very well with the other products discussed in this chapter. Stairways are fairly well standardized in size as far as width is concerned. Length would not be a problem if these materials were made up 4 ft long. This would take care of almost any normal stairway. Any excess material can be sawed off easily using an electric saw with an abrasive blade.

Windowsills and Doorsills

In the average construction, these two items are normally made of wood. They are necessities, yet builders would like very much to use some material instead of wood. They soon discolor when painted or varnished, and are the first parts of a house to be attacked by decay. They are always unsightly, stained by children's hands and feet, and are very difficult to keep clean.

Windowsills and doorsills may be made of polyester compounds by any of the methods discussed earlier. They would never discolor or decay, and would always be decorative. They may be made in either terrazzo or marble patterns.

Laminates

There are a large number of high-pressure laminates on the market today. They are used for table tops, bar tops, kitchen work tops, and many uses in the construction industry.

Some of these laminates are made from phenolic resin; some are made from melamine. These products are of excellent quality, and the properties are very good for areas which receive much wear and tear. They will stand up under many years use in restaurants, in the home, or in the office.

They have one major drawback: cost. The cost of these materials is very high. The process by which they are made requires pressures up to 5000 psi. Sheets 4 ft × 8 in. take huge hydraulic pressures. The materials from which they are made require very long curing cycles, some up to 30 min, at high temperatures. The process is further complicated in that these plastics need a "breathing" cycle. The press closes for a few minutes, then must open to let excess gases escape, then close again for a longer period of time. Manufacturers use "leaf" presses with multiple platens. They may make up to 10 laminates at a time with the same amount of hydraulic pressure. Even so, the costs are very high.

Similar material may be made up with polyester resin at very low pressures. Instead of 2,000 to 5,000 psi, polyester may be done at 200 to 300 psi. Instead of up to 30-min cycle times, polyester can be done in 30 sec or less.

The only differences in the finished material would be slightly less heat resistance for the polyester and a slightly softer surface. Barcol hardness would be about 20% lower in a polyester laminate, and heat resistance would be about 10% lower. Abrasion resistance in the polyester laminate would be perhaps 30% lower. Chemical resistance, stain resistance, and other properties would be approximately equal.

The cost of the polyester laminates would be far less than half that of the high-pressure laminates.

Roughly the same process would be used as is used for the high-pressure laminates, except that much less equipment would be necessary. Presses would be of far less capacity, and dies would be lighter and more economical. Ordinary, two-platen presses could be used, making one laminate at a time, or the leaf presses could be employed, producing up to 10 per cycle.

The decorative effects would be accomplished in much the same manner as in the high-pressure laminates. Printed designs on alpha-cellulose paper are available in all kinds of wood grains, marble patterns, and a multitude of decorative patterns.

A gel coat is sprayed into the female cavity, and the printed design is laid out into this; the matrix compound is placed on top of that, and the press is closed.

Another method that is frequently used is to presaturate the printed paper, lay it out into the mold, and then place the compound on top. This would be more satisfactory for a polyester laminate because of the fast gel time. The former method would probably not give the paper a chance to wet out before gelling.

The matrix compound may be composed of a variety of fillers mixed into polyester resin. Some chopped fiberglass may be used in order to get high tensile strength. Silicas may be used to get hardness, and some clay must be used to get proper consistency for compression-molding.

It would not be practical to try to manufacture these laminates by means other than compression-molding since manufacturing them by this process would allow them to compete more closely in quality.

A number of variations of this material may be manufactured. Very possibly the properties of the polyester laminate can be improved to a point where they will be equal to the high-pressure laminates in every way.

One way to improve the heat resistance, Barcol hardness, and abrasion resistance would be to blend very hard fillers into the gel coat. Glass, in flake form, is now available. These flakes are completely transparent, and when wet out with resin, they disappear completely. The higher the percentage of these flakes that can be blended in to the gel coat, the better the properties will be.

Clean, white silica may also be used for this purpose. There are several suppliers who can furnish silicas that are clean enough. Silica in very fine meshes has a tendency to kill the high gloss of the polyester; however, a blend may be used, containing about 85% 100-mesh silica and 15% 200-mesh silica. If any silica of 325 mesh or below is to be used, the surface gloss will suffer greatly.

Glass fiber overlay mat, sometimes referred to as surface mat, and veil mat, is also very useful in raising the properties of the polyester gel coat. This material will also completely disappear into the resin.

Resins may be specially developed that will also give better abrasion resistance for such an end product. A very good starting point for the development of such a resin is a polymer based in part on HET acid (hexachloroendomethylene tetrahydrophthalic anhydride). Such a resin will not only raise the abrasion resistance, but will make the surface practically scorchproof to cigarette burns, pot burns, and other heat and fire hazards.

By improving these properties, there is no reason why the polyester laminates cannot match the high-pressure laminates.

Synthetic Ceramic Tile: Small Pieces

This application differs from that discussed in Chap. 4 in that we will consider here the manufacture of small, 4 × 4 in. tile, with all the necessary moldings, coves, bullnose, corners, and accessories that are necessary for utilization of this material in bathrooms, kitchens, and other areas.

In the manufacture of very small parts such as these, the process most advantageous would be injection-molding. This process lends itself more to the manufacture of small parts than any other. It can be highly automated; very fast cycles (15 sec or less) are possible, and production lines can be very compact.

In the past, injection-molding has been limited almost exclusively to the thermoplastics, where hot-and-cold cycles were used. The molten thermoplastic was injected into the hot dies, and the dies cooled by volumes of cold water or other liquid pumped through the cores. Later, some thermoplastics were developed that could be melted at very high temperatures without discoloring and scorching, and could be injected directly into cold molds, so the cycle time was shortened greatly.

Now some manufacturers of injection equipment are developing equipment to handle thermosetting plastics. Instead of a hot-and-cold cycle, or a cold die, a hot die is used. The thermosetting plastic compound is injected directly into the hot dies, cured, and automatically ejected from the cavities by pins which operate automatically on cycle.

With epoxies, phenolics, and other thermosetting plastics that have long cure cycles, the material is preheated in the barrel of the equipment before being injected into the cavities. This cuts down on cycle time. With polyesters this would not be necessary, or at least it would not be necessary to heat them to high temperatures. Possibly raising the temperature of the compound to around 150°F for a few seconds before injection into the cavities could prove of value in reducing cycle time. Care would have to be taken that the temperature control and the catalyst system would permit this. A compound gelled in the equipment would be a very serious problem.

Injection-molding has one major drawback, as do most processes: This method of manufacturing parts leaves "runners" between the individual molds. These are thin pieces of material which join each and every part in a multicavity die. They are the flow routes for the compound being injected, so when the entire cavity is filled, these small ducts remain full.

When the cycle is completed and the parts cured, the entire group of parts are ejected, each piece joined to the next by these runners, which must be trimmed off in a manner that will not damage the parts. Automatic equipment has now been developed that does this work quickly and easily.

The sprue, or entrance duct, to the cavity from the injector has been the hardest part to modify for use with thermosetting plastics. It presented no problem with thermoplastics, as the sprue was kept at a temperature high enough so that this small amount of material did not harden. With the thermosetting compounds, this had to be reversed. This duct had to be kept cool enough so that the material did not gel, and thus leave a small, hard quantity of material which would either stick in place and prevent any material from entering the cavity on the next cycle, or would be forced into the first set of cavities by the high pressures behind it, only to plug up one or more of the runners farther on.

This task was no easy one, particularly when designing a cold sprue for polyesters, which gels so very fast at elevated temperatures. But now several manufacturers offer this equipment, which will handle polyester compounds very efficiently.

Transfer-molding could also be considered for the manufacture of these small parts, but production rates could never match those of injection-molding.

In an injection-molding cycle, there is just no means of applying a gel coat. So, in order to produce a synthetic ceramic tile with an appearance comparable to real ceramic tile, the dies used must have an extremely good polish. In order to maintain the finish of the die surface, the compound to be used must be made of nonabrasive materials, and must have a rather high resin content. No flattening fillers may be used because the gloss of the tile would suffer.

A good starting formulation would be as follows:

1. Hexahydrophthalic rigid polyester-monomer................. 35.00 lb
2. Dimethyl analine (mix before adding catalyst).............. 0.07
3. t-Butyl peroctoate.. 0.40
4. Pigment... 3.00
5. Calcium carbonate, calcined............................. 20.00
6. Ground limestone, 20–40 mesh........................... 65.00
7. Barytes, No. 1 bleached................................ 15.00
                                                            _____
                                                            138.47 lb

This compound will be entirely suitable for injection-molding in these new modified machines—either ram type or screw type.

The mix will not be abrasive, and therefore will harm neither the molds nor the injection equipment. None of the fillers in the compound will affect the gloss to any extent, so in proper dies the finished product will be quite comparable in appearance to natural ceramic tile.

These tiles may be solid colors, speckled, or marbelized. Marbelizing may be accomplished by using one or more veining mixes such as given earlier in this chapter for bathroom fixtures. Speckled appearances, such as seen in much of the ceramic tile on the market, may be matched by substituting 1 to 2 lb of a darker, ground limestone (in any color) for an equal amount of that listed in the formulation. It may be the same 20 to 40 mesh, or it may be slightly coarser if larger "specks" are desired.

With equipment of this kind, a production line can manufacture up to 10,000 individual 4 × 4 in. tiles or trim pieces per hr. No other equipment can possibly match this production rate.

Plastic tiles are already on the market, so will present nothing new to the consumer. Polystyrene tiles are being manufactured and sold. The disadvantage of polystyrene tile is high cost. This polymer, being a thermoplastic, will take very small quantities of fillers. Therefore, about 75% of each tile must be polymer. As a result this tile is much more expensive than a polyester version, where only about 25% of each tile will be resin (by weight).

Polystyrene tile has the added disadvantage that it will not withstand abrasion nearly as well as will polyester tile. It will also burn much more readily than will the polyester.

The above formulation may be modified slightly as desired. A requirement will be a good internal mold release. Diammonium phosphate and antimony trioxide, 5% (by weight) of the resin each, may be added for fireproofing if desired.

Synthetic ceramic tile can have a very large market. It will be approximately one-third the cost of ceramic tile manufactured in the United States, and about one-half the cost of some of the imported varieties. It will be much lighter in weight, so shipping costs will be lower. It will be easier to apply, so installation costs will be lower than for real ceramic tile.

An adhesive such as the formulation given in Chap. 4 would be used. This quick-tack contact adhesive suggested for bonding block facings will be ideal. It is completely waterproof and will present no problems in application. Workmen would trowel it on in a very thin layer, either on wood or masonry, with a finely notched trowel.

A plant-applied adhesive, such as that suggested in Chap. 2 for floor tile, might very well be considered also for synthetic ceramic tile. In the field, the workmen would strip off the release paper and place the tile in position. Both of these adhesives will do a good job.

Synthetic Plate Glass: Clear, Tinted, and Decorative

A great amount of plate glass is used in the construction industry for glazing windows, shower doors, sliding patio doors, and for other such applications.

Plate glass has many drawbacks. Everyone in the industry has recognized these faults for many years, but there was no way to correct them and there was no substitute for plate glass.

The cost of this material is very high. The process by which it is manufactured makes it necessarily so. A great percentage of this cost is a result of the polishing part of the process. Breakage during processing, handling, shipping, and installation is also a cost factor that must be considered.

In the home and office each year a number of people are injured by walking through these clear panes, particularly patio doors.

The glass industry has spent large sums in research and development trying to correct a number of the faults inherent in this material. They have made good progress, but this progress has added to the cost of the product.

The latest development has been a plate glass that when broken, does not break up into jagged, dangerous pieces. It breaks up into rounded, smooth pieces and thus presents far less hazards.

Clear plate glass has always been a problem because it transmits ultraviolet and infrared rays of the sun into a building. Rugs, curtains, and furniture fade and deteriorate quickly. Plate-glass manufacturers are now offering a tinted glass, which shuts out a majority of these rays; this glass is very satisfactory, but again, more expensive. Liquid, spray-on materials have been offered so that a homeowner may tint the glass himself. These are quite effective, but are only a temporary solution—they must be removed and replaced each 2 to 3 years.

The possibility of a plastic substitute for a plate glass has been explored for years. Polycarbonate has been the first to make any progress along these lines. Clear, sheet polycarbonate is an excellent material for this purpose. It will not discolor; it has tremendous resistance to abrasion; and it is almost unbreakable. It has one major disadvantage—its cost.

This material costs about $1.10 per lb in its raw state. Since it is a thermoplastic, it may be extruded or injection-molded into sheet form. Processing temperatures are very high, and pressures must be very high, requiring expensive equipment. If extruded, it must be polished before the surface is acceptable. These factors make for very high costs. Polished polycarbonate sheet material may cost up to $2.75 per lb or more.

One company has developed a thermosetting version of a polycarbonate, which may be cast in liquid form between two sheets of highly polished glass, cured into a solid sheet, and used for plate-glass purposes. This material is not truly a thermosetting plastic because it may be thermoformed after it is manufactured. It is called allyl diglycol carbonate, and it is really a monomer. It may be used as such with polyester resins to form a very highly cross-linked polymer with excellent properties. When used alone, it will give a better-quality product than when alloyed with polyesters, but cost will be much higher than a straight polyester or a mixture of polyester and this monomer.

Pure allyl diglycol carbonate has a very high shrinkage during cure, and this must be considered in holding linear dimensions on sheets. The curing process is the largest disadvantage of this material. It must be polymerized very slowly in order to obtain maximum properties. Temperatures must start very low and be increased gradually until cure is completed. This can last from 2 to 6 hr, so the cycle time makes the cost very high.

However, the finished material is of excellent quality, and its optical properties are superior to any material on the market today. Its abrasion resistance is superior to that of plate glass. It will not discolor under normal use in glazing applications.

The acrylics and methacrylates have been used for many years for glazing purposes. They are on the market under a variety of trade names. These materials have been used for clear skylights in buildings, for the glazing applications of the aircraft industry, and for many other applications.

Their cost is considerably less than for polycarbonates and allyl diglycol carbonate. Optical properties are almost equivalent. They will not discolor in normal use, and have good mechanical properties.

The major flaw in the acrylics and methacrylates is their susceptability to wear and abrasion. They have very poor abrasion resistance and cannot be used in applications where such conditions exist.

They excel as materials for glazing for aircraft because they are easily thermoformed, cut, and fit. No similar material exists that is so easy to work with in glazing operations.

A real need exists for a plastic sheet material that is low in cost and has good optical properties and reasonably good mechanical properties for use in normal glazing applications. Polyester resins can fill this need very well. There are many ways to manufacture such a polyester, and there are many different intermediates that may be used in its manufacture.

Polyesters based in part on acrylic acid give water-clear polymers. Polymers based in part on hexahydrophthalic and tetrahydrophthalic acids also give extremely clear resins. Other intermediates that will aid in obtaining very clear resins are fumaric acid and heptaethylene glycols. Proper choice of monomer can aid greatly in achieving clarity. Percentages of methyl or butyl acrylate, ethyl or methyl methacrylate, and allyl diglycol carbonate (mentioned above) will all contribute to the clarity of the finished polymer.

With such intermediates and monomers at hand, there is no problem in obtaining the necessary optical properties for a product for glazing applications.

For most locations where plate glass is used, mechanical properties are not too stringent. Impact strength would surely be the most important property to consider, and in this plate glass is inferior. Polyester sheet would not have as good an impact strength as polycarbonate, allyl diglycol carbonate, or even acrylic. However, its impact strength would be far superior to that of plate glass, and it would withstand very well all normal uses of a glazing material far better than glass. If shattered by a very heavy blow, polyester sheet would break up into pieces with very dull edges, which would not present a hazard to children in any way.

Chart 4 compares the essential properties of plate glass, polycarbonate sheet, allyl diglycol carbonate sheet, and polyester sheet materials.

The process by which polyester glazing materials are manufactured is known as cell casting. It is a fairly well-known process, used in the manufacture of buttons from sheet polyester and of other sheet material that must be manufactured with a highly polished finish on both surfaces.

In cell casting the principal elements in a set of molds are two highly polished sheets of plate glass, or still better, a very high temperature resisting glass. These are kept an equitable distance apart by a silicone-rubber gasket, which is so designed as to seal the perimeter of the sheets of glass to prevent leakage of the liquid resins. An opening is left in the top for filling and for escape of air.

Sometimes these molds are filled while standing completely vertically; other techniques fill them standing at a 45 or 60° angle. The two sheets of glass are held against the silicone gasket with a number of spring-type clamps, which allow for the slight shrinkage in the thickness dimension as the part cures.

The clear resin is mixed with proper catalysts, accelerators, and internal mold-release preparations and poured into the mold. Then the mold passes into the oven for cure.

The curing cycles for this work with polyesters will be very fast since the glass-mold material has good thermal conductivity. With proper formulation and an oven temperature of 200°F, cycle times should be less than 10 min, including filling the mold, curing it, and removing the finished sheet. This type of mold disassembles and reassembles very rapidly. With a proper internal mold release, the mold should not have to be cleaned and polished until after hundreds of uses.

The mold surface must never be touched by the bare hand. A fingerprint or any type of smudge on the polished surface will show on the product. Since these glass plates will always be rather hot, workmen should use gloves, which must be kept spotlessly clean.

The glass sheets must be oversized in order to accommodate the gasket material and the shrinkage. There is no practical limit to the size of the product, and sizes up to 8×8 ft are entirely feasible. Thickness may vary just by changing the gasket material. The thickness should be governed pretty much by the size of sheets contemplated. An 8×8 ft

CHART 4. COMPARISON OF GLAZING MATERIALS

L—low
M—medium
H—high
P—poor
F—fair
G—good
E—excellent

	Cost	Optical properties	Ultraviolet resistance	Infrared resistance	Oxidation resistance	Ultraviolet transmission, tinted	Ultraviolet transmission, blocked	Hardness	Flexural strength	Impact strength	Coef. of thermal exp.	Thermal conductivity	Abrasion resistance	Adsorption (moisture transfer)
Polished plate glass - - - - - -	H	E	E	E	E	L	L	Very high	G	Very poor	L	H	G	H
Polycarbonate sheet - - - - - -	H	E	E	E	E	L	L	M	E	E	H	L	E	Very low
Allyl diglycol carbonate sheet - -	M to H	E	E	E	E	L	L	M	E	E	H	L	E	Very low
Acrylic sheet - - - - - - - -	M	E	E	E	E	L	L	L	G	E	H	L	P	L
Polyester sheet - - - - - - -	L	E	G	G	E	L	L	M	G	G	H	L	F	L

116

sheet should be ¼ in. thick. If the material is to be cut up into small windowpanes, it might be as thin as 3⁄32 in. or less.

Polyester glazing material is much easier to work with than glass. It may be cut, beveled, drilled, or tapped, and any other work may be done easily. An electric saw with an abrasive blade is ideal for this work.

Many variations of the clear sheets may be manufactured. There is already on the market a large amount of tinted polystyrene sheet material. Most of this is textured and is used in bathroom shower doors, decorative screens, louvers, etc. By using textured glass for molds, any given pattern can be duplicated exactly. The polyester sheets may be tinted any color and may be translucent or opaque.

Even with clear sheets it is relatively easy to add ultraviolet blocking agents to the polyester formulation that will stop up to 90% of ultraviolet light that is transmitted into the interior of a building. (This phase of polyester formulation is discussed in depth in Chap. 11.)

By utilizing overlay-mat glass fiber, printed with decorative designs, very beautiful clear or tinted panels may be manufactured, with nothing but the printed design showing. The overlay mat disappears completely into the resin. A multitude of these designs are available, printed with flowers, shrubs, butterflies, and murals. The choice is very wide.

Such products may be used throughout the construction industry. They may be used in windowpanes, door glass, picture windows, shower doors, cabinet doors, decorative screens, church windows, and a host of other items where plate glass is the prevalent material being used today.

This market presents a great challenge to the polyester industry. The volumes involved in these products are very large. Since polyester sheet will be much ligher in weight than plate glass, with much less danger of breakage in handling, this material can be shipped for much greater distances economically. Packaging will not need to be nearly as expensive as for plate glass.

No one connected with the polyester industry in any way should overlook the possibilities for this type of product. The marketing of a substitute for plate glass should not present any great problems. Architects, builders, and owners have long wished for an economical substitute. Decorators have been limited in their work by the lack of such a product. Even the people involved in cutting and installing glass have wondered if perhaps there were not a better material with which to work.

Polyester products can take over a very large percentage of the glazing and decorative panel market in a very short time, when manufactured by proper mass-production schedules.

Six

SPECIALTY CONSTRUCTION MATERIALS

Apart from flooring materials, roofing materials constitute the largest volume of a type of material used in construction today. The percentage of wall boards and roofing materials in sq ft is very much the same in new constructions, but the huge volume of roofing materials used in reroofing buildings is almost as large as the amount used in new constructions.

Most of the roofing materials on the market today have a definitely limited life span. Ten to fifteen years is the expected durability of materials offered to the construction industry.

Perhaps there is more room for improvement in roofing materials than in any building material. Most of these materials are highly flammable; wind and hail damage them very easily, so they leak, impairing the building and furnishings and clothes within it. Carpets must be replaced. Even wood and other flooring materials must sometimes be replaced because of water damage.

Insurance rates are extremely high on buildings with most of these roofing materials, and of course in case of heavy damage, insurance never covers all the damage and costs involved in remodeling, refurnishing, and repainting. Clothes, also, are never completely covered by insurance policies. Loss in books and other personal belongings is always high. Many times, particularly in offices, papers that are irreplaceable are often severely damaged or destroyed. In stores of any kind, all the merchandise can seldom be completely covered by insurance.

When specifications for roofing materials are written, too often only initial cost is considered. This fallacy is very prevalent among architects, builders, and owners. Careful consideration must be given to possible losses, insurance rates, fire hazards, and the life expectancy of the material to be used.

Beauty or unsightliness are factors which seldom enter into discussions about roofing materials. Particularly in the lower-cost roofing materials, a nice-appearing product does not exist. People have become so accustomed to drab roofs that they just don't look at roofs.

Actually, there is little choice. There are good roofing materials, but they are very expensive. Slate and copper cannot be afforded in the average building. In the lower-cost materials, there are all types of wood shingles, and there are literally hundreds of asphalt-compound shingles, some combined with asbestos, others with such fiber as sisal. Some have mica and other fillers and aggregates sprinkled on top. Also, there are the built-up types of roofing, where asphalt-felt paper is applied between layers of molten asphalt, sometimes with aggregates on top. There are a number of coal-tar-fiber compound shingles. However, there is not much variety from which to choose at the more reasonable price levels.

More recently, much work has been done with polymeric types of roofing materials. Some are premanufactured, and others are laid-up in place with spray guns. Among these are chlorosulfonated polyethylene. This polymer produces an excellent roof, which is very durable. Some of these roofs have been in service for over 10 years, and there are no signs of deterioration. When applied properly, a roof with this material should have a very long life expectancy.

As with most materials, this polymer has some drawbacks. It is expensive, and it must be applied at very low solids content. Polymer and fillers make up about 45% of the weight of a liquid compound, and solvents make up the other 55%. The solvent is a cost that is lost, and it presents some fire hazards during application procedures.

Because of the high solvent content, these compounds must be applied in very thin layers, and so several applications are necessary to complete a roof. Thus labor for this material is very high.

Proper bonding to existing substrates is sometimes difficult with this material, and when the surface is not properly prepared, it often turns loose and curls.

More recently marketed are roofing compounds derived from the acrylates and premanufactured materials derived from acrylonitrilebutadiene styrene. These show promise, but the former has almost the same drawbacks as chlorosulfonated polyethylene in that it must be applied at low solids content, and it has some problems in obtaining a proper bond to some surfaces. The latter is too new to be properly evaluated as yet, but it shows good promise if costs can be lowered as production rates increase.

As previously stated, in the roofing industry there is a real need for new materials. Roofs do not have to be drab, unsightly areas of buildings. Polyester resins can have a tremendous future in this industry. Roofs may be built that are decorative, durable, and fireproof. They will be strong enough to withstand any kind of wind and hail damage. They may be walked on without fear of impairment. Termites, woodpeckers, and other such hazards do not have to be considerations.

These materials will cost more than the asphalt-based roofing materials available today when considering only the initial cost outlay; however, when calculating over a 20- or 25-year period, they will be much less expensive.

These materials will be less expensive to install. Labor costs will be reduced, as most of these materials may be made up into 4 × 8 ft panels, with weather-tight joints and sealers.

Insurance-rate differential over a span of years will make up most of the initial cost differential.

Besides these advantages, a *complete* building can look good. These panels may be made in a multitude of styles, colors, and patterns to suit the fancy of any architect, builder, owner, or decorator.

Roofing Materials: 4 × 8 ft Panels

These products will be made up in panel sizes of 4 × 8 ft or 4 × 4 ft if so desired. All edges will be matching, so there will be no disruption of continuity of a particular pattern. The edges will be fitted with joints of the lap type, or they could be a tongue-and-groove type. Later in this chapter special adhesive sealants will be discussed for joining these panels and making them permanently weathertight. These will be applied by a caulking gun, of the cartridge or other type, and will be very fast-applying. These products will be applicable to almost any type of roof, regardless of pitch, since they will be totally sealed. In old buildings, they can be applied directly over most old roofing materials if desired.

The process for producing these materials most suitable for mass-production methods will be quite like that described in Chap. 4. These first five types of roofing materials may be manufactured very well on a production line similar to that shown in Diagram 6.

The polyester-compound facing material simulating a known type of roofing material will have a backing adhered to it just before it leaves the production line.

This backing may be an economical reject type of plywood, hardboard, fiberboard, asbestos-cement board, or even a thin-gauge aluminum or sheet steel.

Any of these last three materials would be of great interest because they would be entirely fireproof as would the polyester-compound face.

Synthetic Slate

Slate is one of the most desired of roofing materials. It looks good, and it lasts forever if no one walks on it. It is very friable, so it will break with the weight of a man not placed in exactly the right position.

Slate roofs are very expensive, so only a very few builders use this material.

An exact duplicate of slate roofing material may be made with a polyester resin. This synthetic slate will look so natural that only an expert would know the difference at close range.

A formulation for this synthetic-slate compound would be the following:

1. Hexahydrophthalic resilient polyester-monomers. . . . . 20.00 lb
2. Dimethyl analine (mix before adding catalyst). 0.04
3. *t*-Butyl peroctoate. 0.25
4. Raven black crushed marble, No. 00. . . . . 80.00
5. Silica, 100 mesh. 25.00
6. Silica, 200 mesh. 10.00
7. Silica, 325 mesh. 5.00

140.29 lb

The above mix will not need pigment. The black marble will be sufficient pigment to give the compound an authentic slate appearance. This mix will be very slightly over 1 cu ft and may be multiplied by the size mixer to be used.

In the manufacture of these roofing materials, no gel coat will be required. The surface of the product will depend entirely on the surface of the molds. Probably in this type of product preferences would be for completely dull, matte finishes.

As in the manufacture of synthetic brick, dimension stone, and other products discussed in Chap. 4, temporary mold liners may be used for the production of these roofing materials. These mold liners, made of silicone rubber, or fluorocarbon, may be inserted into ordinary open molds to give the desired texture and finish to these materials.

In order to achieve true legitimacy in the finished product, the pattern must match exactly the finish on the natural material.

Models or prototypes must be laid up with the natural slate in appropriate-sized panels, forms built around them, and the mold material poured over them. The duplication will be exact, and this prototype, if prepared properly, may be used many times.

Temporary mold liners may also be used, made of phenolic, epoxy, epoxy-phenolic, and other materials.

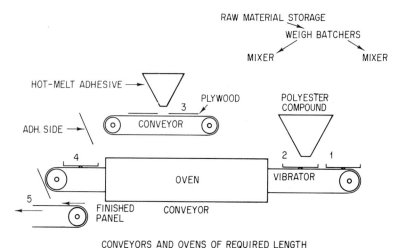

DIAGRAM 10. *Suggested production line for 4 × 8 ft roofing panels.*

For long production runs of a single product, however, temporary molds should not be considered. Cast-iron dies may be prepared by a method similar to the process above; cast aluminum may also be used very well in such a process.

Production rates will depend entirely upon the number of molds on the conveyor, length of the conveyor, speed of the conveyor, and temperature of the oven. With 20 molds mounted on the system, an oven temperature of 300°F, and a conveyor speed of 15 ft per min, well over 5,000 sq ft per hr are possible.

Diagram 10 shows the basic production-line setup and the suggested process sequence. Variations in this may be made to suit techniques developed by the manufacturer.

At station 1, an external mold release would be applied to the mold surface if the mold material used required it.

At station 2, the polyester compound would be poured into the mold in the required amount, and vibrated until it were level. The conveyor would travel on through the oven, curing the material.

At station 3 the hot-melt adhesive would be applied to one side of the backing material. (The formulation given in Chap. 4 will be quite suitable for this adhesive.)

The arrival of the adhesive-coated backing material would be synchronized with that of the cured roofing material at station 4. The backing material would be placed, adhesive-side down, upon the roofing material, which would demold at station 5 and be carried on to the packaging department.

The molds must be designed so as to allow for the joint around the edge of the finished panel. The backing material will be placed very slightly off center to allow for this joint. If the joint is designed to be a tongue-and-groove type of joint, this will not be necessary; however, a lap-type joint probably would be more suitable for this production. A lap of some ¾ in. would be sufficient because of the type of adhesive sealer that will be used to join them. This will mean that the backing material would be placed this distance off center, extending ¾ in. past the polyester face on two sides.

It would be desirable to arrange the hot-melt adhesive application at station 3 so as not to apply this adhesive to the ¾-in. strip on the two sides of the backing material which will form the lap joint.

Diagram 11 shows a proper joint arrangement for these roofing materials.

A formulation for an adhesive sealer for roofing-materials joint would be the following:

1.	Chlorinated rubber, high viscosity	25.0 lb
2.	Toluol, or xylol	25.0
3.	Liquid, refined wood rosin	10.0
4.	Chlorinated biphenyl	5.0
5.	Polybutene, medium viscosity	15.0
6.	Silica, 325 mesh	20.0
		100.0 lb

This adhesive could be packaged in throwaway-type cartridges or in 5-gal cans so that caulking guns of the fill type could be used.

The adhesive will have a high viscosity, and an instant high tack. When panel edges are placed in this adhesive and pressed down, nails may be used, if desired, but will not be a necessity. The bonding strength of this material will hold the panel tightly in place.

This adhesive may also be used instead of nails, if desired, over the entire panel. Small spots of the adhesive may be placed at appropriate distances on rafters or other substrates being covered. When the panel is placed in its position, it will not move. Sufficient bond will form immediately to hold the panel where it is placed, and within 24 hr maximum strength of the adhesive will be reached. The roof will be able to withstand any high winds. The joint will be sealed against any water because as subsequent panels are pressed into position, the adhesive will flow out over the entire surface of the joint, including the two cracks. This adhesive is completely impermeable.

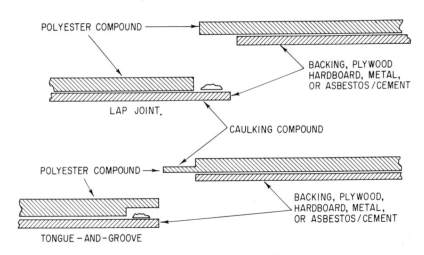

DIAGRAM 11. *Suggested joint arrangements for roofing panels.*

If nails or other fastening means are to be used, the roofing manufacturer should furnish small containers of a matching compound so that workmen installing the materials may touch up the exposed heads of these fastening devices. In this way, no metal would be exposed, which would oxidize and possibly discolor the roofing.

The hot-melt adhesive for bonding the backing material to the polyester compound will be suitable for almost any backing material that may be selected—plywood, hardboard, fiberboard, asbestos-cement board, and even aluminum or steel sheet metal. The adhesive sealer for the joints will also give good service with any of these materials. The manufacturer must make a very careful study of all possible backing materials before proceeding with the process.

All possible aspects of the materials used must be considered; perhaps the matter of flammability should be the most important aspect. The polyester-compound formulation given above will have a flammability rating of nearly zero. By adding small percentages of diammonium phosphate and antimony trioxide, the compound may be rated as nonburning. This will be adequate to protect a building from fire hazards coming from outside a building, but would it be enough to satisfy owners and insurance companies completely?

Plywood, hardboard, and fiberboard are definitely flammable; asbestos-cement board and aluminum and steel sheet metal are nonflammable. With these last three materials, a product can be offered that is nonflammable in its entirety.

Termite damage, normal decomposition, and all other aspects must be considered. Sheet steel would oxidize in time if not protected with a good coating on the underside. Plywood, hardboard, or fiberboard would be subject to termite damage if not treated.

All are factors to be carefully considered before a choice is made. Cost is a very important factor. The asbestos-cement board would be the most expensive backing material. Would the added cost be justified to owners and insurance companies to warrant the difference?

It is possible the manufacturer may decide to use two or more types of backing materials. In this way, he can offer a completely fireproof product, and another exactly the same from the exterior, but with a nonfireproof interior. This would be of some advantage, as he could offer the product at two different price ranges.

Synthetic Copper

Copper is a roofing material that is often used on churches, public buildings, and finer homes. It is expensive, but it is used because it is a lifetime roof.

An exact duplicate can be made up with a polyester-resin compound. The compound may be formulated to match new, bright copper, or it may be formulated to match aged copper that has the "patina" formed from surface oxidation.

Since this material usually does not have a texture or a pattern, the polyester compound may be quite thin, and costs can be lower for this material than for a heavily textured pattern, where thickness must be greater.

Available on the market today are copper-colored pigments that are of excellent quality. A few years ago such pigments would soon become dull and tarnished, but those now marketed will retain their bright copper tone when properly formulated into the polyester resin.

Since this material may be made at lesser thicknesses, the fillers and aggregates must be correspondingly smaller.

A formulation suitable for synthetic copper roofing would be as follows:

1. Hexahydrophthalic polyester resin-monomers.................. 20.00 lb
2. Dimethyl analine (mix before adding catalyst)................ 0.04
3. *t*-Butyl peroctoate... 0.25
4. Synthetic copper pigment................................... 10.00
5. Silica, 100 mesh... 80.00
6. Silica, 200 mesh... 20.00

$$\overline{}$$
130.29 lb

This formulation would be for a bright copper finish. If it is desired to match the patina of an old copper roof, 9 lb of synthetic copper pigment and 1 lb of dark-green chrome oxide would be used. The effect will be extremely close to natural copper. The silicas have no pigmenting effect. Clean, white silicas disappear completely into a mix and do not affect color in any way.

Processing this compound into the finished roofing material would be exactly the same as for the slate above, except that less material would be placed into the mold, and the mold surface would usually be a smooth, unbroken plane with no texture. If certain textures are desired, then this must be accomplished by the surface of the mold itself.

Synthetic Shingles

Any type of wood shingles may be matched in appearance, color, and other characteristics. A pattern may be desired to match the newer aluminum-shingle roofing materials. Any of these may be matched exactly, even the very rough, rustic types of materials now available.

The rougher the type of roofing material being matched, the more polyester compound is necessary. The thickness of the product will depend entirely on the pattern being matched. It is not advisable to design a product that will require more than $\frac{3}{16}$ in. of the polyester compound in the thickest part, as cost and weight would go up considerably.

If a very rough type of roofing were being copied, thickness might go up to $\frac{1}{2}$ in. or more if the pattern were copied down to the last detail. In this case, a simulated master part or prototype must be set up from which to make the molds, which will match perfectly the actual surface of the material, but with less depth. This is no great problem for a good patternmaker.

In any type of a shingle simulation, the lower portion of the shingle is thicker; therefore, this portion is where the thickest part of the product will be. The depth of polyester compound poured here will be much greater than at the other end of the "shingle." Even the cracks or spaces

PHOTO 15. *Polyester roofing material, synthetic shingle.*

between the shingles will be reproduced exactly when the molds are made properly. Colors may vary as desired. These shingles may be the color of new shingles, or old shingles; they may be white or any other pigmented color. A few test panels should be made to obtain the reactions of architects and owners before final color selections are made.

Spanish Tile

The beautiful red Spanish tile, so popular many years ago, has almost completely disappeared from the market today. It is found only on homes built 30 to 40 years ago.

This material suffered its demise because of cost. The process of manufacturing this material was almost completely a hand operation, followed by baking. The cost of labor today makes the cost of this material just too high for it to be used. The little amount still being used is usually imported from Mexico, and used only on a few churches and similar buildings.

This material may be very easily matched with a polyester compound; it can be made into a finished product which is exactly like authentic Spanish tile. Color, contour, and appearance will be the same in every way.

A production line would be similar to the one shown in Diagram

10. The basic difference would be in the molds for this product. Here matched molds, male and female, would be needed to hold the material in the proper curvature as it cures.

Cast iron or cast aluminum would be ideal for this purpose since the surfaces do not have to be smooth. These molds can be taken directly from a prototype set up with tile, or from a plaster mockup, so that the actual thicknesses of polyester resin compound would be less than the natural tile. A good casting firm would know how to manufacture these molds with minimum cost.

The basic formulation for the polyester compound would be as follows:

1. Orthophthalic, rigid polyester-monomers.................... 20.00 lb
2. Dimethyl analine (mix before adding catalyst).............. 0.04
3. t-Butyl peroctoate....................................... 0.25
4. Red iron oxide.. 5.00
5. Quartz, crushed No. 00................................. 75.00
6. Silica, 100 mesh.. 25.00
7. Silica, 200 mesh.. 10.00

135.29 lb

This will be a very flowable mix because of the larger aggregates and lack of highly absorptive fillers.

The relatively small amount of pigment may be noted. Such a small amount gives all the pigmentation necessary because of the thickness of the product and the lack of fillers which would affect the color.

Using a production line, as suggested in Diagram 10, this compound would be poured out into the female mold at station 2 and vibrated slightly to distribute the material evenly. The male mold would be placed on top and then vibrated. The weight of the male mold plus the vibration will cause the material to displace from the lower portion of the mold, filling the cavity rather evenly until the male part of the mold reaches its stops.

Some of the displaced air will form pockets and voids next to the top curvatures in the underside of the male mold; however, since this portion of the product will be adhered to the backing materials, they will not be visible, nor will they distract from the strength of the product to any appreciable degree.

The matched molds will now go through the oven for cure, and at station 4 the male mold will be lifted off. The backing will be placed, and the product will demold at station 5.

An overhead trolley arrangement must be made for the male molds because of their weight. (A proper hook can be placed in their centers to facilitate this.)

Since the female molds will be attached to the conveyor, and the

SPECIALTY CONSTRUCTION MATERIALS

male molds will not, only half as many males as females will be necessary. The continuous overhead trolley can pick up the males at station 4 and bring them back to station 2 for placing back in position.

In this process, it would definitely be advisable to use an internal mold release in the mix, as opposed to an external mold release. In any application where there are matched dies or molds, an internal mold release is much simpler and less costly.

Molds of this type do not necessarily have to be cast. They may also be made quite simply from $\frac{3}{16}$- or $\frac{1}{4}$-in. steel plate. Aluminum plate may also be considered.

Strips of plate 12 in. wide may be formed with the proper curvatures, lapped and welded together to form the female part of the mold, which will reproduce the face of the finished product, complete with the lap effect of natural Spanish tile. The male portion may be one integral plate, formed with the proper curvatures, but without the lapped effect. Since this part would be next to the backing material, this would be even preferable because a greater area of the polyester material would be in contact with the backing.

A combination of molds may be considered: cast-iron or cast-aluminum female and roll-formed male of plate. Even some of the polymer molds would be entirely suitable for short runs of this product.

Since a large part of the investment will be for molds for each different pattern of product to be manufactured, all factors must be considered. Here, again, a good professional mold and die maker would know which route to take in making the molds. Molds such as these are large expenditures, but when properly made, will last for many years. Millions of square feet of such roofing panels may be manufactured in them, and the mold cost per square foot of panel produced will be infinitesimal.

Rustic, Stone-faced Roofing Material

A very popular type of available roofing is stone-surfaced built-up roofing. This is made by multiple applications of molten asphalt and roofing felt papers, topped off with crushed stone.

A stone-faced roof is very practical because the white stones most often used reflect the sun and reduce air-conditioning requirements.

This type of roofing material can be made up very easily in polyester compounds. The same basic production line would be used as shown in Diagram 10, except that the system which applies the backing material would be reversed, and an aggregate-spreader would be added between station 2 and the oven. The backing material, with the adhesive applied, would be placed into the open mold with the adhesive side up. The polyester compound would be poured out onto this, and vibrated until level. At the next station, the aggregate-spreader would apply a proper amount of loose, crushed, white quartz or marble chips. The entire panel would then pass through the oven for curing. The heat generated by the oven and the exotherm of the compound would remelt the hot-melt adhesive, and the panel would be firmly bonded together. The adhesive is quite pliable and so would allow the polyester compound to shrink without forming stresses and causing the backing material to warp.

The panel would go on to station 5, demold, and be carried out to be packaged.

A formulation for the matrix for this product would be as follows:

1. Orthophthalic resilient polyester-monomers................. 30.00 lb
2. Dimethyl analine (mix before adding catalyst).............. 0.06
3. t-Butyl peroctoate.. 0.38
4. Pigment, TiO_2 (or whatever color desired)................. 6.00
5. Silica, 100 mesh.. 75.00
6. Silica, 200 mesh.. 20.00

                                                                131.44 lb

This would be a very flowable mix and would be poured and vibrated into the mold to a thickness of about 0.030 to 0.040 in.

When the larger aggregate is spread into this, the stones will sink down into the matrix until they touch the bottom of the mold, leaving a large portion of each stone exposed. The size of these stones can vary from No. 00 to No. 2 if so desired. The larger the size used, the more each panel will weigh, so this is a limiting factor.

Beautiful stones are available. Quartz is available in pure white, trans-lucent, pinks, and other colors. Marble chips are available in almost every color that could possibly be desired. Other stones, such as flint, rounded river gravel, serpentine, and many others, would also be suitable to use. The white colors form a much better reflecting surface, however, and these will be used on most of these materials. A white roof is also a very beautiful roof, and most owners prefer it.

Aggregates may be mixed, of course, to get some very nice effects in the finished products. Also, a background or matrix may be used that is a very different color from the stones, which produces very nice appearances. There is almost no limit to the number of completely differ-ent products that may be manufactured simply by changing the color of the aggregate, mixing aggregate colors, changing the size of the aggre-gates, or changing the color of the matrix.

The five types of roofing materials previously discussed may very easily be expanded into many more patterns, shapes, and styles. The ones discussed were offered for consideration simply because they have patterns which are already on the market in other materials; thus, they would probably encounter less sales resistance because the market is already accustomed to the general configurations of existing roofing materials. Very likely a manufacturer may wish to design a completely new appearance in roofing materials. Such a procedure would only entail making of the dies or molds for such a material.

PHOTO 16. *Polyeser roofing material, rustic stone finish.*

We are constantly subjected to change in styles of clothes, automobiles, and other surroundings. There is no reason why roofing materials must remain the same. A manufacturer can make up one set of temporary molds and manufacture 50 or 100 panels of a new style material. It can be presented to architects, builders, and homeowners. The reactions of these people will soon let the manufacturer know if the product design will be acceptable or not.

The consumer is more subject to change than is generally believed. Often nonconventional products, designs, styles, and shapes are quickly accepted when properly presented.

These panels will be quickly and easily installed by workmen. Labor costs in installation will be far less than with more conventional types of roofs. More cost will be saved, as there will be less need for a base on which to lay this material since this product is in effect both sheeting and roofing in one piece.

Manufactured, Rolled Roofing Materials

Besides the possible materials discussed above, polyester resins lend themselves to rolled-type roofing materials as well.

Today it is possible to manufacture resins that are, in effect, elastomers. Polyester resins, based in part on polybutadiene and in part on some of the very high-molecular-weight saturated acids, can be very

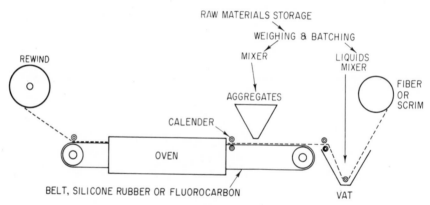

DIAGRAM 12. *Calendering rolled roofing materials with polyester compounds.*

elastomeric in properties. No such resin is available at this moment, but several manufacturers are working on it. The knowledge to make such a resin is available, and the intermediates are available. As soon as there is a market for it, at least half-a-dozen resin manufacturers will be ready to supply this polymer.

The basic process for the manufacture of this product would be web calendering, as shown in Diagram 12.

The two belts involved in the system, the lower conveyor belt and the upper belt, may be either reinforced silicone rubber or fluorocarbon, suitably reinforced. Both these materials are available in sheet form and may be joined together at the ends by a reasonably simple process. The silicone rubber is vulcanized together with its own compound in liquid form, and the fluorocarbon is joined together by heat in the vicinity of 700°F.

Manufacturers of these materials will supply the belts already joined together in the proper-length endless-belt form.

A formulation for calendered roofing material would be the following:

1. Elastomeric polyester resin-monomers...................... 30.00 lb
2. Dimethyl analine (mix before adding catalyst).............. 0.06
3. *t*-Butyl peroctoate....................................... 0.38
4. Pigment (any color)....................................... 5.00
6. Silica, 100 mesh.. 75.00
7. Silica, 200 mesh.. 20.00
8. China clay... 5.00
                                                             _____
                                                             135.44 lb

This compound would be placed in the vat, and the fibrous material would be drawn through the compound to pick up a considerable amount of this material. The fibrous material would go between two rollers, which would remove any excess compound material and leave the proper amount. The saturated fiber would go on to the lower belt and under the aggregate-spreader, where a proper amount of aggregate would be deposited evenly on the surface. It would go on through the calender, where the final thickness would be adjusted and the aggregate pressed into the material. Now the belt would take it through the oven for curing, and at the end of the system, the material would be wound into rolls and cut to proper lengths for packaging and shipping.

Such additives as antimony trioxide and diammonium phosphate may be added to the formulation given to give nonflammability if desired.

No mold release, either internal or external, will be necessary with either of the two belt materials discussed.

The aggregates must be sized according to the thickness of the finished material. The fibrous material should be damaged as little as possible; thus, if a finished thickness of $\frac{1}{16}$ in. is contemplated, the maximum-sized aggregate must be slightly less than this. Any color aggregates may be used—or any combinations of colors. The natural-stone aggregates are available to size No. 0000, properly screened and graded.

With this material, a builtup type of roof may be produced with one single application, whereas with asphalt and felt papers as many as three applications are required. Labor costs will be cut considerably. The roof will be laid with the following material:

Formulation for Adhesive Base for Rolled Roofing

1. Amorphous polypropylene................................. 25.0 lb
2. Hexane... 30.0
3. Asphalt, liquid.. 25.0
4. Chlorinated biphenyl..................................... 5.0
5. Semirefined wood rosin................................... 10.0
6. Polybutene, medium viscosity............................. 10.0
7. Silica, 100 mesh... 25.0
8. Silica, 200 mesh... 5.0
                                                            _____
                                                            135.0 lb

This adhesive base may be applied to the substrate by trowel, coarse broom, squeegee, or heavy-duty, airless spray equipment. Conventional spray equipment is also suitable for this use, with the special large-orifice heads which are available. If spray equipment is to be used, particularly the airless type, the formulation may be changed somewhat. The silicas can be replaced with much less abrasive materials, such as the calcium carbonates. Silicas are very hard on spray equipment; pumps and nozzles are quickly worn and must be replaced.

The lap joints, where successive strips of this roofing material are laid may be coated with the same adhesive base. Laps of 1 in. are sufficient.

With this type of adhesive base, rolled polyester roofing materials may be applied over almost any new or existing roofing substrate. Wood, concrete, or old asphalt-based roofing materials will not present any bonding problems.

After the polyester roofing is rolled out onto the adhesive base, a heavy roller should be used to roll the material evenly out into the base material in a manner quite like that used for conventional rolled materials.

This material will provide an impermeable and decorative roof. When this material is properly formulated, there can be no limit to its life expectancy, which certainly should be well over 30 years.

Spray-up and Poured Roofing Materials

In order to compete with the newer polymeric spray-up roofing materials, such as chlorosulfonated polypropylene, acrylics, and other materials now making an entrance into our markets, polyester manufacturers must also develop a liquid, spray, or pour-in-place type of roofing material.

These products will present no problem with this versatile material. A liquid roofing material made with polyester will have every advantage over the other polymers because polyester has the great characteristic that it can be heavily filled and yet be applied without the use of solvents of any kind.

A 100% solids compound has long been needed. Solvents are added costs, without any benefits, and they are an everpresent fire hazard. Without solvents, roofing applications may be done in one single application to any desired thickness. This will cut labor costs and application time to a bare minimum. Workmen will be able to go on a job and walk off, having finished the same day, without any return trips.

With an elastomeric polyester resin, such as described under rolled roofing materials, this material will far surpass the properties of other polymeric types of roof coatings.

In such an application, the formulation is of utmost importance. Of necessity, it is a two-component system. Spray equipment is available today, both conventional and airless, that is designed for two-component systems. The dual systems each take one of the component liquids and deliver them to the gun, which contains a high-speed mixing chamber. Here the two materials are thoroughly blended and pushed out through the spray head.

Of major importance in the formulation of a two-component compound such as this, are the catalyst and promoter systems. The promoter must go into one component, and the catalyst must go into the second component. Without a promoter present and at ambient temperature, a catalyzed polyester will have a maximum shelf life of no more than 10 days, so the problem is to keep the system from being a three-component system instead of a two-component system.

With the new materials available today, it is completely possible to achieve this. At least two companies have been manufacturing a material known as "molecular sieve" for some years, but only recently are these new uses for it coming to light. This material has always been known to have a tremendous water-absorption property. It was used principally to mix with other materials, dry and liquid, to absorb any moisture present. It is a powerful desiccant.

Recent research has disclosed a new use for molecular sieve. Another material can be absorbed into it, and then both are mixed into any other material, with no effects until the whole is exposed to humidity. The molecular sieve then draws in moisture, displacing the material that was absorbed into the sieve.

This experiment was first tried with epoxy resins. Amines were absorbed into the molecular sieve and blended into epoxy resins. In a tightly sealed container no reaction took place for 6 months. Then the material was poured out onto a piece of plywood and brushed to a thickness of about 0.030 in. In 4 hr it was gelled. In 4 days the material was completely cured and showed properties quite similar to those of a normal, two-component epoxy. This experiment has been tried since with polyurethanes and a number of other polymers. In all, it has seemed to work very well.

However, this material has serious drawbacks. It is expensive, and it must be kept free from moisture. The moisture problem is rather easy to overcome, but in epoxies and urethanes the cost is high.

In epoxy, the amount of catalyst may be from 10% to as high as 50% when certain catalysts are used. The same, more or less, applies to urethanes.

These molecular sieves cost about $3.00 per lb, so entirely too much is necessary to absorb the catalysts for urethanes and epoxies. Four to six pounds of the molecular sieve are necessary for one pound of another material.

With polyesters, the conditions change drastically. In polyesters, only 1% of catalyst is used in most cases; thus, with 4 lb of molecular sieve to absorb 1 lb of catalyst, 100 lb of polyester can be catalyzed. The cost will be roughly $12.00 per 100 lb of resin.

The use of a molecular sieve permits formulation of dual-component compounds that are shelf-stable for 6 months or more, yet will cure when exposed to atmospheric humidity in almost the same time as they normally would. Gel time is actually lengthened about 25%, but cure times does not seem to be affected at all.

The advent of newer catalysts have enhanced the possibility of this type of formulation even more. Several of the catalyst manufacturers have come out with a variation of the usual hydroperoxides, which is very effective, and which will cure polyesters to 20°F or lower. Granted, cures are slower at these temperatures, and this type of material would seldom be applied at these temperatures, but it can be done if necessary.

This catalyst is very readily taken up into the spores or tiny channels of the molecular sieve. No pressure is necessary, as is the case with the catalysts and hardeners for epoxies and urethanes, because of the very low viscosity of the hydroperoxides.

A formulation for the two-component roofing material will be the following:

Component 1

1. Elastomeric polyester resin-monomers...................... 40.00 lb
2. Cobalt octoate... 0.04
3. Dibutyl tin dilaureate................................. 0.02
4. Zirconium naphthenate................................. 0.04
5. China clay.. 10.00
6. Silica, 325 mesh, or calcium carbonate................... 50.00

100.10 lb

Component 2

1. Elastomeric polyester resin-monomers...................... 40.0 lb
2. 0.8-lb hydroperoxide, in 4-lb molecular sieve................ 4.8
3. China clay.. 6.0
4. Silica, 325 mesh, or calcium carbonate................... 50.0

100.8 lb

The fillers used in this formulation must be extremely dry. The resin should be checked as to moisture content. No moisture can be allowed to enter these materials, either before or after they are formulated. After compounding, the cans must be tightly sealed. The containers should be filled completely to the top to avoid air space that will contain some moisture, or the containers may be purged with nitrogen gas to eliminate any air present.

These precautions may seem to be an abnormal amount; however, today they are standard procedure in many plastic-formulating processes, particularly in polyurethanes. All necessary equipment for these procedures will be found in the Appendix.

The two components are packaged either in 55-gal drums or in 5-gal cans. The dual equipment is connected to these and the material is sprayed through a spray head designed for such viscous compounds. There is both conventional and airless equipment available to handle this material. For applications in cold weather, heating units are available to fit either the 5- or 55-gal containers. A small amount of heat will reduce the viscosity of these compounds to normal, so they may be easily sprayed up with this type of equipment.

The application may be at any thickness desired, with one pass. A thickness of 0.050 in. would be sufficient for almost any roof. This material will withstand heavy traffic and any normal wear and tear that may be expected. It will bond well to concrete, wood, and a few of the existing types of roofing materials. It must not be applied over asphalt roofing without a special primer coat because the asphalt will "bleed" through. It would be advisable not to apply it over asphalt at all, if possible.

The above formulations may be pigmented in any color. Pigment was not included in the formulation, as it is not necessary to pigment it at all.

When the material has been sprayed up on the substrate, aggregates may be scattered into the surface if desired. A strip some 3 ft wide may be laid up, and while the spray operator starts the next strip, another workman can follow and scatter the loose aggregates on the surface. The aggregates will be firmly bonded to the material, and any excess may be brushed off later.

This roofing material may also be applied by trowel by premixing the two-component parts well with a small-power mixer, then pouring the material out on the substrate, and then troweling out. It will be self-leveling to a certain extent, so trowel marks will not show. The same can be done with a heavy pushbroom, if desired. This material may be applied in several other ways and means, depending on the particular surface.

The formulations given above are more or less for the level types of roofs, usually referred to as builtup roofs. As given above, these materials would flow too much to be used on a slanting roof, such as a 4:1 surface. However, the formulations may be changed slightly so they may be applied to a sloping roof also. Three to four percent of cellulose acetate butyrate ($\frac{1}{2}$-sec butyrate), blended into the resin when it is being manufactured during the cooling stage, or colloidal silicas or some of the blown, synthetic silicas used at about 3% by weight of the resin, will prevent sag or flow of the material on a pitched surface. There are a few specially treated clays that will do the same job, but these are used in considerably more amounts by weight.

Some very good and beautiful roofs may be laid up with this two-component roofing material. All types of finishes may be obtained with pigments and aggregates used in good combinations. The properties of this material will be such that it should be especially good for flat, concrete buildings, where a builtup roof is usually used.

This material will have at least a 100% elongation, so thermal expansion and contraction will never cause it to rupture. The concrete under it may form small cracks, but this material will not be affected. Cold or hot weather cannot affect it in any way. If desired, it can be made completely nonflammable by adding the materials earlier discussed in this chapter.

Ceiling Materials

Today the construction of ceilings is fairly confined to using the material fiberboard and sheetrock. Lately a new material has made an appearance and is now receiving a share of the market. It is a polystyrene, foamed ceiling material, usually made up into 12×12 in. squares. Some of it is formed so that it is accoustical. It is a very good ceiling material, and its rather high cost at present will decrease as sales volumes increase. This material has an advantage over the others in that it does not have to be painted to give a finished surface.

A very similar material may be manufactured with polyester resins at a lower cost than the polystyrene foam. Polystyrene itself is not usually classed in the medium-price bracket, but this material is, simply because it is premanufactured into tiny spheres, with the blowing agent incorporated into each sphere. These are processed into foam by first preexpanding these spheres with steam until they are about their final size. Then they are injected into cavities and heated until fully expanded. The beads or spheres bond together as they expand. Then the cavity must be cooled somewhat and the material ejected.

The cooling cycle of the mold cavity and then the reheating of the cavity cut down on cycle time tremendously. The preexpansion of the beads does not cut down on total cycle time as it is simultaneous to the final process. It does, however, take an additional piece of equipment.

Polyester foam does not have any of these disadvantages; it may be handled completely as a liquid, with quite different, lower cost equipment. There will be no cooling cycle, and total cycle times can be as low as 10 sec with proper formulations and equipment.

A formulation such as that given in Chap. 4 under the heading, Modular Panels would be used. This formulation would be pigmented suitably so the entire foamed part would be colored and would not require painting.

The same type of dies would be used as are used in making the polystyrene ceiling material, with quick opening and closing action on the equipment. Clamp pressures and toggle setup would be roughly the same.

The great differences would be that the polyester compound can be pumped into the cavities very easily, and that no cooling of the dies is necessary. The dies will remain at about 330°F at all times, and cycle times can be very fast. Ordinary proportioning pumps are available that will place the proper amount of compound in the multiple dies automatically with each cycle.

The polyester foam will be much stronger and more rigid than the polystyrene. Therefore, it will be much harder to damage during manufacture, handling, shipping, and placing.

The polyester foam will not be limited to 12 × 12 in. ceiling tile. It may be made much larger, to 4 × 4 ft, if desired. It will be sufficiently strong and rigid, so that it will not need supports of any kind in these distances. The thickness may be the same as in the polystyrene tile, ½ to ¾ in. In 4 × 4 ft sheets, it should be ¾ in. thick.

This tile may be made with smooth or accoustical surfaces. It may be textured, or it may have intricate patterns built into it. These features will depend entirely on mold design or subsequent processes. In accoustical tile, it may be more economical to use automatic, multihead drills to accomplish this, as most of the ceiling tile is made.

The foam formulation given will be a good one for this process, with the addition of an internal mold release, pigments, and, if desired, fireproofing ingredients.

Thermal Insulating Materials

Polyester may also be manufactured in slab thermal-insulating materials quite easily by a process very similar to that employed in the manufacture of slab urethane foams.

The compound, such as the formulation mentioned above, would be mixed in continuous mixing equipment and poured onto a conveyor belt at a thickness of approximately 1 in. The material would go through an oven for blowing (foaming) and cure and would be sawed into the desired slab thickness by automatic wire saws as it travels on toward the packaging section. The 1 in. of compound would be foamed to a thickness of approximately 35 in. if formulated for a density of 2 lb per cu ft. The density of the foam may be formulated from 2 to 10 lb per cu ft, depending on its end use. It may be slabbed into 2-, 4-, or 6-in. thick slabs just by setting the saws to this adjustment.

This foam will be extremely strong and rigid. It will have over 95% closed cells, and the cell structure will be good. Its K factor will be about 0.19, comparable to the best epoxy or urethane foam and better than polystyrene foam.

Some research has been done on flexible foams for use in automobile seat cushions, mattresses, and furniture. So far, a polyester resin has not been quite suitable for this use. With sufficient research, however, there is no reason why it cannot be made. The problem has been to get a resin which is flexible enough, yet strong enough, to take the punishment which is part of the environment in such applications. A cushion-type foam is usually an open-cell urethane, blown to a density of 5 to 8 lb per cu ft. The urethane is surprisingly strong at this density.

An elastomeric polyester may be developed soon for such applications. If it is, then this market will be well worth investigating. Meanwhile, rigid, thermal-insulation foam has a very large market. It should be considered as a very important part of the future of polyester resins.

Urethanes and epoxies may now be sprayed up in self-blowing insulating materials at ambient temperatures. A great variety of equipment is available for this purpose. Some of this equipment proportions the two components and sprays them on, quite like spraying paint. The material contains a blowing agent—the fluoromethane type—that activates at temperatures as low as 50°F.

In polyurethanes, even water may be the blowing agent. The water reacts with the NCO of the diisocyanate to form carbon dioxide, and this causes the foam to rise.

Many blowing agents and many different types of equipment are available for applications in almost any given situation, and at almost any temperature, for the epoxies and the urethanes. These foams and equipment have been developed because of the tremendous market that exists for this type of thermal barrier.

The foamed-in-place material may be used in many applications that would not be practical for slab-foamed polymers: fuel tanks, refrigeration cars and trucks, chemical storage tanks, and thousands of applications where it would cost much more to apply slab-insulating materials.

As explained more fully in Chap. 4, polyester that may be foamed in place in the field, under ambient temperatures, is not available at this time. It is not just a matter of producing the proper polymer, because this is now possible. The problem lies in matching the blowing agent to the catalyst and both to the exotherm temperature of the resin. The whole formulation will have to be such that it will give the same results at any given temperature from 40 to 110°F. This is not an easy task, but there is no reason why it cannot be done. The market is large enough to warrant a great deal of research. This research should be done by the polyester-resin manufacturers, who have the most to gain from it since the foam will be largely polymer.

Polyester manufacturers complain that there are too many manufacturers for the available market so there is no profit for any of them. This situation can easily be remedied by developing new products to expand the market.

Polyester foams will have the large advantage of being lower in cost than either epoxy or urethane. Once it is perfected, there will be no problem in placing it on the market. Its low cost will immediately give it an outlet.

Ducting for Heating and Air-conditioning

Tubular goods such as these are now formed from light-gauge sheet metal, which is joined and then insulated after installation. The labor costs for most of this work, which is done in the field, are quite high even though the cost of the basic tubular material is very low.

There is no reason why such ducting cannot be manufactured all in one piece—both duct and thermal barrier at the same time. A very rigid polyester-foam material, such as discussed above, has sufficient strength and will provide the thermal barrier, all in one.

Since some ducting is round and other types are square or rectangular, devising a process by which either type can be manufactured on a single production line may be very difficult, or impossible. There is definitely a need for both types because of the design of air shafts, ceilings, and other parts of buildings.

The design of the ducts themselves will be a challenge to manufacturers. Easy and fast means of connecting sections together will be of prime importance. This can possibly be accomplished by the telescoping, or "stove piping," method, where a duct is smaller on one end than on the other, and two slip together, possibly being bonded with an adhesive. Another design to be considered would be the bell joint, in which the length of ducting has the same measurements as the entire length, and one end is belled out to accept the opposite end of the next section.

Since a rigid foam duct would be 1 to 2 in. in thickness of the wall section, another good possibility to be considered would be merely a lap joint, where each end of the section would only be half the wall thickness, with one end the larger dimension, and the other the smaller

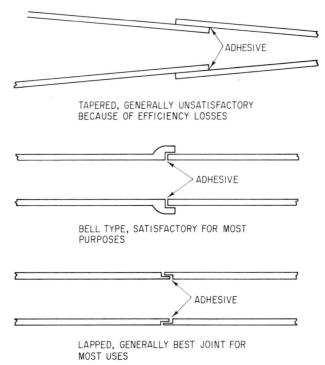

TAPERED, GENERALLY UNSATISFACTORY
BECAUSE OF EFFICIENCY LOSSES

BELL TYPE, SATISFACTORY FOR MOST
PURPOSES

LAPPED, GENERALLY BEST JOINT FOR
MOST USES

DIAGRAM 13. *Suggested joint types for polyester foamed ducting and low-pressure tubing.*

dimension. (See Diagram 13, which shows these three possible means of connecting sections.)

The round ducting would be reasonably simple to manufacture by rotational casting. A quantity of the polyester compound will be placed inside a cylindrical mold, suitably heat-jacketed. The mold would be rotated at sufficient speed for the centrifugal force to hold the compound evenly against its interior face as it foamed and cured. The joint connections would be designed right into the mold. Multiple molds, operated from one power source and one heating system, could manufacture very high volumes of this ducting.

This is a well-known manufacturing process which is used in the production of many consumer items, particularly where vinyl plastics are used. The only variation in the entire procedure would be the molds themselves.

The production of square and rectangular ducts would be an entirely different matter, as rotational casting would not be suitable. These ducts would almost of necessity be produced by multiple matched molds, male and female. These could be positioned in a vertical position on an endless conveyor system, which would carry them through an oven. Proper quantities would be proportioned into each open-end mold and carried through the oven for foaming and curing.

This method would probably present difficulties, particularly if the sections were to be over 24 in. long. Since the foam would be rising between the faces of matching molds, 1 to 2 in. apart, considerable skin friction very probably would prevent the foam from rising to maximum height and minimum density. Tests with different blowing agents and internal mold-release agents and lubricants may solve this problem. An internal lubricant, such as calcium stearate, may prove to be a great aid in production. It flashes to the surfaces very rapidly and creates a very slick lubrication which would be needed in such a process.

Other types of processing may be considered in the production of ducting. In order to be able to compete with conventional materials, the process will have to be very efficient and economical.

Pipe and Tubular Goods

Polyester and epoxy pipe, highly reinforced with glass fiber, are a very fast-growing industry. There are at least four major plants in this country which turn out thousands of linear feet of this material every day, in sizes ranging from 1 in. diameter to 16 in. and more. Such pipe can be designed to take internal pressures to 6,000 psi in the smaller diameters.

In our rapidly growing chemical industries, such piping is an absolute necessity because many of the metals, including stainless steel, will not stand up under constant use with some of these chemicals.

Many other polymers are used in the manufacture of pipe. Polyvinyls, chlorinated polyethers, polyethylene, polypropylene, and many other plastics are used in tubular goods for specific environments.

Several manufacturers are lining metal tubular goods with these materials. The metal provides the necessary strength, and the plastic liner provides the chemical resistance.

Other manufacturers are producing plastic sleeves, for both the interior and exterior of metal pipe. The sleeves are formulated so they may be inserted into metal pipe and expanded to bond firmly to the interior.

Others are oversize and are placed on the exterior of the metal pipe, and shrunk to bond to the exterior. Plastic fittings are made, and plastic-lined fittings of all kinds are available to the chemical industry.

The high-pressure tubular goods, both epoxy and polyester, are manufactured by a process known as "filament-winding." A single strand or a group of strands of glass fibers, are continuously wound around a mandrel, together with the catalyzed polymer, until the desired thickness is reached. The direction of the glass fibers and the amount decide the maximum internal pressures the pipe will withstand. This is very oversimplified, as the process requires much more equipment and techniques, but it is roughly the basic procedure.

The polyester pipe has advantages over the epoxy in cost and cycle time, and for use in certain environments. The epoxy has advantages for use in certain chemical environments and a slight advantage in strength-to-weight ratio.

Some of the newer polyester resins now being developed will be able to overcome the strength-to-weight ratio differential, and others will be able to overcome some of the environmental advantages of the epoxies. There will always be a place for the epoxies in certain applications.

Polyester pipe is a very fast-growing market that must not be underestimated. It is possible that polyester tubular goods may take a very large segment of the present market away from metal goods in such ordinary uses as water, gas, and electrical distribution. Polyester tubing will have every advantage over metals because of the hazards of corrosion by oxidation and by electrolysis. (This will be discussed more fully in Chap. 7.) Polyester tubular goods have an added advantage in that they are electrical nonconductors and thus provide great protection to electrical and telephone cables. (This will be discussed in Chap. 8.)

Tanks, Vessels, and Silos

This is a very large market in which polyester resins are just beginning to make an entrance.

The smaller, integral vessels may now be made much in the same manner as the polyester tubular goods. They may be filament-wound over a mandrel or mold. Molds may be made of inflatable elastomers, soft, flexible polyamides, or other materials which can be drawn out of an opening of the vessel after completion. Or, these molds may be of the soluble type—used once and then dissolved in water and removed. The destructable type of mold may be used, which is made from a plaster-type material and broken out of the vessel in pieces after completion.

With very low-pressure vessels, the hand lay-up and gun lay-up methods are often used to build up the necessary thicknesses of glass fiber and resin.

At least one manufacturer is producing larger, sectional vessels from polyester fiberglass. These are manufactured in convenient-sized sections, which bolt together quite like is often done with metal tanks. These vessels find a market particularly in feedstuff storage, fertilizer bulk storage, and grain silos, where so often corrosion attacks a metal tank.

There is a real need for reinforced polyester tanks of large sizes, suitable for the handling of sour crude oils and highly corrosive chemicals. These tanks are not available today because suitable designs and processes by which to manufacture them have not been developed.

The polyester industry has developed equipment and techniques whereby normal metal tanks may be lined with a layer of reinforced polyester, but no suitable means have been devised whereby large storage tanks may be economically manufactured completely from this material.

In sectional tanks, joints have been a major problem. Either gaskets must be used, or the tanks leak. Proper strength at the joints has been another major difficulty. So far the processes used have been expensive and unsatisfactory.

Polyesters have great advantages over metals for such applications. The strength-to-weight ratios of polyester fiberglass over steel are very favorable. A polyester vessel does not require maintenance of any kind, whereas metal must be sandblasted and painted at regular intervals. A metal storage tank is very limited as to the liquids that may be stored in it, where the polyester has a much wider range of resistance to fuels and chemicals.

In this area, both polyester-resin manufacturers and processors must cooperate to develop new processes and techniques whereby larger vessels may be manufactured. This will not be an easy task, nor an economical one; but it must be done. The investment will pay great dividends in the final analysis.

Concrete Forms

Concrete forms are a rather insignificant part of the construction industry, from the viewpoint of a single construction project. However, when considered as a part of the whole construction industry throughout the country, its part becomes much larger.

For temporary forms, the building industry uses, for the most part, wood and plywood. For permanent forms that must be used many times in order to amortize their cost, the industry turns to metal. Both wood and metal forms have multiple faults. Wood must be treated to give good release, and the grain of the wood raises and leaves its imprint in the finished concrete, which must be ground off in many instances. The life span of wood forms is very limited. Metal forms must be kept painted, or they will oxidize. Some builders keep them oiled, but whether painted or oiled, this constitutes maintenance costs. Metal forms are heavy and hard to handle. If they are subjected to a blow or dropped, they are deformed and must either be repaired or scrapped.

Reinforced polyester forms can find a very good market in this application. Polyester forms will not need releases of any kind; they will not need maintenance, and the concrete can have perfect surfaces when the forms are removed. They will be much lighter in weight than either wood or metal forms. Also, they will be easier to handle and transport from job to job. If handled with reasonable care, their life span will be indefinite.

Reinforced polyester sheet materials have been manufactured for many years. These materials are easy to fabricate into any shape or design and may be reinforced at critical points with ease. Adhesives are available to join this material to itself or to any other suitable material.

The building industry must be informed of the fine possibilities of reinforced polyester for use in concrete forms. Any additional initial investment for such forms will soon be made up in profits because of the advantages cited.

Caulking and Sealing Compounds

Compounds for such uses as caulking and sealing expansion joints in highways, buildings, bridges, and other applications form perhaps the smallest dollar volume in the construction industry. If considered on a nationwide basis, the volume becomes quite substantial.

Very good two-component compounds can be made from an elastomeric polyester resin, such as that considered for the application of spray-up roofing materials. The formulation would be along the same lines, except that the caulking compound would have a much higher filler content. The catalyst would be absorbed by molecular sieve (just as in spray-up roofing materials) and placed in component No. 2.

At the job site, the two components would be well mixed, placed in a proper applicator gun, and applied to joints, cracks, and other locations in which these compounds are normally used.

By proper choice of catalysts and promoters, pot life can be adjusted to suit a particular need. A pot life of up to 8 hr is entirely possible. In this way, workmen can mix a batch in the morning and use it all day.

Reinforced Structural Members,
Beams, and Columns—
Prestressed and Poststressed

In this day of superhighways and freeways and multistory buildings, the prestressed concrete industry has grown very large. Members, beams, and sectional slabs are being manufactured in the plant and transported to the construction project ready to install. This system cuts down on construction time since work is not delayed while concrete cures in place.

Shapes and sizes of such beams and slabs have been standardized to some extent, so the manufacturer need not have a tremendous inventory of forms. Overpasses on highways all have fairly well the same load requirements, and buildings are nearly the same in structural-member design, so many of these can be taken from the same forms.

Concrete is the oldest known construction material; it has been used for many centuries. Steel reinforcing for concrete is more recent, and prestressing and poststressing have been developed fully only during the past 20 years.

By taking advantage of the tensile strength of steel and literally stretching it by placing high longitudinal stresses in force, reinforced-concrete members may be made much stronger, allowing much less concrete to be used for given load bearings.

Even by reducing the total weight of these members by about one-third or more in this manner, reinforced concrete is still very heavy. It is costly to transport and install. These members may be damaged during manufacture or handling, and the percentage of rejects from these reasons is quite high.

Some work has been done toward development of reinforced plastic beams and other members. However, this work has been very limited because of the high finances required in this type of developmental work. Some progress has been reported in various trade publications, but in reality, little total progress has been made. Many designers, architects, and builders know that it can be done, but have not had the resources with which to carry such a project forward. This research work must be done soon in order for the polyester industry to reach its full potential.

Herein lies a tremendous, unexplored market for polyester resins. With the amount of this type of construction being done today, the market is ready and waiting for the polyester industry. Some company or a group of companies must take the necessary steps to take full advantage of this great outlet.

Reinforced polyester beams and members will have every possible advantage over concrete products. First, concrete products are manufactured and must cure 21 to 28 days before they may be handled, according to corresponding specifications. A polyester product would be ready to handle in 7 days, at ambient temperatures, or in 4 hr if heat cures were employed.

Secondly, the weight of these concrete products is over six times greater than the polyester part. The strength-to-weight ratio of polyester, compared to that of concrete, allows far less actual material in each polyester part.

Next, the percentage of members or parts damaged during manufacture, handling, shipping, and installation would be almost nil with reinforced polyester.

The lighter weight plus the reduced danger of damaging these materials would allow them to be shipped to far greater distances than is possible with concrete.

The cost of the polyester finished product should compare very favorably with the cost of its concrete competitor. A plant properly set up could produce many times more of the polyester products per day, and labor cost per unit would be a fraction of that of concrete. Handling and shipping costs would be far lower, and the reduced percentage of rejects would further decrease overall costs.

When all cost calculations are made, with all factors taken into consideration, the polyester product will probably be lower in cost per unit than the concrete. Even such factors as reduced foundation requirements and shorter total construction time must be calculated with these materials.

When considering a project such as this, the magnitude of such a development program will overwhelm many people in the polyester industry. Those who cannot see the great future in such an undertaking should not even consider taking part in it. It will call for great resources, in both capital investment and knowledge.

In considering such a project, perhaps the first step should be to establish what type of reinforcing material would be suitable for best results. At least two must be considered: steel (just as that used in concrete) and glass fiber. Using steel would be a simple route to take because the equipment for the stressing operation is already available. The same equipment possibly may be modified to handle glass fiber as well, but this will have to be tested.

Glass fiber offers great advantages in the strength-to-weight ratio, so if glass fiber were used, the product would be considerably lighter. Glass roving materials are now available in very large sizes. There is no reason why they cannot be made much larger for this application.

Steel cable must be considered also because of its higher tensile strength per pound as compared to steel rods.

Both prestressing and poststressing must be considered very carefully. Each offers many possible advantages in such a process.

The process must be studied also, taking into consideration production, cycle-time, and mold-material requirements, and many other phases of the process.

For large-scale production, it would necessarily be a highly mechanized process. Probably railway cars of narrow gauge would be used. The track arrangement would be an oval or round configuration, with a large portion enclosed in an oven. Molds would be fixed to the small railway cars, which would be fitted with air or electric hoists to handle the reinforcing materials and the molds.

The cars would stop at each corresponding station along the track to place the reinforcing material and to pour and vibrate the polyester compound, and then proceed through the oven for cure. If the product were to be prestressed, this would be done before entering the oven. If it were to be poststressed, this would be done after the product had cooled to room temperature.

The actual process could vary widely, according to the requirements. Only after a complete study can a process actually be devised. Improvements and techniques will develop as actual production is underway.

A project so large and new would entail far more discussion than could possibly be set forth here. This writer can only hope to kindle the spark necessary for the industry to realize the potentials in such a project, and perhaps in a few years such a product will appear on the market.

Seven

CORROSION CONTROL

The control of corrosion in the United States and throughout the world has been the object of extensive research for many years.

Since the end of World War II, much progress has been made, but only the surface has been scratched. Much more remains to be done in the field of metallurgy, cathodic protection systems, and organic and inorganic coatings.

Corrosion control, of course, is not limited to just the maintenance of new and existing structures. It must also include the search for completely new and better materials to use in the construction of these structures. Metallurgists are working with new alloys which show great promise. The electronics and metallurgy industries are cooperating in research on better means of cathodically protecting metals. The coatings and plastic industries are working with new polymers and many different combinations or alloys of polymers to find better protective systems. Many engineers with vision are concentrating solely on replacing metals with plastics wherever possible.

Corrosion control does not just include the protection of metals. It also must take into consideration the protection of wood, concrete, and other materials. It must consider the protection of structures of all kinds, equipment and machinery, automobiles, aircraft, ships at sea, and almost everything around us.

Corrosion encompasses far more than just the oxidation of materials through the actions of water and/or oxygen. It must encompass the destruction of all types of materials in all types of environmental conditions, whether the destructive elements be natural or man-made. The destructive elements may be natural weather conditions or salt air or salt water in areas in or near the ocean. They may be the acidic, alkaline, or salt contents of the soil where materials must be installed. They may be the highly chemical atmospheric conditions near or in chemical plants, or strong chemicals with which the materials must come in direct contact. In many cases, destructive elements are a combination of all these things. The sun itself is a destructive element to many materials. Heat and cold cycles, expansion and contraction, and dust-laden wind can all contribute to the destruction of materials. Electrolysis plays a large role in the destruction of metals. Different metals, in contact or near contact, create very serious problems. The metal which is lower on the electromotive scale is destroyed, to the benefit of the metal which is higher on the scale. This principal is used to good advantage in the cathodic protection systems installed today in so many of our structures, pipelines, ships, and other applications where metals are used. The elements found in the sea and soil create electrolysis, and metals coming in contact with them must be protected.

Many people think that concrete is an inert material that nothing can destroy. This is far from being true. Acidic environments can destroy concrete very rapidly. All concrete is somewhat porous, and moisture and oxygen get to the reinforcing steel. The steel begins to oxidize, and this action causes spalling of the concrete, allowing even more water and air to get to the reinforcing steel. If an electrolytic field is present, as it is in many instances, the destruction of the steel is accelerated.

Wood is destroyed through action of combinations of the elements, natural or man-made. Every type of building material can deteriorate from one or more causes. This is why coatings are used to protect, as well as beautify, almost everything we see around us.

The selection of materials necessary to produce these coatings has changed greatly over the years. We have progressed from the natural rosins from trees to oils from plants, trees, and fish. Great quantities of these materials are still used in coatings for certain uses, but today the great majority of our coating materials are derived from hydrocarbons. They are referred to as plastic or synthetic polymers.

In coatings, these materials form the "binder" or basis of the material. The binder must form the bond to whatever substrate is being coated, holding together the relatively inert fillers which make up a large percentage of the total coating material. Pigments and many kinds of additives are blended into the coating to obtain different properties. Many times, metallic fillers are used, so the coating will be both protective and an anode at the same time. Often, base coats for metals are entirely inorganic, and the metallic film is referred to as "sacrificial." In use, it becomes the sacrificial anode, while the metal being protected is the cathode.

Coatings are regarded as temporary protection for other materials. We must use them until we have building materials that do not need either protection or beautification, such as some of the products discussed in previous chapters.

Protective coatings are manufactured by a great number of companies from a very wide selection of resins, oils, and polymers. Alkyds, a nonreactive type of polyester, have been used for many years, and are a mainstay in decorative and protective coatings. These will not be discussed here. The reactive type of polyester, which is the basis of this book, has been used very little in coating applications until recently. This polyester is just beginning to make an appearance in this industry.

Reactive polyesters have been with us for a long time, but the resins of past years have had serious deficiencies as coating materials. They would not bond well to certain substrates and would not cure completely in the presence of air. In order to obtain good bond, special primers had to be used, and in order to have tack-free surfaces, additives such as waxes and paraffins had to be incorporated into the coating; these would exude to the surface as the coating cured, to form an airtight film.

The above deficiencies made polyesters something less than an ideal coating polymer, in spite of their most desirable properties. Most people in the coatings industry recognized the highly desirable properties of polyester but could not overcome the two outstanding drawbacks.

Many formulators decided that polyesters would never be a suitable polymer for coating applications and turned to other polymers which were somewhat easier to work with. A few researchers kept working over the years, determined that here was a most ideal and versatile polymer because of the properties that could be designed into a given resin. These people felt they could overcome the two major deficiencies.

The basic elements necessary for bond were known. Cohesion, molecular attraction, polarity, and all factors had to be considered. After years of intensive research, polyesters have been developed which will obtain good bond to almost any substrate. Work is still going on, and within a year, or two years at the most, polyesters will be produced that will bond to metals as well as the best epoxies available.

Obtaining polyesters that would surface-cure in the presence of air in thin films has been even a more difficult problem. There are two basic reasons for undercure on the surface of these polymers: The monomers contained in the resin will not polymerize completely when exposed to air, and the remaining carboxylic groups or saturation, reflected in the acid number of the resin, react very poorly at ambient temperatures and in the presence of air.

This undercured surface is highly susceptable to oxidation, and a coating of this nature will soon discolor and deteriorate, particularly in exterior environments.

The addition of wax and paraffin to seal off the polymer from the air is not a good solution. Either this film must be removed after the polyester has cured, or the wax will detract from the appearance of the coating. The wax will kill any surface gloss and itself will soon oxidize, discolor, and deteriorate.

Much research work has been done to find solutions for the surface-curing problems of polyesters. Other polymers, alloyed with polyesters in relatively small percentages, help considerably. Instead of straight monomers, polystyrene, polyacrylates, diallyl phthalate polymer, and others work very well as cross-linking agents. The only problem here is that if too large a percentage of polymers is used, viscosity goes up, and often solvents must be added to apply them as coatings.

New intermediates and monomers have been developed, which eliminate most of the problem. Two new polyhydric intermediates help in obtaining air-cured properties. Dicyclopentadiene and neopentyl glycol are both very good. New saturated acids include hexahydrophthalic and tetrahydrophthalic acid. Both are most useful in coatings. Most of the chlorinated-saturated acids also will produce good surface-curing resins. HET acid, chlorendic anhydride, and others are very good. Pyromellitic dianhydride, used as a portion of the saturated group, produces excellent properties.

The chlorinated monomers, such as o-chlorostyrene and M-chlorostyrene, do not inhibit surface-cure nearly as badly as the more common monomers. Both also have the ability to impart better bond to a given resin.

The more highly reactive a resin, the better the surface-cure. There are many polyhydric components that may be used, including glycerine, pentaetheritol, sorbitol, and others, which, used in very small percentages, will produce a resin that is highly reactive. Polyethers, polybutadienes, and polyactones all are most useful in obtaining highly reactive resins when substituted as a part of the alcohol portion of the formulation.

The residual carboxyl groups of the polyester resin must be reacted, so a polyester may be packaged at zero acid number. If this were to be done by lengthening the cooking time, the molecular weight of the resin would be much too high, viscosity would be much too high, and the compatibility of the resin to common monomers would be impaired seriously.

There are two methods of reducing the acid number of a polyester resin to zero, without increasing molecular weight and viscosity. One method is by reacting the residual carboxylic groups in the kettle with ethylene oxide or ethylene carbonate. Since ethylene oxide is a gas and very difficult to handle, this is best accomplished with ethylene carbonate. The reduction of acidity is by chain termination rather than by chain linkage. There is no increase in either viscosity or molecular weight of the resin.

The second method of producing a resin with an acid number of zero is to use digallic acid (tannin) for the saturated portion of the resin. It may be cooked until the acid number is zero, without viscosity being too high. Molecular weight, however, does increase, and this resin will be slightly less compatible with a number of the common monomers. This may be overcome by adding the monomers during the cooling stage of resin manufacture at temperatures slightly higher than normal.

In Chap. 11 more complete data is given on the manufacture of surface-curing polyesters, unaffected by the presence of air.

The important thing is that today polyester-resin manufacturers have the knowledge and the raw materials and intermediates with which to work to produce polyesters that are highly suited to further processing into coatings.

With the addition of the molecular sieves to the long list of raw materials available, excellent two-component polyester coatings can be manufactured, which will be entirely shelf-stable for 6 months or longer.

These coatings are most desirable for many environments where the epoxies, alkyds, urethanes, and many others would not be suitable. These coatings will be economical, 100% solids coatings that may be applied in one application to almost any thickness desired. This is just not possible with coatings containing solvents.

Protective Coatings for
Structural Steel

Polyester coatings are especially suited to any structural steel exposed to an environment of acid, acid fumes, sulfides, salt, and salt air. Some polyesters, such as the bisphenol A polyesters and the chlorinated polyesters, will also give very good service in highly alkaline environments.

The preparation of the steel to be coated must be the same as when it is prepared for any other organic coating. Sandblasting is always preferable to provide both clean metal and an anchor pattern for additional mechanical bond. In applications where sandblasting is not possible, a phosphoric acid wash will give a good surface over which to coat. Sometimes two such applications are necessary to remove mill scale or heavy oxidation. In a few instances, the phosphoric acid wash must be aided with chipping or power wire brushes to remove very heavy scale.

These coatings may all be applied over new concrete, wood, and other substrates without unusual surface preparation. Concrete that is extremely dense or that has a glaze on the surface should be power-brushed with a coarse wire brush to roughen the surface slightly and remove any glaze.

All surfaces to be coated must be dry and free of loose dirt and foreign matter such as oil and grease. New concrete must be a minimum of 21 days and preferably 28 days old.

With previously coated surfaces, polyester coatings may be applied over epoxy, polyurethane, or other polyesters. The surfaces of the old coating, if in good condition, will only need to be slightly roughed up with wire brushes or sandpaper and wiped down with a 50:50 solution of toluol and styrene monomer.

Polyester coating may not be applied over alkyds, epoxy esters, vinyls, or linseed-oil-based coatings. Whenever there is doubt, the polyester should be applied to a small area about 12×12 in. and allowed to stand 48 hr. If no "lifting" of the old material takes place, then it is safe to proceed.

On all new steel and concrete that have not been coated previously, a primer coat of 3 to 5 mils is indicated. The primer is allowed to cure, preferably not more than 48 hr, before the top coat is applied. The top coat may be applied to any desired thickness in one application.

The distinct advantage of these 100%-solids polyester coatings is that since there are no solvents present, there is no practical limit to the thickness of a single application.

On vertical surfaces, polyester coatings will have to be formulated with a sag-control agent or agents. Cellulose acetate butyrate ($\frac{1}{2}$-sec butyrate) and the colloidial silicas are very good for this purpose. There are many other additives that may be used in these coatings to obtain characteristics desirable for ease in application; the selection of these depends largely on the purpose for which the coating is intended, application method to be used, length of pot life desired, and curing method. Formulations will vary considerably from an ambient-temperature-curing system to a heat-curing system.

Chart 5 shows nine basic polyester-resin formulations suitable for use as coating polymers and the uses to which they are particularly suited.

CHART 5. COATING POLYESTERS

Dihydric and polyhydric components	Moles	Unsaturated acid	Moles	Saturated acid	Moles	Monomers	Moles
Formula 1. Steel primer: Neopentyl glycol Bisphenol A	1.0 1.2	Maleic anhydride	0.6	Isophthalic acid	1.4	m-Chlorostyrene Allyl chloride	0.5 0.2
Formula 2. Concrete primer: Propylene glycol	2.2	Maleic anhydride	0.6	Isophthalic acid	1.4	Styrene Vinyl toluene	0.3 0.4
Formula 3. Salt: Dicyclopentadiene Propylene glycol	1.1 1.1	Maleic anhydride	1.0	Isophthalic acid	1.0	Styrene m-Chlorostyrene	0.2 1.0
Formula 4. Heat and flame: Neopentyl glycol Dicyclopentadiene	1.1 1.1	Chloromaleic acid	1.0	Chlorophthalic acid HET acid	0.8 0.2	m-Chlorostyrene Triallyl cyanaurate	0.6 0.5
Formula 5. Resilient: Neopentyl glycol Dicyclopentadiene	1.1 1.1	Maleic anhydride	0.8	Isophthalic acid Hexahydrophthalic	0.6 0.6	m-Chlorostyrene Diallyl phthalate	0.6 0.4
Formula 6. Acids: Neopentyl glycol Dicyclopentadiene	1.1 1.1	Maleic anhydride	1.0	Hexahydrophthalic	1.0	Styrene Divinyl benzene	0.6 0.6
Formula 7. Alkalies: Bisphenol A Dicyclopentadiene	1.6 0.6	Chlorofumaric acid	1.0	Tetrachlorophthalic	1.0	m-Chlorostyrene Diallyl phthalate	0.6 0.6
Formula 8. Exterior: Dicyclopentadiene Polybutadiene	1.8 0.4	Fumaric acid	0.9	Tetrahydrophthalic	1.1	m-Chlorostyrene Methylmethacrylate Diallyl phthalate	0.4 0.2 0.4
Formula 9. Very reactive: Dicyclopentadiene Neopentyl glycol Glycerine	1.0 1.0 0.2	Fumaric acid	1.0	Tetrahydrophthalic	1.0	m-Chlorostyrene Methylmethacrylate Diallyl phthalate	0.5 0.4 0.3

NOTE: These resins will be reduced to an acid number of about 15-20 and then treated as stated with ethylene carbonate to 0. The inhibitor is hydroquinone for ambient-temperature cures.

The intermediates and monomers may be changed in type and quantity to obtain very different properties. These formulations are set forth only to show the types of intermediates that are most suitable for resins that are to be formulated into coatings for the environments described here.

The polyester resins to be used in coatings will be higher in cost than the resins recommended in previous chapters which are used in compounds for building materials. Resins properly manufactured for coatings will cost the coatings manufacturer from about 36 cents per lb, for such a resin as in Formula 1, to as much as 80 cents per lb, for such a polymer as in Formula 4.

The cost of a particular resin will depend very largely upon the specific application for which it is intended. A resin manufacturer will supply resins which are properly formulated for use in coatings for specific purposes. There is a very wide range of environments for which these resins may be used, when manufactured with the specific purpose firmly in mind and when proper components are used in their manufacture.

The manufacture of good coatings materials from polyesters requires complete cooperation between the resin manufacturer and the coatings manufacturer. The resin manufacturer must know exactly the end use to which the resin will be applied. Then he will have no trouble in supplying the resin most suitable for this use.

All coatings that may be manufactured from resins similar to those shown in Chart 5 will give excellent service. The two primer resins are formulated so as to remain tacky until the top coats have been applied. This is necessary for optimum bond. The primer-coat resin given in Formula 1 will remain tacky some 48 hr, during which the top coat should be applied. Formula 2, for concrete primers, will remain tacky indefinitely, so there is no time limit in which the top coat must be applied.

The other seven resins will all be finish-coat resins and will cure tack-free in varying lengths of time, depending on the catalyst and promoter systems used. They may be cured in as little as 2 hr at ambient temperature, or they may be formulated to give long pot life for applications where this would be desirable.

Chapter 11 gives more complete data on the manufacture of polyesters for specific environments, together with their formulations complete with promoters, catalysts, fillers, pigments, and other additives.

Protective Coatings for
Pipelines: Interior

The oil and natural-gas transmission industries spend many millions of dollars per year in the United States alone for new pipeline installations. Hundreds of thousands of miles of old pipelines lie buried all over the country—on land and under rivers, lakes, and seas. Swamps, some of which are salt or brackish water, are crossed and recrossed with these pipelines. More and more of these lines are being laid daily to serve the needs of the nation.

Every section of pipeline that is laid must be protected, usually inside as well as outside. Interior and exterior coatings will be considered separately since the applications are so completely different.

The interiors of pipelines are coated for two reasons: First, they must be protected from corrosive elements which are present in the fluids being pumped. In natural gas, oil, and even in finished-petroleum products, acids, alkalies, or sulfides are often present in sufficient quantities to destroy the steel in a short time. Frequently, these products have quite a high salt content, and always some moisture is present. These pipelines would corrode very quickly if they were not adequately protected from such elements.

The second major reason for coating the interior of a pipeline is to gain added through-put per hour. It has been proven that a very smooth-surfaced coating inside the pipe will allow considerably more gas or liquid to be pumped through it than if the steel surface, often rough, were exposed.

In some areas of the country, there is a third important reason for coating the pipelines. Some fields produce a crude oil that has a high paraffin content. As the oil flows through the pipeline, paraffin separates from the oil and begins to build up on the interior surface of the pipe. In a few years, the coating of paraffin builds up to a point where the capacity of the line is seriously impaired. Very costly cleaning methods are required to remove this buildup of hard paraffin from the interior of the pipe, and the line must be taken from service for rather long periods of time.

A good coating material, applied properly, protects the interior of the pipe from corrosion and reduces the coefficient of friction to where maximum through-put per hour may be obtained. At the same time, it provides a surface to which paraffin does not adhere.

Well over 90% of the pipe laid today, from the small to the very large diameters, are coated inside. This is not only true of pipelines which carry oil and gas, but of lines for water, salt water, and many types of finished petroleum products.

Some of this pipe is coated at the pipe mill by the joint before it is shipped. More is coated by the joint or in double joints in the field before being laid. When the pipe is welded together, short sections from each joint are burned off, cleaned, and coated after the pipe is welded.

Other pipe is coated after the entire line is finished. Equipment and processes have been developed to permit this to be done, and in many instances it is more satisfactory because there is no problem of burn-back at each weld. By these processes, even old pipe which has been buried in the ground for many years may be cleaned and coated inside. Such coatings can lengthen the life expectancy of the pipeline for many years.

Pipelines are being coated today largely with epoxy formulations. These are very good for use in many environments but have serious deficiencies; particularly, they are not suited for use in pipelines that carry acidic materials.

Other deficiencies include the manner in which they must be applied. For an epoxy to be used at 100% solids in such an application, modifiers must be used which will lower the viscosity of the coating material. The glycidal ethers, which are principally used for this purpose, detract tremendously from the properties of the finished polymer. If solvents are used to lower the viscosity of the coating, this presents two problems: (1) The coating material must be applied in two or more applications or the finished film will have multiple pores or pinholes. This is entirely unsatisfactory, since it does not offer complete protection to the steel. (2) If applied in films of more than 2 mils in thickness each, a "solvent wash" is formed. The solvent evaporating from the coating material causes the coating to sag toward the bottom of the pipe. Multiple coats are far more expensive and less satisfactory in every way.

This application is ideally suited to polyester coatings, particularly where acids, salts, and sulfides are the corrosive elements involved. Polyesters are at least equal to the epoxies in paraffin control and give equal performance in reducing the coefficient of friction inside the line. Even for use with mild alkalies, the bisphenol-chlorinated polyesters should equal epoxies that have been modified with the glycidal ethers.

The polyester may be applied to any thickness in a single application, cutting costs in time, labor, and equipment correspondingly. They are ideal for both the pipe which is coated by the joint and the in-place pipeline coating.

A good starting formulation for this application, designed for service under acidic conditions, would be as follows:

Component 1

1. Polyester resin (such as Formula 6) .... 40.00 lb
2. Promoter 0.08
3. ½-sec butyrate (in the resin) 1.50
4. Colloidal silica 1.00
5. China clay 10.00
6. Barytes, superfine, bleached 5.00
7. Silica, 400 mesh 43.00
                                                          100.58 lb

Component 2

1. Polyester resin (same).................................... 40.00 lb
2. Catalyst, 0.80 lb in 4-lb molecular sieve.................... 4.80
3. ½-sec butyrate (in resin)................................ 1.50
4. Silicone (surface-tension control)......................... 0.05
5. Pigment (chrome oxide, etc., for acid resistance)............. 4.00
6. China clay... 10.00
7. Silica, 400 mesh.. 40.00

                                                           100.35 lb

The catalyst and promoter may be adjusted to give almost any pot life desired after the two components are mixed. The catalyst usually may be adjusted from 0.75 to 1.5%, depending on the individual catalyst. The promoter may be adjusted to any desired level, from 0, for heat cure, to 0.05 to 0.30% for ambient-temperature cure.

The small amount of silicone resin used to promote flow-out at the surface to form a very smooth film must be a material especially manufactured for polyester resins. The silicone oils sometimes used in other polymers would not be suitable in polyesters. Several companies offer this resin. The amount may be adjusted somewhat to get the desired flow-out at the surface, but it should never be used in quantities which exceed 0.5% of the resin (by weight) because it will cause cratering or "fish-eyeing" in higher quantities.

The butyrate content may also be adjusted as desired. As shown, in conjunction with the colloidal silica and china clay, it will prevent running or sagging on any normal surface. If insufficient flow-out is obtained, the formulator should first lower the butyrate content; if this does not do the job satisfactorily, then the silicone content should be raised in small increments until exactly the proper surface is obtained on the film. The colloidal silica or clay content should not be lowered by any large amount, as the material will tend to settle out in the containers. The pigment and the silicas may be adjusted to obtain good working viscosities for the process being used in the coating application.

A similar formulation may be used in applications requiring resistance to salt, mild alkalies, or sulfides, or in almost any given environment by changing the polyester resin to another which is formulated for the specific purpose, and by changing pigments and fillers to those that best resist the particular condition. Chart 3 will serve as a guide to pigments and fillers, and Chart 5 to polyester resins. (More complete data may be found in Chap 11.)

These coatings may be applied with the same equipment that is currently used with epoxies, urethanes, and other coating materials. The processes and techniques are also very similar, with little or no change in normal procedures.

Protective Coatings for
Pipelines: Exterior

Pipelines have been protected by a wide variety of materials since their advent as a means of transporting liquid and gaseous materials. Asphalts, coal tars, roofing felts, glass fiber, and tapes of all kinds have made appearances through the years. Most recently, epoxy coal tars and urethane asphalts have made considerable progress as coating materials. Today pipelines are protected by a combination of a coating material and a cathodic-protection system, the theory being that no matter how well-coated the pipe is, it will have a certain percentage of "holidays" or pinholes whereby the elements can get at the steel. The cathodic-protection system, to a great extent, furnishes protection to any bare sections of pipe. The anodes and other equipment involved in the system must be constantly checked, and the anodes must be replaced at regular intervals.

Today, pipelines are very well protected, particularly those that have been installed over the past 5 years. The materials, equipment, and techniques used in their application do a much better job than in earlier years.

Polyester resins so far have been unable to compete in this very large market. The proper resins were not available for such applications, and dependable catalyst systems had not been devised in order to obtain the necessary working times or pot life required for such application procedures.

Much of this work is done in the plant in single, double, and even triple joints, leaving off a short section where welding will be required. The remaining work is done in the field after all other work is completed. This is known as "over-the-ditch" coating.

Polyester resins, catalysts, and other ingredients necessary for work of this type are available today. The same equipment, techniques, and procedures that are being used with other materials may be used with polyester compounds. A polyester can be formulated that would be highly suited to either in-plant or field work. The polyester could be used as a coating, as some pipe is protected, or it could be used in the wrap process, where layers of materials such as glass fiber, burlap, and other fibrous materials are spirally wrapped around the pipe, held together with layers of polymer. The wrapping material almost totally absorbs the polymer, forming a highly reinforced shield around the pipe. With very slight modification of existing equipment, a process can easily be developed whereby the fibrous materials can be presaturated before being wrapped around the pipe. This process would be ideal for polyester compounds, and it would reduce costs considerably.

The pipeline industry is constantly searching for new and better means of protecting these multimillion-dollar investments in transmission lines. Polyester can provide an answer to many of the problems that have beset this industry for many years. The market for pipeline protective coatings is very well established. It only remains for the polyester industry to recognize the potential presented by such volumes of coating materials, and to start making this field a major outlet for polyester products.

Heavy-weighted Coatings for Underwater Pipelines

Where pipelines must cross rivers, lakes, swamps, and often many miles of open sea, the problems of the transmission industry are multiplied.

A pipeline which exceeds certain diameters and wall thicknesses when carrying gas, or when empty, will float. Besides designing corrosion protection for a pipeline, it must be coated with a material to supply much added weight. Many types of "weight coats" have been tried. Concrete has been applied by air placement, known as "gunnite." It has been applied by a wide variety of especially designed machines, some which literally throw the grout mix onto the pipe by high-speed conveyor belts. Sometimes forms are used to pour concrete around the pipe. The thicknesses applied increase as pipe size increases.

At first glance it would seem that here is a market in which polyester could not compete because of the great difference in costs between concrete and polyester compounds. However, this is not necessarily true.

Concrete, however applied, is a porous material, and will not, by itself, afford the protection these very expensive installations require. The pipe must first be sandblasted or run through a stationary grit-blasting machine. It is then primed with any one of a variety of coating materials. Then it receives a wrapping operation of one to three layers of wrap, with binder, or it will be taped. The tape is usually a polyvinyl or polyethylene tape which has an adhesive on one side. Only after these multiple operations are performed can the concrete be applied. The pipe is racked for a minimum of 21 days, and sometimes a sealer coating must be applied over the top of the concrete.

Due to the mechanical properties of concrete, even though in most cases it is steel-reinforced, it is very often damaged in handling and installation to the point where it must be redone.

A second method used to apply weight to the exterior of pipe is an extrusion process, whereby a compound of either asphalt or coal tar with fillers and aggregates is extruded onto the exterior of the pipe.

With this process, roughly the same preparation of the pipe is necessary. Again, the mechanical properties of the material make it highly subject to damage.

Polyester compounds could compete in this market, regardless of the difference in the costs of the various compounds because the process of applying polyester would be much shorter and would require less individual steps.

The cleaning operation would not change. The pipe would be either sandblasted, grit-blasted, or acid-pickled. Here the process would change drastically. No primer coat is necessary with the polyester compound. No wrapping or taping materials need be used. The polyester compound can be applied directly to the cleaned pipe, and the pipe can be handled, transported, and installed in a very short time. The compound will be completely impervious to water, air, and most chemicals that would be present in areas where such pipe would be installed. It can be formulated to have extremely good electrical properties, a most important part of such applications, for complete protection of the pipe.

The cost of such a polyester compound would not be as great as might be expected, as it could be formulated with very low resin content. The mechanical properties of the pipe covering would be so much better than other types of coverings that there would be little possibility of damage of either pipe or covering at any stage of production or installation.

A formulation that would be ideal for such an application would be as follows:

1. Resilient isophthalic polyester-monomers.................... 100.0 lb
2. Promoter (mix before adding catalyst)...................... 0.2
3. Catalyst.. 1.0
4. Crushed stone, to 2-in. size.............................. 900.0
5. Crushed stone, to $\frac{1}{4}$-in. size............................. 400.0
6. Coarse sand, 6–20 mesh................................ 200.0
7. Fine sand, 50–100 mesh................................ 100.0
8. Graded silica sand, 100–200 mesh........................ 50.0
1751.2 lb

A normal isophthalic resin would be used, and the stone would be any normal stone used for the same purpose with concrete. Stone with high specific gravity is much sought after for these applications but is seldom found within reasonable transporting distances from the job site. The higher the specific gravities of the stone, the thinner the material that may be applied to reach a total desired weight per linear ft of pipe. Conductive aggregates, such as limonite, magnetite, and hematite, should be avoided, and these are very seldom available to the plant at any rate.

The stone usually used is ordinarily river rock, rounded by years of being tumbled along stream beds. This material will do very well in that it is mostly jasper, granite, and other very hard, nonconductive stone which are principally silica in composition. These stones are very dense, and will not absorb the polyester resin. Loadings of aggregates can be even higher than those given in many instances.

This material would be applied to the pipe quite like much of the concrete shells are applied—by casting into forms around the pipe. About 3 in. at each end of the pipe should be left unprotected until the pipe has been welded together. Then this small void is formed and filled as is done with other materials.

The big difference in doing this entire operation with polyester compund is in the time element involved. With a proper plant setup, joints of pipe can be formed, cast, and cured in a matter of minutes, instead of the many days required by other methods. The joints can be filled in with a highly promoted compound which bonds and cures very quickly, avoiding the high damage rate of the other methods.

Although the polyester compound itself would be more costly, the entire operation would be less costly with polyester resin than with either concrete, asphalt, or coal-tar compounds.

The pipe would have far greater protection, and the line would need much fewer cathodic-protection systems. The pipe would be strengthened by a considerable degree. The normal slight shrinkage of the polyester compound would aid in obtaining an extremely good interface between the compound and the pipe. This is of utmost importance in order to prevent the undercreep of corrosion from any possibly damaged section or from any future oxidation from any source.

This application may not be a major outlet for polyester resins, but it is a much larger market than would be suspected. It is well worth investigating.

Protective Coatings for Concrete

Few people realize that in certain areas concrete must be protected from deterioration just as most other building materials.

Particularly in highly salty areas near the ocean, concrete must be sealed to prevent the highly corrosive elements from reaching the reinforcing steel in the structure. When the steel begins to oxidize, the concrete begins to spall, and more of the salt air reaches the steel. If measures are not taken in time, the structure must soon be replaced.

The applications discussed here are very different from those included in Chap. 3, such as bridge toppings. Buildings, homes, churches, and all types of structures are to be considered. In locations such as these, the concrete should be sealed and coated as soon as it is properly cured.

The coating serves a number of purposes: First, it protects; secondly, it beautifies; and thirdly, it seals the building against moisture penetration. Concrete buildings are particularly deficient in their adsorption of moisture in areas of high humidity.

Schools, swimming pools, floor slabs, and thousands of individual applications require this type of treatment. They are too numerous to name them all.

In these applications, some flexibility of the coating is required to withstanding the expansion and contraction of the concrete. Most concrete, being highly porous, will require a primer coat.

A good formulation for the primer coat for concrete would be as follows:

Component 1

1. Polyester resin (such as Chart 5, Formula 2)................. 50.0 lb
2. Promoter.. 0.1
3. China clay... 5.0
4. Silica, 400 mesh....................................... 45.0

                                                          100.1 lb

Component 2

1. Polyester resin (same as above)......................... 50.0 lb
2. Catalyst, 1 lb in 5-lb molecular sieve.................. 6.0
3. China clay... 4.0
4. Silica, 400 mesh....................................... 40.0

                                                          100.0 lb

These would be mixed together when ready to use. They will be of such viscosity that they may be applied by either conventional or airless spray. Brush, roller, and other means may also be used.

Pigments may be added if desired, so as to see better the areas covered.

Since this coating will have a tacky surface, there is no time limit as to when the top coat should be applied.

A formulation for a top coat for concrete would be as follows:

Component 1

1. Polyester resin (such as Chart 5, Formula 5)................ 40.00 lb
2. Promoter.. 0.08
3. Colloidal silica....................................... 1.00
4. China clay... 10.00
5. Silica, 400 mesh....................................... 49.00

                                                          100.08 lb

Component 2

1. Polyester resin (same as above)............................ 40.00 lb
2. Catalyst, 0.8 lb in 4-lb molecular sieve..................... 4.80
3. Silicone (surface control)................................. 0.05
4. Pigment, any color....................................... 4.00
5. China clay.. 10.00
6. Silica, 400 mesh.. 42.00

100.85 lb

These two components would be thoroughly mixed when ready to use and applied by any of the methods normally used in coating work. The thickness may be built up to any normal requirement in one application. This material will not sag or run on vertical walls, up to 0.025 in. thick.

The coating will cure to a hard, glossy surface, with no surface tack present. It will be extremely weather resistant and, if proper pigments are used, will not fade in the sun. See Chap. 11 for more complete details on formulation.

There are many applications where a high gloss is objectional. This may be remedied by substituting 8 to 10 lb of synthetic silicas, known as "flatting agents," for an equal amount of the china clay specified above. The result will be an almost matte finish. Smaller amounts will produce very nice semigloss finishes. The resulting coating will be hard and tough, yet will have enough resilience to withstand all the expansion and contraction in concrete structures. It will be impervious to moisture and to many strong chemicals. Smog, sulfides, and gases in the atmosphere will not discolor this coating.

It is a more expensive coating than normal house paints, but there is no comparison in quality and durability. A building coated with this material should need no further sealing or beautification for at least 20 years.

The initial cost will be more than made up in subsequent low maintenance costs and the protection afforded the building.

Wood Coatings

Coatings similar to the above are entirely suitable to wood. Wood requires even more flexibility than concrete to prevent cracking, blistering, etc., when it is exposed to the sun and other elements.

The formulation above would be ideal for new wood in almost any given location. It would not be suitable for use over previously painted wood, unless the old material were either an epoxy, polyurethane, or another polyester. Alkyds, epoxy esters, vinyls, or acrylics should be removed before coating with this material.

Marine Coatings

This is a market for coating materials which is indeed very large. Marine coatings have been the object of much research over the years, and people are still searching for new and better materials to use in protecting ships, barges, sheet piling, marine oil and gas installations, and many other applications where metals must be used in and around saltwater.

Considerable progress has been made over the past 10 years. Better coating materials, cathodic-protection systems, and biocides have lengthened the life-span of marine installations by nearly 100%.

Besides permanent installations that cannot be recoated after construction, the major use of such coatings is for floating craft.

Ships and barges must be drydocked very frequently for sandblasting, coating, and new anodes. The productive time lost by these repairs is in itself a major loss to the owners, besides the expense of the repairs themselves.

Marine engineers are always ready to test any new materials that may lower maintenance costs of vessels, and that may lengthen the life span of permanent marine structures. Every shipyard and every marine builder has permanent test racks set up for testing these materials.

New metals are tested as metallurgists develop them. New types of anodes are constantly being tested for efficiency. Coatings are perhaps the most tested of all materials used in marine work because these materials decide the time element between costly overhauls on floating craft; also, this material determines the life span of permanent installations.

The United States Navy has conducted extensive research on coatings for marine use for many years. A large part of the progress in this field may be attributed to this work.

Unfortunately, coatings manufacturers have contributed very little to this overall effort, with a few notable exceptions. Two of the larger national manufacturers have done a considerable amount of research in this field, while the rest have been content to await further developments. As developments by others came to light, all the rest would be quick to use this work to further their own line of materials offered to the market.

Often, little or no thought went into the preparation of a coating material, so much of it was entirely unsuitable for the work for which it was intended. If success was obtained by others with vinyls, everyone began manufacturing vinyls. If epoxies were found to give good service, then the entire industry began manufacturing epoxy marine coatings. Practically no consideration was given to anything except the base polymer itself.

A coating material designed to be used for a specific end purpose cannot give good results just because the proper base polymer is used in its formulation. A coating must be a composite of all materials which will best withstand a given environment. Many formulators, even now, think that since all fillers, pigments, and other materials in the formulation are totally encased in the polymer, they have no important role in the end properties of the coating. These are far from the facts. Every ingredient that goes into a formulation should be designed and chosen because of its ability to withstand the environment for which the coating is intended.

Polyesters have many properties that make them ideal for use in marine coatings. Because of the wide variety of intermediates from which to choose, resins may be manufactured with the particular properties in mind that are so necessary in these applications.

A marine coating must have a number of outstanding properties:

1. Either a very high toxicity to marine life, or a surface that is highly unsuitable for marine growth, or both

2. A dense, nonporous composition, with minimum water absorption and minimum hydrogen permeation

3. A composition which is least conducive to adsorption

4. An outstanding resistance to salt (this includes every ingredient used in the formulation)

5. A resistance to mild alkalies, which build up, in the form of carbonates, from the metals present in seawater at areas of highest cathodic potential

6. Outstanding electrical properties in order to withstand the galvanic action or electrolysis caused by the metals in seawater and by the dissimilar metals of the vessel (propellers, etc.)

7. Sufficient flexibility to withstand the constant movement of steel plate which covers a vessel

8. Optimum bond

9. Sufficient toughness and abrasion resistance to withstand the erosion caused by the tiny particles in seawater which abrade the surfaces at high speeds

These properties are the most sought after in marine coatings. It is no simple matter to formulate all these properties into a polymer and then manufacture a coating from it because of all the other components that must go into the coating to obtain these requirements.

A good starting formulation with polyester would be the following:

Component 1

1. Polyester resin (such as Chart 5, Formula 3)................ 40.00 lb
2. Promoter.. 0.08
3. Colloidal silica.. 1.00
4. Biocide, fungicide (mercury compound, or cyanide)......... 8.00
5. China clay (aluminum silicate).......................... 8.00
6. Silica, 400 mesh....................................... 43.00

100.08 lb

Component 2

1. Polyester resin (same as above)......................... 40.00 lb
2. Catalyst 0.8 lb in 4-lb molecular sieve.................... 4.80
3. Colloidal silica.. 1.00
4. Silicone... 0.05
5. China clay... 5.00
6. Pigment (toluidine, phthalocyanines, etc.)................ 5.00
7. Silica, 400 mesh....................................... 45.00

100.85 lb

This formulation would be for a finish coat for any marine application. Note the choice of fillers, pigments, and other materials selected as best meeting the requirements of the end product. The fungicide or biocide is of utmost importance. The materials based on copper give excellent protection against the organisms and microorganisms that are so destructive to marine coatings, but because of their low electrical resistivity and the relatively large amounts necessary, they detract from this property in the coating. In addition, copper is much higher in the series of electromotive forces; hence it becomes the cathode, and the steel which is protected becomes the anode. This is not desirable. Thus, the mercury compounds and such cyanide compounds as potassium, sodium, and others are more advantageous for use in these coatings because of their high electrical resistance and relative nonactivity in the electromotive-force scale.

The silicas are chosen both for their electrical properties and for their excellent resistance to seawater. The pigments are chosen for these same two properties. Wherever possible, metallic pigments and fillers are to be avoided scrupulously, particularly in the top coat for marine use.

The above formulation will give a coating that will provide excellent service under marine conditions, when applied over properly prepared surfaces and completely cured before a vessel is placed in the water.

Sandblasting is the only satisfactory method of cleaning marine steel. On new steel, all mill scale must be removed, and a good anchor pattern must be obtained. Sandblasting is the only way to accomplish this, unless the steel has been acid-pickled before fabrication. On vessels being re-coated, where all old coating materials must be removed, sandblasting is the most practical and economical method for this work.

Primer coatings for marine steel are a subject of great controversy in the industry. The question on which most of the disagreement is based is whether the primer coating should, in fact, be an anodic or "sacrificial" coating, which would furnish cathodic protection to any subsequent bare spots on the surface of the metal, or whether the primer should be merely a medium for good bond between metal and top coat, furnishing the proper interface to prevent "undercreep" of oxidation at locations where the top protective coating has been damaged.

All sides of the controversy have merit. Totally inorganic primers, such as the zinc silicates, based on zinc dust and either ethyl or sodium silicates, do form an anode continuously on the surface of the metal. So also do coatings based on cadmium, chromium, aluminum, magnesium, and strontium oxides. In primer coatings, these metals may be made into coatings with either an inorganic vehicle, as above, or they may be formulated into organic primers.

Besides these two methods of getting one of these metals onto the surface of the steel, there are various methods which use heat and apply them in molten form. There are a number of flame sprayers and other kinds of equipment on the market which will apply these metals in molten form directly on the steel, with no vehicles present.

Other researchers argue that instead of being anodic, the primer should be cathodic, or higher in the electromotive scale than the steel. Primers of this type would be principally lead compounds of all types, and nickel, antimony, and copper compounds. These metals may also be applied either by the organic, inorganic, or molten methods.

The remaining viewpoint is that the primer should be neither anodic or cathodic, but should, in fact, be an organic coating with extremely high dielectric strength to prevent either anodic or cathodic action from affecting the steel.

All three viewpoints have merit, and all three may be proven in at least theory. The important thing to consider is which one actually works in the protection of steel to the greatest extent under actual marine conditions.

With the sacrificial metallic coatings (the anodic type), there are a number of advantages and disadvantages:

Advantages: When steel, coated with zinc, for example, is properly applied, a very good bond is obtained to the steel. This is particularly true in cases where it is applied in a molten form by a heat gun. This zinc film is porous, so an organic top coat can get a good bond, thus forming a good two-way bond between primer and steel and between primer and top coat. If the top coat is damaged during use, leaving the primer exposed to the seawater, it will protect the underlying steel for a time, depending on the thickness of the zinc coating. Seawater, in direct contact with zinc, will oxidize away approximately 0.003 in. per year. This amount must be added to the amount of zinc used up as the sacrificial anode. It will be another 0.002 to 0.006 in., depending on the size of the exposed area.

Disadvantages: With this amount of zinc lost per year, the coating of zinc must be relatively thick in order to obtain long-term protection, that is, from 5 to 9 mils of zinc per year of protection gained. These zinc coatings are expensive, and if this amount were to be applied by the inorganic silicates method, it would take two to three coats to reach this thickness. For 5-year protection, it would take 10 to 15 coats. By the heat-gun method, any thickness may be built up in one pass, but this is also a very expensive operation. If zinc is applied in an organic-polymer system, the entire purpose is defeated. It is hampered in its anode role by the presence of the polymer.

Conclusion: If zinc is used as a base, or primer coat, it should be applied at a sufficient thickness to afford protection for the desired time, and it should be applied preferably by the heat-gun method because this method gives denser, less porous films less likely to break and chip off the surface. Zinc coatings at these thicknesses are very expensive to apply, so they should be avoided if at all possible.

Now, the metallic coatings that are higher on the electromotive scale than steel (which become the cathode, with the steel the anode) also have advantages and disadvantages:

Advantages: These metals also may be applied by the silicate-based inorganic-vehicles method or by the heat-gun method. The latter is the most satisfactory. Good bond is obtained to the metal, and the film is porous enough for the organic top coat to obtain good bond. Since this coating is not sacrificial, it is not lost by electrolysis, and the seawater does not oxidize these metals to any extent. This means that they may be applied in very thin films, 2 to 3 mils in thickness for best results.

Disadvantages: On any areas where the protective top coat is damaged, there is enough porosity to this coating for seawater to penetrate to some extent. Since the steel is the anode, it will suffer far worse localized damage than if it were completely bare. Localized pitting could become as much as 8 to 9 mils per year in these areas, even though the entire vessel or installation were totally protected with a cathodic system.

Conclusion: This type of primer is not ideal, whether applied in the inorganic or organic systems. There is too much danger of localized damage to the steel.

To consider the advantages and disadvantages of a polymeric type of primer, many aspects must be considered:

Advantages: A properly formulated primer, such as an epoxy or polyester, will get sufficient bond to the steel without the aid of metallic primers. Metallic fillers, if very close to steel on the electromotive scale, may be incorporated into the organic primer to aid in this bond. Such materials as the chromium compounds and the cadmium compounds are so nearly in the same position on the scale with steel that they may be used in these formulations. Even lead compounds are close enough to steel on the scale to give good results, even though they are somewhat more of a cathode than cadmium. When properly formulated and applied, such primers can give very good service, particularly when the vessel or installation is further protected with a good cathodic system. Any areas that may be damaged in the coating will be protected by a good cathodic system. An organic primer will be only a fraction of the cost of an inorganic primer.

Disadvantages: An organic primer is more subject to damage than an inorganic primer. Usually, when the top coat is damaged, the primer will suffer the same damage since the bond of the organic top coat to an organic primer is greater than the bond of the top coat to an inorganic primer. Upon damage, usually both will be damaged, leaving the steel unprotected in this area.

Conclusion: An organic primer is far less expensive and will do an excellent job if the vessel or installation is well protected with an independent cathodic-protection system.

The above advantages and disadvantages of the various systems is a very brief look at the problems involved. Volumes could be written on the subject, but these are the basic facts, however understated.

A good starting formulation for a polyester marine primer would be the following:

Component 1

1. Polyester resin (such as Chart 5, Formula 1) .... 40.00 lb
2. Promoter 0.08
3. Colloidal silica 1.00
4. Lead chromate 20.00
5. Magnesium silicate 5.00
6. Silica, 400 mesh 34.00

100.08 lb

Component 2

1. Polyester resin (same as above)........................... 40.0 lb
2. Catalyst, 0.8 lb in 4-lb molecular sieve..................... 4.8
3. Colloidal silica... 1.0
4. Cadmium oxide.. 15.0
5. Lead oxide, mono (litharge)............................. 5.0
6. Magnesium silicate...................................... 5.0
7. Silica, 400 mesh.. 30.0
                                                          _____
                                                          100.8 lb

The two components will be different colors and so will be obvious when well mixed. This primer may be applied with conventional spray equipment or with airless equipment. The airless equipment is far better because the great pressures at the nozzle aid in wetting out the surface properly and will form a better interface with the anchor pattern.

The primer should be applied at a 3- to 5-mil thickness and should be followed by the top coat (discussed earlier) within a maximum of 24 hr for best bond between the coats. The top coat may be applied at any given thickness in one application up to 25 mils or more.

This coating system, complemented with a good cathodic-protection system, will give excellent service in any saltwater environment. It will stand up well on steel sheet pilings, underwater pipelines, drilling and production platforms, piers, and all types of vessels. It should be applied to all surfaces under the waterline and as high as any anticipated wave action.

Protective Coatings for Pipe: Cast-iron, Concrete, Asbestos-cement, and Vitrified Clay

There are many low-pressure applications for which pipe of these types could be used if they could be made to withstand the materials the pipe would be used in.

Cast-iron pipe is widely used in freshwater systems and must be concrete-lined. This concrete lining is very costly to apply, hence the high cost for city waterlines.

The same work can be done with a polyester compound at far less thickness and at less cost. A polyester coating may be applied to the interior of these cast-iron pipes with existing 360° spray heads attached to airless equipment. This coating will be applied at a thickness of about 10 mils and will afford far better protection than the concrete linings.

Such a coating may be formulated from a resin similar to Formula

7 (Chart 5). It will withstand very well the chlorines and other chemicals added to potable water and will pass any FDA standards for materials for such purposes.

An application of this kind can furnish a market for a very large volume of polyester resins.

Concrete pipe is fairly limited to use in sewer work at present. This material could be used in many other applications if it were suitably coated on the interior with a polyester coating material. It could be used for drain lines for chemical plants and for other applications where suction and drain lines require a certain chemical resistance but are not subjected to high pressures.

Asbestos-cement pipe has been a mainstay for many years in many applications. It is used for waterlines, electrical and telephone conduits, and for many other uses. Here again, this material could be used in many other applications with a proper polyester coating inside. Polyesters are most suitable for an application such as this. The pipe is strengthened, and at the same time made impervious to chemicals.

In many sections of the country, vitrified-clay pipe is used extensively. However, there are many applications where it cannot be used because of its lack of chemical resistance. Polyester coatings can rectify this problem, and the pipe can be used for many additional purposes.

All these types of pipe are more reasonable in cost than steel pipe. If a steel pipe were to be used in such applications, it, too, would have to be protected, both the interior and exterior. Many of these types of piping could be used by coating only the interior because the exterior of the pipe would withstand soil conditions without protection. Much cost can be saved with the use of such pipe.

All these applications furnish additional markets for polyester resins and coatings made from them.

Industrial Coatings: Automobiles, Aircraft, and Equipment

Industrial coatings has been one of the most competitive markets for coating materials for many years. The volume of these coatings is very large. Every automobile, every piece of equipment and machinery, and every aircraft produced takes very considerable quantities of coating material.

Today, automobile manufacturers are using principally the acrylic lacquers, applied by highly automated production lines by a variety of means. Some use electrostatic coating, some use fluidized bed processes, and others use corona deposited particles. Some coatings are applied in solvent solutions, and others use water-dispersion techniques. The fluidized bed process uses very fine, dry particles of polymer.

Automobile manufacturers are constantly searching for better coatings. Since 1925, automobile coating materials used have changed dozens of times. The quest is not just for better-looking coatings, but for coatings that will withstand the rigors of rain, sun, salt air, and all the elements. The search is for coatings that will not fade or lose their high-gloss finish. Constantly, processes and techniques change as better means are found for applying these coatings at less cost to the consumer.

Many types of polymers have been thoroughly tested. All kinds of additives, alloys, and combinations of polymers have been investigated. The coatings used today are, for the most part, very good. They stand up well in use if they are reasonably well cared for.

A great amount of research has been made for coatings that will not water spot and that will repulse dust and dirt. This research is still going on. Silicone resins have shown very good results as far as water spotting is concerned. By adding antistatic agents to silicone, these coatings will even repulse dust to a great extent. Their major problem is cost. The silicones are just too expensive to be used in these applications. Competition among the manufacturers limits very closely the cost of a finished product, so an additional $15.00 to $25.00 for the coating material would have to be transferred to the consumer.

Many of the coatings used in these applications today have small percentages of silicones in them as additives. They are useful in most polymers as leveling and surface-tension-control agents. The percentages used are small enough not to affect the cost of the coating to an appreciable extent.

Herein lies a vast, unexplored market for polyester resins. Polyesters, properly formulated, would be ideal in these applications. Resistance to the elements, appearance, and cost would be very favorable. The cost of applying these coatings to the product would be very comparable with, or lower, than coatings used now. Cure schedules could be very fast, and much more coating material could be applied in a single coat.

Polyester resins can be manufactured which would be most suitable for this type of coating. Formula 9 (Chart 5) would be an example of such a resin.

With such a resin as a base polymer, coatings would be suitable for automobiles, aircraft, and all types of machinery and equipment.

Coatings of this nature would have to be processed very differently from the industrial coatings discussed earlier. They would have to be processed in normal paint and coating manufacturing equipment to give the smooth, brilliant finishes desirable.

Some recent developments in inhibitors for polyester coatings can help to gain more closely controlled gel and cure times in coatings which are applied in very thin films. Such materials as cyclohexanone, benzaldehyde, and pyrogallol all show good results as coatings inhibitors. Dimethylaminomethylphenol has shown excellent results in coatings which are baked at temperatures above 300°F.

Recent developments for polyester coatings show the value of incorporating small portions of other polymers, particularly to polyester primers. Epoxy resin, the highly polar ketone resins, and the chlorinated polyphenyls are all useful in such primers.

The polyester industry has reached the point where it must find these completely new and unexplored markets. No possible coating application may be ignored.

Eight

THE ELECTRICAL INDUSTRY

The electrical industry today consumes many millions of pounds of organic polymers per year. A very large percentage of this consists of the polyvinyls, polyethylene, polypropylene, and others used in electrical insulating sheaths for wires and cables.

Other polymers are used in the insulation of motor windings, in dipping, potting, and encapsulation of electrical component parts, in printed circuitry, and in thousands of other electrical applications calling for good electrical properties. Today, the majority of these needs are being filled by the phenolics, epoxies, allyls, acetals, polycarbonates, polyamides, and some of the newer polymers such as polyphenylene oxide and polysulfone.

Most of the plastics used in applications other than wire and cable sheathing are among the most expensive of our organic plastics. The silicones are among the most desirable of all plastics for use in electrical applications but are just too expensive for most applications.

Some applications in the electrical industry call for both excellent electrical properties and very high heat resistance. This reduces the selection to only a few polymers which may be used, and these are higher-cost polymers derived from the silicones. In the applications requiring only medium heat resistance, the phenolics and the acid-cured epoxies may be used, along with many of the higher-cost polymers. At low temperatures, the lower-cost materials such as the polyvinyls, polyethylene, and polypropylene may be used.

Almost all the organic polymers have medium to excellent electrical properties. The particular application for which they will be used will depend on the cost of the material. As the temperature of the application rises, the cost of the polymer that will be required will rise.

In many cases, the base polymer will be further enhanced in electrical and mechanical properties by pigments and fillers. Very pure silicas, glass fiber, glass flake, mica, synthetic mica, and many synthetic fibers are used in all types of compounds for electrical applications.

Many of these polymers are very limited as to the amount of such fillers that may be used, resulting in lower percentages of the lower-cost fillers and consequently higher product cost. This is particularly true of thermoplastics. Filler loadings are most often very low in order to be able to process these materials.

There is a very wide range of thermosetting and thermoplastics which are used today in the electrical and electronic industries. Consumption is in the millions of pounds per year, and it is growing each year. The applications to which they will be used will range from ambient temperatures to above 500°F. At temperatures above 450°F, only the silicones will give good service, so these products will be expensive.

Polyesters can be manufactured which may be substituted for any of the above polymers in any of the above applications, with the exception of the silicone. These polyesters can have excellent electrical properties from ambient temperature to 450°F. They will be suitable for use in almost any given electrical application, from wire sheathing to medium-high-temperature potting and encapsulation. Their electrical properties will be equal to, or better than, most of the polymers used today, with the exception of silicone.

These polyesters will be able to take very high filler loadings, so the percentage of resin may be much lower. The high percentage of proper fillers will increase the electrical properties considerably. The additional advantages of decreased processing time required for polyesters will make them an even more desirable polymer for these applications.

Chart 6, Electrical Polyesters, lists four types of polyester resins that would be suitable for a variety of electrical applications, from the very

CHART 6. ELECTRICAL POLYESTERS

Polyhydric components	Moles	Unsaturated acid	Moles	Saturated acid	Moles	Monomers	Moles
Formula 1. Very flexible: Polybutadiene Triethylene glycol	1.1 1.1	Maleic anhydride	0.4	Terephthalic acid	1.6	Vinyl toluene Diallyl phthalate	0.3 0.5
Formula 2. Resilient molding resin: Propylene glycol Glycerine	2.0 0.2	Maleic anhydride	0.8	Phthalic anhydride Cyclopentane dianhydride	1.0 0.2	Diallyl phthalate Vinyl toluene	0.4 0.7
Formula 3. For dip, encapsulating, potting: Neopentyl glycol Dicyclopentadiene	1.1 1.1	Fumaric acid	1.0	Hexahydrophthalic	1.0	Diallyl phthalate m-Chlorostyrene	0.6 0.7
Formula 4. High heat resisting: Neopentyl glycol Dicyclopentadiene	1.1 1.1	Fumaric acid	1.0	HET acid Pyromellitic dianhydride	0.5 0.5	Diallyl phthalate m-Chlorostyrene	0.6 0.4

Note: These polymers will be cooked down to an acid number of 15-20 and reacted with ethylene carbonate to reduce acid number to 0. After cooling, monomers are to be added at about 130°F. The inhibitor may be hydroquinone or catechol.

flexible, which would be quite suitable for wire and cable sheathing, to a resin that will withstand a constant temperature up to 450°F. All will have excellent electrical properties. When properly compounded with fillers and pigments (and in some instances reinforcing fibers), they will all be highly competitive with more expensive polymers in the electrical field.

Electrical Wiring and Cable Insulation

A polyester resin, such as given in Chart 6, Formula 1, will be a highly flexible polymer with excellent electrical properties. It will be most suitable for such applications as wire and cable insulation, requiring very good low-temperature flexibility, good tensile strength, and excellent electrical properties from −30 to 180°F.

The method by which this material, properly compounded, would be used, would require more or less the same processes used with the vinyls, polyethylene, and polypropylene, except for a few modifications in the extruder. Barrel temperatures would be low to medium, depending on the catalyst system used. Instead of a cooling cycle after the material had been extruded onto the wire, there would be a very short heat section to cure the polymer compound.

This process should produce the finished product at costs very close to those now obtained with the other polymers. The electrical properties of the sheath with polyester are quite superior to those of other polymers. This sheathing has far greater temperature resistance than the others in that when wiring becomes overheated, as it often does, the sheath will not melt off. The polyester sheath would be damaged by heat distortion, and its electrical and mechanical properties would suffer, but it would remain in place at temperatures up to 350°F or higher.

This market is very large, and polyester manufacturers and others in the industries connected with electricity and electronics would do well to look into these resins.

High-voltage Transmission-line Insulators

The manufacture of insulators for high-voltage transmission lines is a major industry. These insulators are used at a rate of nearly 30 million per year, in varying sizes, from a few ounces to a 100 lb each or more. They are used in all types of installations, from thousands of volts to our standard home current. They are used in telephone installations, radio and television, in radar, and everywhere that current of any voltage is required.

The major market, however, is in the very large sizes, used in high-voltage electrical transmission all over the nation. The nation is already cobwebbed with these lines, and more are being constructed each year.

The insulators being used today are ceramic. The process by which they are manufactured is very expensive, requiring very high temperatures and very slow production schedules.

Ceramic is heavy and highly friable, and a very large percentage of insulators are damaged beyond use during manufacture, handling, transporting, and installation. The cost to the consumer and the electrical industry is extremely high. The large sizes can cost over $150 each.

These ceramic insulators have excellent electrical properties, and have been used throughout the years simply because there was no equal substitute.

Today, these insulators may be manufactured from polyester resin compounds at a fraction of the cost of ceramic material. The cost for the polyester insulator would be low because of the very low percentage of resin that would be required and the fast production rates.

To be of first-rate quality, these insulators must be manufactured by any process utilizing a moderate pressure. Casting would not be satisfactory, because some tiny voids would be present, detracting from the electrical properties.

Compression-molding, injection-molding, transfer-molding, or pressure-casting (autoclaving) could be used to produce these products. Pressures of 100 to 250 psi will be more than sufficient to produce quality products.

A good molding compound for this product would be as follows:

1. Polyester resin, resilient (such as Chart 6, Formula 2)........ 15.00 lb
2. Promoter (if used, mix before adding catalyst).............. 0.03
3. Catalyst... 0.15
4. Crushed quartz (pure silica), No. 00...................... 60.00
5. Silica (pure), 100 mesh.................................. 10.00
6. Silica (pure), 200 mesh.................................. 5.00
7. Chopped S glass, $\frac{1}{4}$ to $\frac{1}{2}$ in............................. 10.00

100.18 lb

In a mixed compound of this type, utilizing chopped glass, it is very important that the chopped glass is not broken up and damaged to any extent. The glass fiber must be added last, after all the other ingredients are thoroughly blended. The chopped glass is added, and the mixer is turned only sufficiently to blend it in. This is best accomplished by adding the glass a little at a time, as the mixer turns very slowly.

Such a compound will have a consistency that will be handled nicely by the processes mentioned.

The silicas may be replaced, in part or completely, with such materials as muscovite (white mica) or synthetic mica. The silicas (if very pure) and the synthetic mica will give highest electrical properties to the finished product. The S glass is chosen because it is an almost pure silica glass, quite different from E glass and normal glass fibers. Polyester fiber could be substituted for the glass.

Pigments can be added; internal mold releases, and other materials may be used, always keeping the electrical requirements in mind. The pigments that would be suitable are pthalo colors and organic dyestuffs. No metallic pigments or fillers would be suitable. Colors will be somewhat limited, but this is not an important factor.

These insulators may be manufactured by any plastics manufacturer who has the types of equipment recommended. A major expense in diversifying to this production would be in the dies. All other equipment would probably be unchanged. The mixing procedures would be quite similar to any heavy compound of this type. The liquid components would all be premixed in a high-speed, high-shear mixer and then added to the dry fillers in a large, double-arm mixer. Almost any equipment suitable for handling molding compounds will serve the purpose.

The finished product will be very much like the ceramic insulator in electrical properties, with slightly lower dielectric constants at the higher temperatures. Since these insulators are exposed in almost all instances to ambient temperatures, this would not present a factor. At the higher-cycle range, the polyester insulator would have a slightly higher constant.

The end electrical properties, as stated, would depend to a very large extent on the fillers and pigments, etc. Metallic and other conductive impurities would have severe adverse effects.

The physical and mechanical properties of these insulators would be quite another matter. The polyester insulator would be practically unbreakable. It could be dropped with little or no damage. It would be somewhat lighter in weight than the ceramic insulator, depending on the fillers used. If a formulation similar to the above were used, the differential would be about 20%. It would require less packaging, and shipping costs would be reduced.

Installation costs would be lower because of the weight differential and the reduced danger of breakage.

This market presents a great challenge to the polyester industry. There is no reason why polyester insulators cannot entirely replace ceramic insulators.

Conduit Tubing

The electrical industry consumes a tremendous amount of conduit tubing through which to install wiring and cables. This tubing ranges in size from ½ in. in interior diameter to over 8 in.

Practically all major cities placed overhead wiring underground, including electrical and telephone lines.

Utility companies use a wide variety of tubing in which to enclose the wiring. Some of it is lead-sheathed cables; more often, clay, asbestos-cement, and galvanized pipe are used.

In homes and buildings, galvanized tubing is most often used, and in some cases, aluminum. Some building codes are more lenient than others, so there is usually a wide selection of materials from which to choose.

Reinforced polyester tubing would be ideal for these conduits, whether buried or enclosed inside a building. In buried installations, it would offer much longer protection than any of the materials now used. Polyester pipe would be impervious to water and to the chemical elements of the soil around the conduit. In addition, it would offer optimum electrical properties for such a conduit.

Most of the conduits used today are low in price. It would be very difficult for polyester tubing that is manufactured by the processes used today to be able to compete on a reasonably similar price level. Most of the polyester glass-fiber pipe today is manufactured by filament-winding processes over a mandrel, and this is too expensive a process for conduit tubing.

A conduit of this type does not need the tremendous strengths obtained by filament winding. This process is entirely suitable for high-pressure pipe, where strength is the most important factor. New processes will have to be developed in order for polyester conduit tubing to be able to compete with the lower-pressure tubings and conduits.

Larger tubing possibly may be made by centrifugal casting. This process involves an exterior mold, with a polished interior surface. The compound and suitable reinforcing material are spun at high speeds. The centrifugal forces spread the material evenly on the interior wall of the mold, while exterior heat cures the unit.

In this process, the major problem is finding a convenient method of placing the reinforcing material in the cylindrical mold. A number of methods are available. One is the preform process, where chopped-glass fiber is vacuumed onto a screen in the desired form. The chopped glass is sprayed with a light coating of catalyzed polyester resin, then baked, and is then strong enough to handle and place in the mold. This method would be more difficult in this case, however, because of the length of the preform. Special handling devices would have to be installed so as not to damage the preform between its fabrication and its placement into the mold.

Another possibility would be to use a light mat for reinforcement, lap and join the edges over a mandrel slightly smaller in diameter than the mold, and mechanically insert the mandrel and the glass fiber into the mold and then withdraw the mandrel.

This method seems more promising than the preform operation and possibly is less expensive.

A third possibility would be to use hinged molds that would open out into twin semicircles. A chopper gun could apply a layer of glass with a very small amount of resin, and the molds closed, the compound inserted, and the mold rotated. This method would leave a product with a fine seam down each side, but this probably would not be objectionable.

Other techniques may be considered. Since this product must be manufactured very efficiently to keep costs at a minimum, all possible methods must be carefully considered.

The smaller-diameter conduit tubing presents a still greater problem, but it should not be too difficult to solve. This very probably could be extruded by a process quite similar to the thermoplastic tubing. The compound would consist of resin, fillers, and chopped fiber, forced through the extruder to the shaping and sizing die, and into heating chamber for cure, all in one continuous tube. When leaving the oven, it would be cut into appropriate lengths.

It is necessary to keep a very slight air pressure from the inside of the extruded tubing until it has gelled. The same general technique is used on most of the thermoplastic tubing production.

Here, again, there are many possible means of producing small-diameter conduit tubing. Careful consideration must be given to all possible and probable methods in order to select the one most suited to efficient production.

For both types of tubing—the large diameters and the smaller sizes— means of connecting joints together must be designed. In the larger-size tubing, if centrifugal casting is used, the connection may be designed right into the mold. This may be either a bell type or an interlapping type of joint. Separate, slip-on couplings may also be considered. These would probably be the best solution, particularly for the smaller sizes.

A fast-curing type of polyester adhesive would be suitable for joining any of these types of tubing. It would be very similar to the polyester caulking compound described in Chap. 6, but with slightly less fillers for use as an adhesive.

These conduit products can very well be a high-volume market, which should be thoroughly investigated by any manufacturer looking for a new product to develop.

Transformer Cans, Inspection Boxes, Terminal Boxes, Panels, and Switchboxes

In electrical distribution systems, telephone networks, and every application where current of any kind is used, a large volume of boxes, enclosures, and panels are involved. Today the great majority of these are metal. They must be galvanized or painted. They are unsightly, and, due to corrosion, their life span has a limit, depending on locations of the installation.

Any product that is rectangular, semicircular, or square, if the depth is not too great, may be compression-molded very economically with reinforced polyester-resin compounds. When the depth is more than an inch, it is most advisable to design a slight draft or taper into the product, with the deepest part having just slightly smaller dimensions than the front. In this manner, parts up to 24 in. or more in depth present no problems.

Many of these enclosure products are designed to be used underground, while others are above-ground installations. Those to be used below grade will have to be designed so as to be completely watertight. This may be no easy task.

When such a product is being considered as a possible project, the similar products in metal should be studied at length to see how designs will have to be changed in order to produce them in polyester. Almost any design may be changed slightly, with no detriment to its end use. Practically any part that has been fabricated from metal must be changed somewhat in order to be duplicated in polyester.

Closures will probably be the most challenging part of the project. Inspection boxes, switchboxes, and other such products will require very good design principles on any type of opening, hinged or otherwise. For those that must be completely watertight, this will be no easy designing task, but it can be done.

This type of material lends itself to easy fabrication and may be bonded together easily with polyester or epoxy adhesives. The boxes themselves can be one piece. The face side must be two pieces—frame and opening. Suitable gaskets may be used where necessary.

For a molding compound of this type, a polyester resin such as that given in Chart 6, Formula 2, would be ideal:

Formula for Molding Compound

1. Polyester resin (such as Chart 6, Formula 2)................ 40.00 lb
2. Promoter (if desired, mix before adding catalyst)............ 0.04
3. Catalyst, such as *t*-butyl peroctoate...................... 0.25
4. China clay... 10.00
6. Silica, 200 mesh... 15.00
7. Chopped-glass fiber, ¼ to ½ in.......................... 35.00

100.29 lb

Such a compound may be easily compression-molded at pressures of 200 to 250 psi. It will be a thick, heavy paste but will flow easily in the matched dies at these pressures and will fill out very thin sections.

A suitable internal mold release may be added to the above, and pigments as desired.

The finished product will be excellent for use below or above ground. Its electrical properties will be excellent, and it will require no maintenance of any kind.

Such products will be well accepted by the electrical industry as a most necessary substitute for the metal presently used in these applications. It will be possible to install panels into these products with little or no precautions against grounding. Panels and terminals may be installed into them permanently with adhesives, rather than with screws or bolts.

Production of such a product will have to be on a large scale in order to compete with metal products. All possible modern equipment and automation can turn out a finished product which is well within the price ranges of the competitor.

Filament-wound Light Poles and Tubular Goods for Street Lighting and Highway Signs

Today, steel and aluminum tubular goods are used in street lighting, highway sign posts, street markers, and other applications, which require a certain amount of strength and reasonably good appearances. The steel posts must be galvanized and kept painted over the years to ensure durability. The aluminum products require less maintenance, but the initial cost is somewhat higher.

These products can be manufactured from polyester resins and reinforcing materials. They will require no maintenance, and their appearance will be much better than either the steel or aluminum product. They can be strong enough to withstand any amount of wind and to hold the weight of any signs, lighting fixtures, or other appurtenances fixed to them.

The weight of the poles themselves will be much lighter, permitting them to be shipped to distant points at lower costs. Ideally, these poles should be evenly tapered from bottom to top so they will nest together, one inside the next. Shipping space will be reduced to a fraction.

A product of this type, with a taper of 3 in. or more from bottom to the top, does not lend itself to centrifugal casting. The differential in forces from the larger diameter to the smaller diameter would be too great as the polyester compound rotated, and the larger end would receive a much thicker section than the small end.

Extrusion processes also present many problems in a tapered product. These are almost impossible to overcome with present equipment and techniques.

Filament-winding may be considered. Much less strength is required in this application than in high-pressure or even medium-pressure tubing. It may very well be the best method of producing this material. The wall thickness may be designed for the loads calculated, and the amount of glass filament may be applied accordingly.

Another possible process is the hinged mold, with the two halves opening out into two semicircles. The resin and chopped fiber may be deposited on the walls to the required thickness, and then the mold is closed to cure. Drawbacks to this process would be a slight seam at the two sides and reduced strength at the seams.

The filament-winding process seems to be the best method available today for producing these tubular goods. With modern equipment and techniques, this method should turn out finished products at costs which would place them well in competition with the steel and aluminum poles.

For this use, a slightly resilient resin would be necessary to produce the required mechanical properties for such an application. A resin such as Formula 2 (Chart 6) would produce good properties, mechanical as well as electrical. A compound of such a resin will give good results in weathering characteristics also when proper fillers and pigments are chosen.

This market is very large and is growing larger each year. Highways, freeways, and other arteries are being constructed at ever-growing rates. Thousands of such supports are used daily in these projects.

Printed Circuits

All types of electrical applications, radio, television, computers, radar, and every conceivable electronic equipment manufactured can provide an extremely profitable market for polyester resins in printed circuitry.

Some years ago, printed circuits made a strong appearance in these fields. Costs on the finished products could be lowered by a considerable margin by the use of the printed-circuit system instead of the solid-state system. With most products, there was simply no method to automate solid-state wiring. It had to be done by time-consuming, hand labor, hence the cost was passed on to the consumer.

A great amount of research went into processes by which printed circuits could replace the costly solid-state system. Much of this work was done in foreign countries, and manufacturers in the United States had to follow suit in order to be able to compete with the much lower-cost foreign products.

A great amount of the first printed circuitry was inferior and caused much public resistance. Repairs were frequent and costly. Shorts occurred, and equipment generally was unsatisfactory. Much resistance to printed circuitry was voiced by unions affected by this system. In many instances workmen assembling equipment with printed circuits intentionally damaged the panels in order to further their cause.

In short, printed circuitry has not yet realized even a small part of its potential. It is still used in many applications where space is at a premium, but has been discounted for thousands of applications for which it is suited. In this day of great necessity for lower costs and more efficient methods, printed circuitry must make strong gains in applications where this system alone can reduce costs of the finished products.

The first printed circuits for television, radio, computers, and other such uses were not well designed or engineered. The materials, both insulating and conductive, were in many cases not well chosen for this application. Too little thought went into such factors as the effects of heat, humidity, and durability. They were, for the most part, designed to give a very low-cost end product, without thought as to its expected usable life span.

Printed circuits can be designed to be equally as good as solid-state systems and to eliminate a large amount of human error that often is a factor in solid-state equipment. If properly designed, printed circuits can eliminate many of the problems occurring in the solid-state systems, such as conductive dust and lint, moisture, insects, and many other hazards. The printed circuits will cost a small fraction of the cost of solid-state panels.

Most industries using printed circuitry in their product are using the silk-screen process to print each individual circuit on the panel. The panel is sometimes polyester fiberglass, and sometimes it is a phenolic alpha-cellulose material. As each circuit is printed on the panel with a conductive compound, it must be followed by a clear insulating coat, leaving gaps where two or more circuits may connect.

Each circuit and each insulating coat require a screen. A product which requires as many as 50 separate circuits requires at least 50 separate silk screens. The silk screens are expensive and need considerable care. Labor is expensive because each panel produced requires so many separate applications of the conductive and nonconductive materials.

In some instances these costs may be lowered by using stencils or shields and spraying or flow-coating the insulating materials in place. Automated systems reduce costs further.

Even with so many separate steps needed to produce these printed circuits, the end cost is much lower than that of solid-state systems. However, in order to interest the great majority of the market in such applications, printed circuitry must be developed that is more easily produced, better in quality, and lower in end costs.

Some researchers in this field are working with compression-molding processes to produce the finished panel. They are devising techniques whereby up to four circuits may be imprinted into a panel with each cycle of the press. Work is continuing and very possibly can be improved still further.

Another group is trying to devise methods by which multicircuit panels may be laminated. The theory is to precut each circuit from a conductive sheet of material and precut each insulating layer from a material with good electrical properties, arrange them in the proper sequence, and press them together, forming a single panel, with all circuits enclosed completely by insulating materials.

This process, when carried to the point of complete automation, can be very fast, efficient, and can produce top-quality circuits. It has one very serious drawback: The thin sheets of conductive materials are expensive, and when used in sheet form with the individual circuits stamped out of them, there is a very large amount of waste material left (which must be reprocessed into sheets again).

Another drawback of this process is the large amount of equipment required. A number of products require panels with many circuits, and each circuit requires stamping tools. Capital investments are very high and can only be justified if production rates are very high in the same basic product.

Special equipment and techniques must be developed for this work. Not enough research is being spent on finding methods by which this work may be done faster, better, and more economically.

Polyester resins should be able to play a large part in this development. No other polymer can match the very fast cycle times that are possible with polyesters, combined with the excellent electrical properties and very low pressures by which they may be processed.

At first glance this market may seem to be a rather small-volume one for polymers since some of the panels are very minute. Requirements for polymers may range from a fraction of an ounce per panel up to many pounds in other products. However, when the total volume of the individual panels necessary to supply the demand is considered, in all the many end products where such panels are used, the volume is very large indeed.

If a manufacturer can devise large improvements in the production of such panels, the market for his product can be almost limitless.

Potting, Encapsulation, Dipping, and Motor-winding Applications

Almost every component part in the electrical, electronic, and telephone industry is at least in part a plastic composition. These parts may range from very tiny diodes, the size of a pencil eraser, to motor windings for huge electric motors.

Many of these component parts are electrically insulated by either potting, encapsulation, dipping, or other means of encasing the part completely in a polymer with good electrical properties. Many of these parts are subjected to quite high temperatures, and therefore the silicones must be used. Other parts reach temperatures that even the silicones will not withstand, and therefore ceramics must be used as the insulating medium.

By and large, the great percentage of these parts operate at temperatures well below 400°F, so the more expensive materials are not necessary. Epoxies have been used to a great extent in these lower-temperature applications, although many of the thermoplastics, such as the polyamides, may be used in some instances.

Applications permitting dipping of the parts often use such polymers as the allyls, where much thinner films will give considerably higher electrical properties. In all the many polymers used in these applications, there are few instances where polyesters could not be substituted to the benefit of the manufacturer. In any application requiring heat resistance of under 350°F, a resin such as that shown in Chart 6, Formula 3, will serve the purpose very well. In applications where temperatures may reach 400 to 450°F, a resin such as Formula 4 should be used.

These polyesters will be equal in electrical properties to any organic polymer, with the exception of the silicones. They may be used as straight catalyzed materials, or they may be compounded with the proper fillers and pigments, and even better electrical properties may be obtained.

The electrical properties of the four resins given in Chart 6 will be very near these values.

Property	ASTM Method	Resins			
		1	2	3	4
Dielectric constant	D150-47T				
25°C, 60 cycles		3.5	3.6	3.7	3.7
25°C, 1000 cycles		3.3	3.4	3.5	3.5
Dissipation factor					
25°C, 60 cycles	D150-47T	0.003	0.004	0.003	0.003
Power factor					
25°C, 60 cycles	D150	0.0009	0.0008	0.0008	0.0009
Volume resistivity					
Ohms/cm $\times$ 10^{16}	D157	2.2	2.4	2.5	2.5
Surface resistivity					
Ohms/cm $\times$ 10^{15}	D157	9.7	9.4	9.4	9.3
Dielectric strength					
Volts/mil, 25°C	D149-44	475	500	550	550
Arc resistance, sec	D495-48T	118	125	135	135
Moisture absorption, % 24 hr		0.01	0.008	0.006	0.007

Values are shown for ⅛-in. compression-molded resins, with no additives, fillers, or pigments. These values can go much higher, with proper choice of fillers and reinforcing materials.

The above properties make these resins highly suitable for use in every type of electrical application up to 450°F, for Formula 4. The properties will not be surpassed by any organic polymer, with the exception of the expensive silicone.

Lighting Fixtures: Interior and Exterior

Lighting fixtures is another field where polyester resins may be manufactured into products to compete with metals and other plastics.

Today, over 90% of all lighting fixtures, both interior and exterior, have metal bases and shades, with either glass or plastic faces. Interior indirect lighting of all types have changed principally to plastic for the face or visable portion of the fixture. Exterior fixtures, such as street lighting, are still using glass in the majority of products.

There is no reason for using metal bases for fixtures, except that metal has been used ever since electricity was invented and no one has seen reason to change it. Metal for this purpose is simple to process into the shapes and forms necessary; costs are not considered simply because there has been no material to compete with the metals.

The simple shapes and forms normally used in all types of lighting fixtures are very simple to compression-mold with polyester compounds. A molding compound very similar to that given for use in transformer cans, inspection boxes, switch boxes, etc., is ideal for this use. Here again, processing may be done at pressures of 200 to 250 psi on very fast cycles. A press with four sets of dies in an automated system and with fast press closing and opening can produce over 1,800 parts per 8-hr shift.

Fifteen-second cycles for production of these products can match any process known for producing metals. The costs of the materials will be reasonably similar, so there is no reason whatever why all parts of lighting fixtures cannot be made of polyester compounds.

The faces of the fixtures, whether they be the clear type used in exterior lighting, or the highly complex indirect type used extensively for interiors, may also be easily manufactured from these polyester compounds.

The clear, simple lenses can be either cell-cast or plunger-molded, depending on the complexity of the curvature. Many of the interior-lighting shades and covers may be cast or compression-molded. Highly complex, checkerboard, and other types may have to be fabricated from sheet material.

Polyester sheeting may be made at any thickness desired. It may be clear, colored, or highly filled with compounds, which may be stamped out into the necessary shapes just as in metal and the other plastics. The fabricating techniques would be very similar to those used with the other materials.

There are many light fixtures where possibly the entire part could be redesigned slightly and molding and other operations could be made much simpler. Mold design is of utmost importance and of course will be a large part of any capital investment to produce these products. Simplifying designs can save many thousands of dollars in mold costs. In compression-molding, pressure-casting, or any other type of operation, proper mold design can not only be less expensive, but can also cut cycle times and increase production. The mold design must coincide very closely with the rest of the automation in the production line, regardless of the process used, for better facilitation of loading and unloading the dies. In many systems, air injection on both male and female dies will be required for positive ejection of parts. In other dies, vacuum cups must be mechanized to demold the parts. Much depends on this phase and the method chosen to place the compound into the dies. In injection-molding, this is no problem, nor is it usually a problem in transfer-molding. In straight compression-molding, it sometimes becomes a problem if the mold charges are very small; the method must be extremely accurate.

The finished cost of a given manufactured product will depend on factors such as these. The engineering that goes into these phases is of the utmost importance. Almost all other equipment necessary for such production lines is fairly well standardized, and works well in any given compound, regardless of the polymer used.

But in polyesters, where the molding cycles are so short, extra seconds saved in the cycle by the loading and unloading of the dies becomes even more important than in the other polymers, where mold cycles are much longer. A 2- or 3-sec cut in a molding cycle of 120 to 180 sec is not much of a percentage, but in polyesters, where cure cycles are 15 sec or less in such thin-walled products, a 2- or 3-sec cut in the cycle is a very large percentage, and production rates rise considerably.

The products described in this chapter and many other products that are used in the electrical, electronic, telephone, and related industries, can be manufactured better and at a lower cost with polyesters than with the raw materials now being used. Polyester compounds can easily replace metals and many of the plastics in a great percentage of the applications in these industries.

Nine

THE OPTICAL INDUSTRY

The optical industry is a very large and growing part of our world. Optical lenses are used in such a wide variety of products that the present processes of making and working glass have not been able to keep up with the demands.

The highly skilled technicians and professionals needed in the manufacture of optical lenses from glass are not available to expand production because the training of such personnel takes many years. Thus, this industry needs very badly new processes for manufacturing lenses.

The optical industry must produce a very wide range of products: very tiny contact lenses, corrective lenses for eyeglasses, special aspheric lenses for cataract sufferers, prescription sunglasses, camera lenses for every conceivable type of camera including television, rifle scopes, surveyors' instruments, sextants, magnifying glasses for thousands of uses, microscopes, and telescopes (some with lenses of even more than 200 in. in diameter).

These millions of lenses per year must be produced by relatively few people working in this industry. They cannot keep pace with the growing population and the growing need for these products.

About 10 years ago, researchers from two large optical companies began work with plastics to see if such lenses could possibly be produced in this material. They began work with small contact lenses, with the help of good plastics engineers. The acrylics were chosen as the most probable polymer, and work began.

First, the acrylic was cell-cast and cured. The resulting sheet was sawed up into small pieces, and contact lenses were ground from them, quite like glass is worked. Different grinding methods and grinding mediums were tried until perfect lenses could be made from these materials.

In this way, the acrylics and acrylates became the mainstay for use in contact lenses. These materials were much easier to work than glass, and if handled very carefully, they would give good results. Since the acrylics are rather soft and have poor abrasion resistance, special cleaning fluids and tissues were designed for them.

Research continued to look for means and methods of producing some of the other very difficult types of lenses. Aspheric lenses for cataract patients have always been a nightmare for the optical industry. Since there are no true radii in these lenses, it took a highly skilled technician from 2 to 3 days per lens to produce them from glass. A few aspheric lenses were produced with the acrylics, and because these materials are easier to work with, the lenses were produced in about one-third the time per lens.

The research group was not completely satisfied. It wanted to be able to produce lenses to prescription in one single operation if this were possible. Molds were made, with the prescription ground into the dies in reverse. Injection-molding, compression-molding, and casting were all tried with little success. Always at least one side of the lens would have defects.

Next thermoforming was tried from a sheet of polymer. This would not give the desired optical properties, so they turned again to casting.

It was reasoned that the high shrinkage of the catalyzed acrylic monomers being cast was responsible for the defects. The shrinkage was minimized by partially polymerizing the monomers before the material was introduced into the mold. But the defects remained, although to a lesser degree.

Molds were designed, with male and female rigid heat-resisting glass, with a soft gasket between the dies and the two halves held together with a spring-loaded clamp. This was poured with the partially polymerized material, and perfect lenses resulted. The soft gasket and the spring allowed the dies to close together slightly as the resin cured and shrunk. The defects were overcome.

Now, the complex aspheric lenses could be manufactured, and contact lenses could be made in the same general manner. They were cast to prescription, and the edges could be manually trimmed to fit eye or frame. A great deal had been accomplished.

As these products were sold on a very limited basis, the results began to come in. They were too soft and damaged very easily. If cleaned with a handkerchief, tiny abrasions could be seen, and the optics were badly damaged.

Work began on many other polymers to try to find one that would be harder and more resistant to abrasion. Chemists worked with all combinations of the acrylic and methacrylic monomers. The methyls were found to be considerably harder than the ethyl derivatives. The higher-boiling butyl and 2-ethylhexyl were still slightly harder. Isodecyl acrylate and cyanoethyl acrylate were tried. All the higher acrylates were improvements but were still too soft when used alone.

Researchers turned to other polymers. Epoxies were tried, but the percentage of light transmission was too low. Polyesters of all types that were available were tried, with acrylate monomers, but they just did not transmit enough light. They were not clear enough.

Polycarbonates were tried but were just too difficult to work with in monomer form. Cures were far too slow to be practical. Diallyl phthalate, and triallyl cyanurate were dismissed for the same reasons.

The researchers finally came upon a monomer that looked as though it might do the job—allyl diglycol carbonate, a sort of cross-bred monomer between the allyls and the polycarbonates. It, too, was slow to cure, but could be speeded up somewhat by partially polymerizing it into a thick syrup and then pouring it into the molds. Total cure time approached 6 hr, but the lenses were almost perfect. They were very clear, and optical properties were very close to that of glass. This material was very abrasion-resistant and practically unbreakable.

Work was begun with this material, and production soon could supply the great majority of the contact and aspheric lenses in the country. The manufacture of all prescription lenses in this manner is now being considered.

Opthalmological Lenses

The polyesters of today are far different from those tried only 3 or 4 years ago for this type of application. New intermediates and some of the old ones that had not been previously thought of for use in polyesters can now make resins with light transmission up to 94% in

¼-in. sections. The best plate glass at the same thickness has 92%, polycarbonate 90%, allyl diglycol carbonate 93%, and the acrylics up to 98%.

A polyester resin with a 94% light transmission would be the following:

1. Propylene carbonate..................................... 1.1 moles
2. Heptaethylene glycol.................................... 1.1
3. Fumaric acid... 1.0
4. Acrylic acid... 0.5
5. Tetrahydrophthalic..................................... 0.5
6. Methyl methacrylate.................................... 1.0
7. Allyl diglycol carbonate............................... 1.0

Many variations of such a resin can be manufactured. The methyl-
methacrylate is a low-boiling monomer, so for use at high curing temperatures, substitute 2-ethylhexyl acrylate or butyl acrylate. The carbonate monomer cross-links well with any acrylate.

This is a polyester, even though it has many characteristics of an
acrylic, particularly the clarity. This resin will cure in under 1 min
at 300°F when properly catalyzed for these temperatures.

With such a material as this, the manufacture of optical lenses can
become a much different industry than it is with polymers that take
one to 6 hr to cure. Production will be multiplied many times. Costs
will be just a small fraction of the costs of lenses manufactured by
any other polymer or glass. A very small, compact production line can
turn out large quantities of lenses with one person operating the entire
line, except for inspecting and packaging.

Total cost per lens, regardless of the complicity of the prescription,
will be the same. Manufactured cost of each lens will be well below
$1.00.

In the manufacture of most polyester products, the purchase of molds
and dies usually constitutes a very substantial part of the entire investment. In this instance, the molds and dies will require the greatest percentage of the total capital investment.

Diagram 14 shows a typical die arrangement for the production of
these lenses. Apart from the dies, the production line will consist of
a small mixing chamber, fitted with a vacuum for deaerating the resin
as catalysts and other additives are blended in, and a means of filling
the dies. The latter may be a small hydraulic pump, a gravity-feed
operation, or a small pressure tank, in which a small amount of air
pressure is used to force the resin into the dies.

The dies themselves may be made from a heat-resisting glass, or they
may be steel or chrome-plated and highly polished. The two halves
of the die, male and female, will be separated by a silicone-elastomer
gasket and the whole held together by spring-loaded clamps, hasps,

or other means to permit the slight contraction necessary to allow for the shrinkage.

There are many possibilities for the die arrangement. The dies may be made into separate parts if desired. Each individual cavity may be a different prescription and a separate part. The long part of the dies may be plain mild steel, with suitable spaces for receiving each individual male and female insert. Both the male and female portion of the dies must be suitably channeled for hot-oil or steam heating.

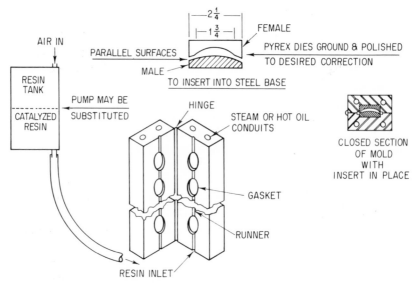

DIAGRAM 14. *Diagram for manufacture of ophthalmological lenses.*

Each set of dies may have as many individual pairs of dies as is desired. Conceivably there may be up to 100 cavities per set. It may be more convenient to have more sets of dies, with fewer cavities per set.

The most convenient position for the sets of dies is vertical, with all filling taking place from the bottom. In this manner, all air is forced from each cavity as the resin is injected into it, and through the runners to the next cavity, and so on. All air is ejected through the top of the set of dies, and the operator can see when all cavities are full when resin comes out the top runner.

When polyester resin begins to heat, just before gel occurs, it will expand 3 to 5%, depending on the resin and the temperature. After gel, as the curing stage or polymerization proceeds, the polymer will begin to shrink or contract. This also may be 3 to 5%, depending on the resin and the cure temperature. In general, the higher the cure temperature and the higher the exotherm temperature of the resin, the greater the shrinkage.

The silicone-rubber gasket, together with the spring-clamp arrangement, will allow for this expansion and contraction and prevent one or both sides of the polymerizing lens from separating from the die surface. Any separation, as cure develops, will result in a reject lens. The optical properties will be damaged.

The rate of production in a production line such as this will be very fast. The heated platens or outer dies will never cool. They will remain at the temperature set for the hot-oil or steam medium. The inner dies will cool very slightly between cycles as they are unloaded and loaded. With an efficient technique, total cycle time can be as low as 2 min, including filling the cavities, curing, and unloading the finished lenses.

Each lens will be connected to the next with a thin strip of polymer, the runner between the cavities. Thus the entire group of lenses will be demolded in one piece; later they are separated into individual lenses, the rim is trimmed off, the finished lens is ready to use. For purposes of shipping, it may be advisable to leave the rim in place. The optician, in fitting the lens to the patient's glasses or in fitting the contact lens, may remove the rim easily.

A good starting formulation for this use is the following:

1. Polyester resin (such as that given above)................... 10.00 lb
2. Catalyst (peroctoate or percarbonate)....................... 0.15
3. Internal mold release...................................... 0.05
                                                              _____
                                                              10.20 lb

To such a formulation, tinting agents may be added for producing tinted glasses or sunglasses. Organic dyes may be used in this application. Very small quantities are required, and they will not interfere with the optics of the lenses.

The resulting lenses will be of excellent quality when perfectly ground dies are used. The dies will not require cleaning between cycles when the proper mold release is used internally. The polymer will be abrasion resistant and will have very good impact strength. The percentage of light transmission will be slightly higher than that of glass or polycarbonate and allyl diglycol carbonate lenses. It will be slightly less than that of a straight acrylic lens. Abrasion resistance will be much higher than that of the acrylic lens but somewhat lower than that of the polycarbonate or allyl diglycol lenses.

These lenses will be so low in cost that a person may purchase two or more pair as needed to always have a spare set. If one pair becomes broken, scratched, or lost, he can always have a spare nearby, as the cost will be a small fraction of normal lenses. A person will be able to afford several sets—one for reading, one for driving, etc.—instead of perhaps using bifocals or trifocals.

Every known prescription may be manufactured by this process. The manufacturer must have a very large inventory of the small individual pairs of dies. For prescriptions that are most common, he will need many pairs of dies. For prescriptions that are rarely needed, he may only need one pair. All dies will have to be clearly marked so the prescription will be permanently imbedded into the rim or detachable part of the molded lens. Since a relatively few prescriptions are the most commonplace, production will largely be in these prescriptions.

One well-setup production line in a rather small room or building can supply the entire nation with these lenses. Eye patients will no longer pay high prices for expensive hand-worked glass lenses. Even the very expensive aspheric lenses will be available at very low prices. Bifocals, trifocals, and single-vision lenses will all be the same price, perhaps slightly different prices because of the added cost of tooling the dies. At any rate, the difference would be very small.

Each pair of dies will last indefinitely if handled with care. No repolishing or reworking will be necessary, since no abrasive materials of any kind will ever come in contact with them. Care will have to be taken not to drop the dies or to touch the surfaces. A fingerprint on the surface of the male or female die will be plainly visible in the finished lens.

This application does not present a large market for polyester resins, but it is excellent for a manufacturer because of the tremendous volume of lenses used each day. The amount of raw materials going into them will be small, but the quantities of finished products will be very large.

Safety Glasses and Shields

All other types of glasses may also be manufactured by the same process described above, whether there is a prescription involved or not: safety glasses for industrial workers, safety shields for grinding equipment, glasses for athletes, and thousands of applications where normal glass presents many hazards to the people using it.

Many times athletes wear contact lenses, which are very frequently lost during play. With normal contact lenses, the cost can be very high. With these polyester lenses, cost will be almost negligible.

Workers employed in manufacturing plants frequently break the normal safety glasses issued to them, and cost may be considerable to the manufacturer. With these polyester safety glasses, goggles, and helmets, the cost will be negligible.

Sunglasses: Prescription and Plain-vision

Each year, millions of pairs of sunglasses are sold. In many cases, they are not corrective-vision glasses but merely for partially blocking the sun's rays from the wearer's eyes. In other cases, the sunglasses must be ground to fit the wearer's correction.

Suitable blocking agents are available, which may be added to the formulation for clear lenses, and which will afford the wearer maximum protection from both ultraviolet and infrared rays. Other additives will merely reduce the amount of these rays permitted to enter. These additives blend into polyester very easily and do not add to the cost appreciably.

These glasses can be truly protective to the eyes of the wearer. In addition to the blocking agents, they may be tinted as desired to further the comfort for the wearer. These additives will not interfere with the optics of the finished lenses.

Organic dyes are most suitable for tinting these polyester lenses, and the benzophenone derivatives are usually best to use as blocking agents. These are commercially available. Many times, crotonic acid derivatives can be used as blocking agents, and certain zirconium compounds afford excellent light-blocking properties.

X-ray Shields, Gamma-ray Shields, Welding Lenses, and Goggles

X-rays, known as roentgen rays, and such rays as alpha, beta, and gamma rays may be partially, or totally, blocked from passing through these polyester resins. Welders' eyes need good protection from the rays emitted from acetylene torches, arc welders, and other equipment used in this work. X-ray workers must have protection from the damaging rays used in medicine, chemistry, and many applications today.

Lenses, goggles, and shields all may be made with polyester resin, with proper blocking agents added to the formulation.

Camera Lenses: Television Camera Lenses

Every type of camera used must have one or more lens. Some of these are telescopic, and others are nontelescopic but have certain properties that make them suitable for certain situations.

These lenses may be manufactured at very reasonable costs with polyester resins and the process discussed earlier. The cost of these items will be a small fraction of the present costs where these lenses must be hand-ground from glass.

Magnifying and Microscope Lenses

The lenses for magnifying glasses used in hand-magnifyers and in microscopes are very expensive items today. Thousands are used, and each one must be hand-ground to specifications.

The same process described above can be used to manufacture these items on a large scale, at very low costs.

Telescopes

As our exploration of space grows, the need for larger, more powerful, and better telescopes becomes critical. There are far too few suitable telescopes in the world to adequately study the space around us.

The cost of these tremendous installations has been the major deterring factor. A great percentage of the cost of a large telescope is the lenses themselves.

Some of these lenses must be 200 in. in diameter and larger. Each one must be custom-ground by hand, and the cost of a single lens can run into hundreds of thousands of dollars.

With a single pair of dies, thousands of these lenses can be produced, and there may be adequate telescopes at every convenient location throughout the world.

Smaller telescopes can be made available to schools, colleges, and to individuals for use as a hobby. Costs can be low enough so that anyone will be able to afford a home telescope.

The process described here with polyester resins is most suitable to telescope lenses of all sizes. Mass production of these lenses from relatively few pairs of dies can completely change the aspect of space exploration.

The polyester lens will weigh approximately two-fifths the normal weight of these lenses, so supporting tubes and other equipment will be much lighter weight and lower in cost.

Every optical application where glass is being used today can benefit by changing to polyester resins and processes. No possible application should be overlooked, regardless of size. Any single application requiring more than a half-dozen lenses can very profitably be filled in this manner.

The cost of the dies for any application is little more than the cost of a pair of lenses, and from these, many lenses may be economically produced.

Artificial Eyes

Other applications where polyester resins can be used to good advantage in the optical industry include the manufacture of artificial eyes. This process must include several stages for the artificial eye to match perfectly a natural eye.

Molds are quite similar to those described for the manufacture of lenses. The individual cavities are in different sizes because the human eye is quite distinctive in size as well as coloring.

For good processing and for maximum authenticity in the finished product, three sets of dies are required. One set of dies produces the cornea, one set produces the pupil, and the third produces the entire eye.

The cornea and pupil are finished, placed together properly, and inserted into the cavity for the entire eye. The polyester resin is then forced into the cavity, cured, and the part is complete.

With proper techniques and color matching, the artificial eye will be a perfect match for the natural eye. Good craftsmen can even match the tiny blood vessels which are visible in the human eye.

Some patents exist on the manufacture of optical lenses and other optical parts from a number of the plastics. It is advisable to check on existing patents before proceeding into a manufacturing process on such items.

Ten

MISCELLANEOUS MANUFACTURED PRODUCTS

An existing manufacturing company may be looking for new products to expand its present line of goods, or may very well be considering diversification into completely different lines of merchandise as insurance against slack periods in the present business. Diversification into new fields seems to be accepted presently by many large corporations as the best method of assuring future growth and stockholders' security. Many companies are venturing into manufacturing fields which are far removed from present lines of endeavor, and in which they have had no previous experience whatever.

Drug companies are entering the plastics field. Oil companies are entering the intermediates and petrochemical fields. Insurance companies are venturing into many different enterprises in order to keep their capital working to best advantage. Roofing-materials manufacturing companies are going into flooring products. Coal-tar processors are diversifying into plastics manufacture and building-materials fields. Metals manufacturers are entering the plastics-products fields. Foods processors are spending large sums in research and development of packaging materials for their own products, rather than depending on others. Paper manufacturers are going into the construction-materials fields.

This is only a small sample of the growth and diversification going on around us. Some think the best way to go about diversification is to purchase, or to merge with, a company already in existence that has need for growth capital and better management. Others are looking for a company with tax write-offs accumulated on its books. Many companies wish to start from scratch and build a new industry from the bottom up.

All approaches have merit, depending on a particular firm's policy, financial position, and market orientation. A factor that often enters the thinking is perhaps an excess of good sound management potential, which is not presently being used to its fullest ability. Capital surpluses often must be reinvested or the tax will be excessive.

There are many reasons for a company to expand or diversify. Good management knows that any company must grow or become stagnant; so many times when there is no room in the market for greater production in its own field, a company must look to other products and fields for room to grow.

Not all growth is owing to the expansion and diversification of established manufacturers and businesses. Much growth is a result of the incorporation of completely new enterprises formed from a nucleus of people previously employed in other endeavors.

So much of our growth and expansion today is in the field of plastics in one form or another—whether it be intermediates and petrochemicals, polymers, or finished plastics products—that it is without doubt the fastest growing industry in the United States. Here is where practically untouched markets exist and where growth can be very rapid. Other industries have in many cases reached their summit, with little hope for future expansion.

There are no foreseeable limits to the growth of the plastics industry. New polymers are being developed each year from raw materials and intermediates that were unknown 2 years ago. Each new polymer that is developed opens new possibilities for end products. Relatively old polymers have been improved to a point where they may be used in many applications that were not even dreamed of 2 years ago.

This field offers more opportunities than any other field at this time. However, by the same token, it offers much capital risk to those inexperienced in this field.

Polyester resins offer more to a new or expanding industry than any other polymer known today because of the very wide range of products for which it is suitable, and because of the wide range of processes by which such products may be manufactured with these resins.

Any firm, new or established, considering new products to be manufactured, should carefully consider all possible aspects before making decisions.

Orientation

If the firm is an established firm, to what general fields is the present firm oriented? If a new firm is being established, to what fields are the executives best oriented? Chances of success are far better in fields where considerable knowledge is already available in both manufacturing procedures and the marketing of similar products.

A few fields that may be considered for new polyester products are the following:

1. Building-materials field: structural shapes, gratings
2. Marine applications: boats, barges, pontoons, buoys
3. Automotive products: bodies, bumpers, wheels, hubcaps
4. Aircraft component parts
5. Furniture: office, household, outdoor
6. Appliances: refrigerators, washing machines, cabinets
7. Food and beverage packaging field
8. Consumer goods: decorator items, lamps, art, sculpture, murals, mosaics, stained-glass windows
9. Tooling; draw dies, vacuum dies, drop-hammer dies
10. Coatings and corrosion fields
11. Portable buildings, house trailers, offices, campers
12. Luggage: trunks, suitcases, bags, portfolio cases
13. Street and highway signs and markers, signals, posts
14. Containers: garbage cans, wastebaskets, chemical containers
15. Swimming pools, fountains, birdbaths, waterfalls
16. Mortuary products: caskets, headstones
17. Flowerpots, planter boxes, hothouses
18. Outdoor advertising: signs, letters, signboards
19. Safety equipment for industry and sports
20. Sports equipment: skis, surfboards, bowling balls and equipment, archery equipment, fishing rods
21. Fiber, fabric, filament for clothes, tires, reinforcing
22. Polyester film and sheeting
23. Abrasive tools for grinding, sawing
24. Fans, blowers, scrubbers, hoods, smokestacks for industry
25. Tanks, acidizing vats, annealing vats, anodizing vats
26. Polyester substitution parts for any plant handling corrosive fertilizers, chemicals, gases

This list, of course, represents only a very small portion of the fields where polyester resins can be the basis of new products. A great number of products now being manufactured with other materials as well as completely new materials can be manufactured with polyester, with great advantage to the manufacturer and to the consumer.

Studies: Products to Be Considered

A firm contemplating such new products must study every possibility. A large number of products should be considered that could be manufactured by the same general process, so in the event the market did not work out as expected for one, others could be produced to supplement or replace it.

In the contemplated field, every product and all its aspects must be studied: the material presently being used in its manufacture, present design, its weight, selling price, and probable plant-manufactured cost.

Is the product presently being manufactured from wood, metal, glass, ceramic, concrete, or other plastics? Is the present design conducive to manufacture from polyesters, and if not what changes would have to be made in basic shape, form, or size? What is the weight of the present product, and what would be the comparative weight if made from polyester compounds? What is the appearance of the product? Must it be painted after manufacture? Does it have to be printed on or decorated in any way? Can the entire operation be done more efficiently in polyester?

What is the present cost at retail and the probable manufactured cost? (Careful calculations of these costs can be very close, when sufficient time and effort are given to the calculations.) What would the cost be for an identical product in polyester compounds? My calculating the weight of the product in cubic inches of polyester compound necessary, material costs can be very accurate. Processing costs, equipment costs, and other factors may be calculated very close to what the actual production costs will be.

When the products presenting the best possibilities have been chosen, then it is time to proceed with the actual tooling to make a few prototype parts of each product, establishing the actual formulations, designs, and processing methods and techniques that are to be used.

Research and Development

Tooling and equipment will be the first phase of the project. If compression-molding is the process selected, a small press and related equipment, means of heat, dies, etc., should be installed for the production of a limited number of prototype products.

The proper resin for the process, proper catalysts, promoters additives, fillers, reinforcing fiber, and pigment are all selected to give the best end properties for the environment in which the product will be used. Proper selection will be no simple matter, and many different resins and materials may have to be tried before results are satisfactory.

Cycle times may be established, and exact costs, designs, and processes and techniques can be developed in this manner. After working for some time in one process, it might be decided that the products which are contemplated lend themselves more to another process. It could be found perhaps that injection-molding would be a more efficient, and hence lower-cost, process for the particular products. Therefore, equipment would have to be installed to fully investigate this method of production.

For developmental purposes, it is far more economical to rent or lease the necessary pilot-plant equipment. Almost all equipment manufacturers have small experimental equipment for this purpose. Many times, they have facilities in their own plants, already completely set up and ready to use for this purpose. In this case, the firm only has to have the necessary dies or molds made up and the proper materials sent in.

A manufacturer of hydraulic presses will have small presses either available for rental or set up in his plant for use. Injection-molding manufacturers, transfer-molding-equipment manufacturers, and others will offer the same facilities. Heating-medium equipment, grinding-equipment manufacturers, and many others will cooperate in the research and development of any new product. Resin manufacturers and the manufacturers and suppliers of all the other materials will offer all possible aid. They all know that the development of a new product and a new plant means business for them.

In this manner, the development of a new product may not be nearly as expensive as would be expected. Possibly the most difficult part of the entire project will be to find the proper personnel.

Often, personnel may be borrowed on a temporary basis from another industry in products which are simular to, but not in direct competition with, the projected new industry. Many times the resin manufacturers have competent personnel that may be borrowed; also, the equipment manufacturers have experienced personnel trained for precisely the purpose of helping new industries and products get started.

In this way, a process and a product may be tested out, and numbers of prototypes may be produced for testing, showing, and feeling out the market.

Proper techniques, mold and die designs, cycle times, total equipment requirements, plant requirements, and costs can be arrived at with an accuracy of plus or minus 5%.

Having completed this part of the research and development, and with the size of the market in mind, the next step is to calculate the probable gain to the firm through such a product or products.

Pro Forma

With all plant requirements, equipment, material costs, and labor costs established quite accurately by the above methods, a pro forma can be made up.

Calculations may be desirable over a 5- or 10-year period, or even longer.

Trade publications and government statistics can provide information as to the size of the market. From the probable cost of this product, its properties, and other factors, good marketing consultants can make quite accurate predictions as to the percentage of the market the product can expect to fill during the first year, the second year, and in the years ahead.

Such factors as equipment and plant depreciation, maintenance, utilities costs, overhead, packaging and other costs can be calculated with very close accuracy. Costs of marketing, advertising, promotion, and related costs also can be arrived at within a small percentage.

With all this information at hand, the pro forma can predict the probable success or failure of the industry.

Three factors remain, which are of utmost importance, and which, together with the pro forma, will decide the ultimate success of the undertaking.

Capital Requirements

No industry should be begun without assurances of all necessary capital plus a comfortable margin. A great percentage of businesses fail because of lack of required finances.

Good Management and Personnel

Possibly more businesses fail for lack of good management and proper personnel than for any other reason. Good management is difficult to find, and good professional and technical personnel are even harder to find.

The key personnel for a new industry must be available before it begins. Gaps and slots can be filled in between this skeleton framework, but the key people must form the foundation for a successful enterprise.

Marketing

The method of marketing the products is of utmost importance. Depending on the particular product, it may be wise to market through established dealers, establish factory representatives, or sell directly to the consumer through a sales force.

However it is done, marketing is a most important factor and must receive just as much consideration as the other phases of the industry. The method should be established before production is begun, as it is often very hard to change marketing methods after a product has been manufactured for some time.

Land and Plant Requirements

When planning the requirements for the land and plant, many factors must be considered: future expansion, modes of transportation of raw materials and finished products, availability of water, gas, and electric power. State and local taxes and the proximity to the major markets must also be carefully checked, compared, and considered.

The land should be planned at least 10 years ahead. The plant can be constructed for only present requirements, but there must be room to expand.

Rail, water, or highway transportation must be convenient. A large plant must have a railway siding built into the plant area, and good highways must exist nearby. The plant must be as near as possible to its source of raw materials and within reasonable shipping distances of its principal markets.

The availability of utilities and their costs can often make a rather substantial difference in the cost of a product. A plant that must drill water wells and perhaps install its own power supply must have far more available capital.

State and local tax laws may in some cases be critical to the survival and growth of a new industry.

Equipment Requirements

When calculations as to size and capacity of the required equipment are made, it is often found that it is not economical to purchase equipment sized to the exact present needs. Very often, much larger equipment, with greater possible output, can be purchased for very small differences in initial cost.

If present production schedules are planned for 10,000 parts per day but there is a good possibility of marketing 20,000 per day within a year or two, it will be most economical to plan the initial production line for this capacity from the start. The difference in initial investment is often less than 15%, whereas to install later a duplication of the first production line would double the investment.

The advantage is not entirely just in the equipment requirements. In almost every case, the same amount of labor can run a production line for 20,000 parts per shift that would be required for producing 10,000 if the production line is planned into the initial production line.

Supervision, auxiliary equipment, instruments, materials handling equipment, conveyors, and other factors are often equal for the smaller and larger production. Overhead must be set up in such a manner that it will be reduced in direct relation to the total production. This is where profits are made.

Planning Eventualities and Future Production

Sound planning for both present and future requirements is a must. The total capital investments for a product can be quite substantially lowered in this way.

The difference in a manufacturer showing a modest profit and a very substantial profit is most often found in the planning stages of the plant itself, its equipment, and the provisions for future production. Processes, techniques, and materials can be improved as production progresses, but total production will depend on the provisions made in the installation of original equipment. Production will be limited rather rigidly by the capacities of the machines and equipment purchased.

A compression-molding line is capable of only a certain number of cycles per 8-hr day, depending on the cure time of the compound used, the speed of the opening and closing of the press, and the time required to charge and unload the dies. Production will be limited by these factors multiplied by the platen area of the press. If a press is designed to hold four sets of dies instead of two, then production can be doubled when necessary, even though this larger capacity is not needed at first.

The cost differential in planning for the larger capacity is only in the press size, platen area, and hydraulic capacity and will be surprisingly near the price for the smaller-capacity equipment. The same holds true with injection-molding and transfer-molding equipment, autoclaves, or with any other type of processing equipment.

Every possible eventuality must be considered during the planning and developmental stages of a new venture. If one product does not do as well on the market as expected, there must be other products fully developed, ready to be produced on the same equipment line, possibly with only the dies needing to be changed. Several alternative products should be in the developmental stages during actual production of the plant in the event that another manufacturer may come out with a product at a lower cost and thus reduce the market for the present product.

Every possible patent should be obtained on products, processes, and on any equipment especially developed for specific applications. Patent protection could be very valuable to the firm in a few years in minimizing competition.

There are many aspects to be considered in planning any new product or a plant to produce it. Very careful planning can easily mean the success or failure of any industry.

Besides the products discussed in earlier chapters, there are many thousands of other products that must be considered as good possibilities for polyester compounds. Some of these will be discussed here. Some products will necessitate very large capital investments and mass-production schedules. Other products can be manufactured with modest investments.

In general, large investments are required in products that are in great demand on the market, and that must be produced in large, automated plants in order to be able to compete with similar products already on the market. These products have a small margin of profit per unit, so must be manufactured on a very large scale for any profit to be made (percentagewise) on the capital investment.

Smaller investments are required for products that are more or less new to the market, either in style, type, or material, so the pressure of competition will not affect the profit margin right away. Some items may be manufactured with relatively small investments and still produce a high margin of profit for a time, but others will see these products, calculate costs and profits, and will be tempted to go into the business. So, a manufacturer who starts out in a rather small way must continue to expand and produce his product more efficiently, at a lower cost, or he will be inviting competition.

This has happened in so many cases in the plastics industry over the years. A small manufacturer will do all the research and development on a product, produce it, and place it on the market in a small way. Probably it will be an item on which no patent protection could be obtained. The market develops, and the demand is greater than his production. The profit margin is obviously good, by the small production line established. Others see this and install a large plant to produce the same product by more efficient methods and equipment, selling at a much lower cost per unit. They benefit from all the work the small manufacturer has put into the development of both the product and the market. So the small manufacturer must be ready, as soon as the market begins to develop for his product, to install more and better equipment, automation, and bulk-material handling facilities, so he can purchase his raw materials at much lower costs. If these things are not done, he will soon find another company selling a similar product at much lower cost than he can produce it.

Building-materials Field

Besides the products discussed in the first six chapters, there are literally thousands of items that may be produced with polyester compounds that can compete very well in the building-materials field.

Extruded Shapes. With modern equipment and technology, almost any conceivable shape may be extruded with polyester compounds: I beams, H beams, angles, channels, window and door extruded shapes, siding, quarter-rounds, half-rounds, cove molds, and chair molds, in every necessary figure, shape, and size.

These materials may be extruded with the modified extruders now available through cross-head dies. Many of them can be manufactured with compounds of polyester resins and low-cost fillers, such as wood flour. Others will have to be reinforced with such materials as sisal, glass fiber, or synthetic fibers. Technology is now available whereby the reinforcing materials can be fed to the extruder head separately and independently and immersed in the resin compound in the cross-head itself.

Most of these materials will be so tightly compacted when emerging from the extruder head that they will not need support of any kind as they go through the oven for cure. Some, such as angles and other shapes, may need support to hold the form until gel occurs. The conveyor system can include provisions for such support with interchangeable attachments on the conveyor belt.

There is no practical limit to the sizes of such extrusions. The product will come through the oven in one continuous extruded shape, then to be cut up into desired lengths. These products can compete with metal extrusions and shapes for many applications in the building field.

Hardboard and Chipboard. There are many kinds of hardboard and chipboard on the market today. The major raw material from which they are made are the waste products of the lumber industry—sawdust, shavings, and chips. Some of the cheaper kinds of hardboard even utilize the bark of a tree.

These raw materials are bound together with a great variety of materials. The better types use urea, phenolic, and other polymers. The cheaper types use resorcinol, animal glues, caseins, and such binder materials.

Some of these products are extruded, and some are compression-molded. They are most useful applications for polyester resins. The amount of these kinds of materials sold each year make the market prospects very large. When bound together with polyester resins, hardboard will be of excellent quality and in many cases lower in cost because of easier handling, faster curing, etc. They can still be manufactured by the same process; and the only change would consist in substituting polyester for the binder currently being used.

Plywood. Millions of sheets of plywood are manufactured and sold each month. Some of it is very low in quality, and some is of excellent quality. The ultimate quality and price depend on the quality of the wood itself and on the adhesive used. Low-cost interior plywood will fall apart if any amount of moisture gets into it, and marine grades of plywood are very expensive.

Polyester resins can be put to good use in this huge industry. Low-cost polyesters, in the range of 24 cents per lb, can be used in laminating the individual sheets of veneer together, and the plywood will withstand any amount of water, weather, and other environmental abuse.

The process for the manufacture of this plywood would not change in any way, except for the adhesive binder. Polyester is better for this use than any polymer being used today, and the cost will be quite comparable. The quality of the end product will be greatly enhanced.

Doors: One-piece, Compression-molded. The manufacture of doors by conventional methods is a long, drawn-out process, involving considerable hand labor. Costs are correspondingly high.

Doors can be made in any size or thickness very simply by compression-molding them in a polyester compound. Wood flour would be the major ingredient, with polyester merely the binder. They could be pigmented if desired, so the door would be produced in a totally finished state.

The complexity of the doors would present no problem. Plain doors (sometimes referred to as slab doors), panel doors, or even decorative entrance doors can be made with no problem whatever. Each type and size of door would require separate dies, but there are not a great number of types and sizes of doors.

Some of these applications are just modifications of existing production methods, with the substitution of polyester for a binder now being used. In other applications, entirely new products, such as the doors, may be the basis for entirely new industries.

Besides the products mentioned, there are many more. Look around any construction site. Many materials are being used that could easily be manufactured from polyester compounds. These polyester products can very easily compete with the products now being marketed.

Marine Applications

Because of the inherent resistance of polyesters to saltwater, marine applications are a major area of unexplored possibilities for this polymer.

Boats. For many years, we have known fiberglass boats. These have been the small pleasure craft used for water-skiing and fishing. The great majority of them have been manufactured with polyester resins. Only a relatively few have been made with the epoxy resins.

A few larger craft have been built, up to 40 ft or more in length, but equipment and techniques used in the smaller craft make the cost of the larger boats too high. If matching molds and vacuum-injection are used, the cost of the molds is very high, hence many boats must be sold exactly alike in order to write off the mold cost. This is not practical because while duplicity in smaller boats is not objectionable, it is usually not desirable in the larger, more expensive cabin cruisers and other pleasure craft.

For work boats and competition-sailing craft, duplicity is an asset, as everything can be standardized, but even here the matched-molded hulls are expensive to manufacture. The molds are very large and unwieldy and must be heavily reinforced in order to withstand constant handling.

In so many smaller craft, hand-layup and glass-chopper guns are still prevalent. This is all right in the small boats, but present equipment, as good as it is, just does not apply sufficient quantities of glass fiber and resin per operator hour. It would take many sets of equipment and many operators to lay up a large craft properly, without gel occurring between laps.

For large craft, completely new equipment must be developed. Guns that will apply up to 50 lb per min of fiberglass and resin are entirely possible. No one has developed them because there has not been a market for this type of gun.

Such a resin and glass-chopper gun will have to be very large and unwieldy; therefore, it will have to be mechanized to a large extent. The hose, gun, glass chopper, and incoming strands of glass must be supported entirely from a boom, and the operator will merely direct the boom, quite as a crane operator does his machine. Multiple heads could be mounted on one boom.

The accepted ideas in molds will have to be drastically changed. Instead of one large female mold, there will have to be sections of a mold, mounted on tracks, and powered by either electric motors or air or hydraulic cylinders to place them into position and break them away from the finished hull. The hull mold sections would fit together tightly, so little or no seam would show in the finished surface.

After the exterior hull of the vessel is laid up, prefabricated ribs, keel, and other supports would be placed into the bare hull, and the resin and fiberglass covered over all on the next pass, binding hull and members tightly into one piece. These ribs, keels, and braces could be metal or extruded polyester and glass-fiber members.

Such a framework could have tremendous strength when designed properly. Large vessels could be manufactured entirely in this manner. Ocean-going ships could be manufactured at costs that would compete with steel-hulled vessels. Also, with this material, there would be no need for maintenance, drydocking, cathodic systems, sandblasting, and painting at regular intervals.

The only requirement would be that at least 20 to 50 vessels be manufactured from the same mold in order to write off the cost. Many sections of the molds quite possibly could be designed so they could be used on more than one size and type of vessel, thus reducing the mold cost per ship.

Barges, Pontoons, and Buoys. All types of marine craft could be manufactured in much the same manner, with large production guns mounted in multiples on booms. It would be completely feasible to build large barges, drilling barges, floating drilling rigs, and other types of craft with such equipment.

One of the large expenditures in marine craft is the periodic drydocking for overhaul of the hulls. With materials of this nature, no drydocking would ever be required, unless the hull were seriously damaged by ramming by another vessel or by running aground.

These applications for polyester resins must be seriously considered. We have the know-how to make such equipment as would be necessary. The mold design and structural design of the vessels would present no problems to marine engineers. This could very well be the first major development in shipbuilding since the advent of the steel hull and the exit of the wooden hulls of the older sailing ships.

All types of marine equipment can be manufactured by much the same methods: pontoons, light buoys, signal buoys, channel markers, and every other application where metals are now used. Salt water has been the enemy of this equipment for many years. Maintenance and the time lost due to overhauls have been a tremendous expense. There is no possible reason why all this equipment should not be manufactured with reinforced polyester and be completely maintenance-free.

Automotive Products: Bodies, Bumpers, and Component Parts

A few years ago, a small number of automobile bodies were manufactured from polyester resins and fiberglass. The automobile industry watched these closely to see the results of these materials in actual service.

These bodies were very expensive principally because of a lack of processes to turn them out on a mass-production basis. The resins used in their manufacture were orthophthalics and were very friable. Even small blows would cause the body to shatter, which was very costly to repair.

Neither resins nor pigments were suitable for constant exterior exposure. The colors tended to fade and the high initial gloss was lost unless it was constantly waxed and polished.

The general opinion within the industry was that the glass fiber and polyester automobile body was not a roaring success. Too little research and development went into the manufacture of these automobile bodies. The proper resins were not used, mostly because they were not available at the time. Poor choices were made in pigmentation, monomer systems, and catalysts.

The tooling for the production of these bodies and the equipment used was just not suitable for large-scale production; hence the costs were very high.

Glass fiber was the best reinforcing material available at the time, so it was used. This material, while imparting tremendous strength to the polyester, has the disadvantage of being friable and will break on impact, as will a very rigid polyester. Small accidents left large, jagged breaks in the body, which were difficult to repair by the hand methods used at the time.

It is time now for the automobile industry to take a second look at reinforced polyester bodies. Resins have changed tremendously. The isophthalics are much more impact-resistant than the orthophthalics. By using intermediates and monomers now available, these bodies can be completely impervious to sun, rain, and other elements to which they must be exposed.

Completely new reinforcing materials have been developed. Very recently, a new fiber, polypropylene, has been placed on the market. It is now available in filament, strand, mat, and woven fabric.

The reinforcing properties of this material are such that much less may be used in weight because of its mechanical properties and its reduced specific gravity. It is much easier to work with as it is very flexible and conforms to shapes and curvatures far better than glass fiber.

This material is more expensive per pound than glass fiber, but because of the lesser weight percentages used, the cost of the finished product is very nearly the same.

In a product where the weight percentage of glass is 50% and the percentage of polyester is 50%, the polypropylene fiber can be substituted at 35% (by weight) and 65% polyester used. The weight of the finished product will be approximately 25% less, yet mechanical properties will be very nearly the same. The impact strength, however, will be about 50% higher than for a similar product made with glass fiber.

This fiber has many advantages over glass in this type of application, besides the lesser weight of the finished product. The bond of the polyester resin is superior to this material than to glass fiber. It wets far faster in the polyester, causing far less work in rolling out the entrapped air. It will stretch, bend, fold, and lay down easily to conform to the mold contours. Perfect parts, with minimum of rejects, are easier to manufacture with this fiber.

In applications such as body parts, the gel coat should be a polyester such as a hexahydrophthalic or a tetrahydrophthalic, manufactured with such polyhydric components as heptaethylene glycol and dicyclopentadiene, and monomers such as ortho or monochlorostyrene, acrylates, and allyls for maximum weather resistance, gloss retention, and reduced maintenance requirements. This gel coat should be a minimum of 0.010 in. in thickness for maximum protection of the pigmented reinforced material below.

The reinforced body should be an isophthalic resin with a flexural modulus of about 650,000 psi, unreinforced. This will be about midway between a rigid and a resilient polyester, and when reinforced with 35% (by weight) of the polypropylene fiber, would have a modulus of approximately 800,000 psi. This material will withstand blows of tremendous force without breaking or shattering. It will "give" with a blow, and then regain its original form instantly.

With the pigments available today, a body such as this will be most beautiful and durable. It should need a very minimum of maintenance.

Many other parts of an automobile body can be made with these same materials. Dashboards, instrument panels, firewalls, and many other smaller parts may be manufactured to a great advantage.

Bumpers have been a problem to automobile owners, manufacturers, and automobile-repair men since the beginning of the automobile. A automobile bumper, if it is to give any protection to the car and its occupants, must be very heavy and strong when made of metal. This added weight is undesirable, so manufacturers use light, chrome-plated steel. The slightest blow will damage these bumpers, and they are almost impossible to repair. New ones must be installed at great cost to the owner or his insurance company.

They do not protect the car or its occupants, as there is not enough strength in these bumpers to withstand even minor accidents. When an accident occurs, the bumper is deformed, and the automobile body is also deformed.

Mostly, automobile bumpers today are for appearances only. Most manufacturers are ready to admit this and are making them lighter, and more decorative each year. They are being attached directly to the body itself, so there cannot possibly be any protection.

Reinforced polyester bumpers would be ideal. They could match the body in color, or they could be chrome or any contrasting color desired. They would be much more resistant to damage from minor accidents in that they would not dent, bend, or deform. They would recover instantly from minor impacts with no ill effects.

A compound such as that described for automobile bodies could be used, with much higher reinforcing content.

The best process for manufacturing automobile bumpers on a large scale would be compression-molding. In this manner, the polypropylene fiber could be as high as 60 to 65% of the finished part. Very high strengths may be obtained in this way, without sacrificing the ability to recover from blows.

A car and its occupants could have much more protection at the time of accident, as the "give" of the bumper would provide a kind of cushioning effect. Both car and occupant could survive more of the minor accidents with far less damages and injuries.

Since the production of automobiles is a highly automated, large-scale process, the production of bodies, bumpers, and other component parts must be likewise.

The processes that were used to produce the first few polyester bodies would not be feasible for such production. This was the major reason why the automobile manufacturers decided against the use of these materials. They did not lend themselves to mass production as well as light sheet metal. The metal parts could be formed very rapidly by draw dies or drop-hammer dies, either reinforced plastic or cast iron. Since metal cleaning, priming, and coating were later operations, they did not interfere with the fast production schedules required.

In order to become attractive to the automobile industry, these parts will have to be manufactured as fast as the metal parts. They will have to cost no more than the metal parts, plus the metal treatment, priming, and coating. This should not be a major problem with today's knowledge, equipment, and materials.

Recently two companies developed completely automated devices for cutting, handling, and placing reinforcing materials in the dies, which has long been a major cost of compression-molding these parts. With this breakthrough, completely automated production lines may be set up, whereby neither materials nor finished parts are touched by human hands. Labor costs are cut tremendously, and cycle times are reduced considerably.

There are several processes by which automobile body parts can be manufactured, but it is doubtful if any of them can produce them as economically and as fast as compression-molding. The cost will be in direct relation to the speed of the process and will be correspondingly lower as production increases.

The dies for the production of automobile parts will be very expensive but should be amortized very rapidly during the year in which they are first used. Possibly a few parts would be unchanged from one year to the next, so in some cases the same dies could be used for two years or more.

An automobile body can be produced completely in 1 min if there is a production line for each part. Counting the bumper, firewall, and instrument panel, there would be approximately 14 parts per body. This would necessitate 14 hydraulic presses and 14 sets of dies, with all the other auxiliary equipment for these presses.

With the proper equipment and materials, there is no problem to setting a cycle time of 1 min per part, which includes gel coat, loading the die with reinforcing material and resin compound, curing, and demolding the finished part.

Such a plant would be a very large investment to the automobile manufacturer or to his supplier of body parts, but it would not be too much greater than the total investment required for a plant to manufacture metal parts plus all the subsequent equipment needed for metal preparation and coating operations.

The actual assembly of an automobile with polyester parts would be less expensive as to labor than with metal parts because many of the metal parts must be hand fitted. With the polyester parts manufactured in this manner, each part would be precisely its size and shape and would need no fitting, grinding, filing or welding of any kind.

A changeover from present sheet-metal body parts to polyester parts would require that the plants be completely retooled and refitted. The presses and equipment now used in the manufacture of metal parts would not be suitable. The expense would, of course, be great but could be amortized in a very short time.

The cost of the finished automobile with polyester parts should be approximately the same as with metal parts. An individual part will cost more, but it will be a finished part and will eliminate all the cost for labor, equipment, and materials involved in the finishing processes required for metal parts.

With these reinforced polyester bodies, each automobile will be better built. The bodies will be considerably lighter than metal bodies, even though the thickness will be greater. Repairs, paint touch-ups, and body damage will be reduced.

This is a very large application for these materials. The number of automobiles built in this country each year make the market well worth going after.

Aircraft Component Parts

Reinforced polyesters have been used for a number of years in aircraft for certain component parts of the wings and fuselage. A number of aircraft have reinforced polyester fuel tanks and oil reservoirs.

The aluminum alloys used for the majority of structural parts and coverings for aircraft have some disadvantages. Stress cracking of critical structural members have been responsible for a large number of crashes. These alloys will not withstand the constant flexural stresses to which they are subjected, and many aircraft have been called in for reinforcing and replacing of parts.

Tests on reinforced polyester resins have been the subject of considerable controversy among aeronautical engineers. There are a great number of methods of testing these materials, and each method gives very different values. In some tests, the materials show excellent results, and in others very poor results. A few recent changes in ASTM specifications for testing materials have shown more applicable testing methods for these products that are much closer to the actual environmental stresses to which they would be subjected in use in aircraft.

The results of these tests have shown great promise for certain reinforced polyester compounds for use in structural members and wing and body parts for large aircraft. The best results of the tests are for resins with a modulus in the range of 700,000 psi rather than for higher-modulus resins. When materials with a modulus above 800,000 psi are tested, the results on constant flexing are not good with any of the resins tested so far.

Using resins which will test out at a modulus of 700,000 psi without reinforcing materials, and compounding these into a finished product with 55 to 60% glass fiber gives a material with an end modulus of approximately 950,000 psi. It has excellent tensile strength, flexural strength, and does not reach a point where it is brittle until it reaches —40°F.

All the best results so far have been obtained with resins based on isophthalic acid. Tests are continuing in the laboratories of several major aircraft manufacturers, the United States Air Force, and the United States Navy. A lot of work is being done in cooperation with all concerned and with the help and blessings of the Civil Aeronautics Board.

It is hoped that these materials may be improved to a point where they may be used on supersonic aircraft; however, to date, their heat-distortion point has been too low for use on anything but subsonic aircraft. Work is now progressing into resins with a high percentage of trimellitic and HET acids in order to try to raise the heat-distortion point. The resins manufactured so far with high percentages of these acids have been too brittle, and so to overcome this they are being combined with other saturated acids.

These reinforced polyester parts compare extremely well with the aluminum alloys in strength-to-weight ratios. They will not entirely replace these alloys for use in aircraft, but they will be used for many sections of the wing and fuselage assemblies, including many critical structural members.

Improvements are being made in these materials constantly, and the time will come in the near future when at least 75% of the materials used in aircraft will be reinforced polyesters.

While this market is not as large as the one presented by the automotive industry, it is well worth cultivating.

Furniture: Office, Household, and Outdoor

The furniture industry presents a huge market for polyester products. Polyester is particularly suitable for school, office, household, and exterior furniture.

For a period of 10 years, reinforced polyesters have been used extensively in theater and school seats. Some office and household furniture has been manufactured from these materials, but it has not found a very enthusiastic market. This may be attributed mainly to the lack of imagination in the design of most of this furniture. For the most part, it does not have the eye appeal so necessary in this type of furniture.

In school furniture, there is no great need for eye appeal; however, present-day designs can certainly be improved, not only in looks, but also in comfort. Besides the well-known chair with a small writing surface on one arm, desks with attached chairs are entirely possible to design in polyesters. Chairs can be much more comfortable than the present designs, and the small writing arm can be much larger so the student will have more working space. These arms can be made to fold down, completely out of the way, when not in use.

Theater chairs, auditorium seats, and many other kinds of seats that are upholstered or bare are most suitable for these materials. Present designs leave a lot to be desired for maximum comfort. There is much room for improvement in the designs used in stadium seats where, because of outdoor exposure, they cannot be upholstered. The great majority of these seats are very uncomfortable, whether made of wood or reinforced polyester. In too many cases where polyester has been used, poor choices of resins and pigments have caused them to crack, fade, and deteriorate rapidly.

In patio furniture, polyester compounds have been used considerably, but here, again, there is far too little imagination in design and often poor formulation.

There is no reason for a chair to be straight and uncomfortable. It may be very light in weight and simple in design but still very comfortable.

Complete sets of outdoor furniture can be manufactured in these materials, including tables, swings, and replicas of the expensive wrought-iron furniture. Wrought-iron sets are extremely heavy and very expensive. These can be duplicated to the last detail in polyester-resin compounds.

Reinforced polyester is a natural material for use in office and household furniture. The large majority of the chairs and sofas for these locations are upholstered, usually with wood frames. Polyester offers a material that can completely change these basic designs and make them more attractive and at the same time more comfortable. Tables, cabinets, lounge chairs, desks, and almost every piece of furniture that goes into a home or office can be manufactured from polyesters most economically.

The only advantage of wood over the polyester compound is the fact that furniture can be custom-designed, with only one or two sets made of that design. Reinforced polyester cannot be handled in this fashion.

Very little furniture is custom-designed and built. The great majority is produced in thousands of sets of one design by large manufacturers who have assembly lines quite similar to those of automobile manufacturers. Large production lines such as these lend themselves to the production of these items with polyesters. Since, for the most part, the individual component parts are small, compression-molding is the most economical method of production. The largest portion of the investment would be for the purchase of the matched metal dies. When the cost of the dies is divided into thousands of sets of furniture, the die cost per piece is extremely low.

Polyester furnishings will be much lighter in weight than either wood- or steel-frame furniture. They will be strong and will take much abuse in handling and moving. The cost should be very nearly the same as present furniture, and may very well be lower.

Other methods of manufacturing furniture may be considered in addition to compression-molding. If reinforcing fabric is considered a necessity in any design, then compression-molding will be the most economical for large-scale production. If the design of the furniture will permit the use of polyester compounds, together with chopped fiber, then injection-molding by all means should be considered.

Much greater strengths may be obtained by using reinforcing fabrics instead of chopped glass, but there are many applications in furniture where the chopped-glass compound will be quite adequate. In many instances, the chopped glass may be combined with low-cost fillers such as wood flour and china clay.

All types of furniture manufactured from polyester resins will open up a very large market that has been almost untouched so far. It will be the responsibility of furniture designers to put these materials to good use through the design of new types of furniture that are attractive, comfortable, and within the price range of present wood furniture.

Appliances: Refrigerators, Washing Machines, Hair Dryers, and Radio and Television Cabinets

Almost all household appliances today are made principally of metals of one kind or another. In most cases, these have to be painted, chrome-plated, or otherwise finished after manufacture.

Some plastics have been used successfully in appliances. Washing-machine impellers, dishwashing-machine impellers, and the covers of some of the smaller appliances have employed such plastics as highly filled phenolics, melamines, and, to some extent, ureas. These have given good service, but the use of the organic polymers in these appliances has not grown as it should. In recent years, some of the newer plastics have been used in small appliances, but no manufacturer seems to want to take the first steps in using plastics to make the larger appliances.

Refrigerators, washing machines, dishwashing machines, television cabinets, and the large appliances are made from sheet steel. They are stamped out with draw dies made of either cast iron or reinforced plastic. They must be trimmed, hand-worked, treated, and two or more coats of coating material must be applied. This is a long and expensive process, even though the basic material is relatively inexpensive. Paint chips off, cabinets rust, and the appliance looks old in a relatively short time.

Major appliances such as these, with all cabinet parts, covers, doors, and exposed parts, should be manufactured from a polyester compound. These appliances present forms that lend themselves to either compression-molding or injection-molding techniques.

No great strength is needed in these applications, so there is no need for reinforcing fabrics. The compounds to be processed can include polyester resin, highly filled with china clay, chopped glass or synthetic fiber, and good nonfading pigments.

Appliances manufactured with this material will be no more expensive than present appliances. The difference in the cost of the basic metal is more than made up by the expenses involved in the subsequent processes necessary to finish the article.

The finished product will be more durable than a metal counterpart in that the pigmentation will occur throughout the piece and scratches, blows, and other damages will not show. An article made with this material cannot oxidize or stain with ordinary household use.

In major appliances such as these, styles do not change much from year to year. Each model is about the same as the last. Perhaps there is a slight difference in chrome trim, handles, hinges, and decorations, but the basic design seldom changes. This type of production is ideal for polyesters, where expensive dies are required. The same sets of dies may be used year after year until the basic design changes. When the cost of the dies is amortized over many thousands of parts, this cost is negligible.

For parts that will need a gel coat, compression-molding is usually the least expensive method for production; for parts that do not require a gel coat, injection-molding in most cases will prove the most efficient and economical production method. However, this is not always the case, because the size of the parts, wall thickness, and other factors must be considered. In very thin-walled parts, compression-molding as a rule will turn out fewer reject parts.

All possible factors must be studied, and a process should be decided upon that will best suit the purposes of the manufacturer and the particular products.

The Food and Beverage Field

In these fields, plastics have been used on a wide scale for a number of years in packaging meats, vegetables, and other food items. In these applications, polyesters are not suitable. The packaging of such items requires a thermoplastic that may be heat-sealed or used in bubble-packaging that is now so popular in many food items. Other thermoplastics are being used in milk cartons, both returnable and nonreturnable. Thermoplastics have many properties that make them most suitable in such applications.

In recent years, polypropylene has been used in manufacturing cases for beer and soft drinks. However, they have not made much progress in the market because of their high cost. Polypropylene and other thermoplastics have the great disadvantage that they cannot take appreciable amounts of fillers. Therefore, in any application for which thermoplastics are used, the article must be at least 75% polymer (by weight). This makes for high costs and makes the product very noncompetitive on the market.

In applications such as cases for soft drinks and beer, wooden cases have been the only material used, apart from some cardboard cartons. They are unsightly and their durability is very limited. They must be painted and printed.

Polyester compounds would be most suitable for such applications. The market for this article includes millions of individual cases per year of almost all the same size and shape. Colors will vary from product to product. Printed matter will vary, but the basic case remains the same for literally hundreds of products from dozens of companies. This article is unusual. There are few manufactured items that are used in such quantities that do not change. Here, with one production line, a product may be manufactured from the same basic dies for dozens of customers.

This application is most suitable for either compression-molding or injection-molding. The same dies are used at all times. Insert plates will be installed along the sides of the dies to imprint the brand names and other printed matter. These inserts will be interchangeable and can be made up for each individual company. The raised or inset lettering can easily be made a contrasting color if desired.

For such an application, a very low-cost compound would be used. The polyester resin would be a resilient orthophthalic and would cost about 24 cents per lb. The rest of the formulation would be clay and some chopped fiber. A low-cost fiber such as sisal would be adequate for such an application.

These cases may be manufactured at a plant cost of under $2.00 each. They will be extremely durable and will look attractive in any store. They will be a complement to any product shipped in them. This is a market that must not be overlooked by the polyester industry. The volume of this product makes it a most attractive item for any manufacturing plant.

There are a large number of applications in the food and beverage industries where the polyesters can be put to good use. Small portable ice chests, used for picnics and camping, can be very economically manufactured from polyester compounds. These can be manufactured easily in two shells—one slightly larger than the other—and the void filled with foamed material for insulation. Even the foam may be polyester, as described in Chaps. 4 and 6. These chests will be much stronger and more durable than either the metal or polystyrene chests now so widely used.

Such ice chests are a very large production item, as many millions are sold each year. Often, manufacturers of soft drinks or beer partially subsidize these items and offer them with brand names and advertising printed on the sides. So in many cases, these ice chests would be sold directly to the soft drink and beer companies, along with the cases discussed earlier.

At one time or another, several research people have tried to blow-mold polyester and other thermosetting resins. Very little work has been done along these lines, but there is no reason why it cannot be done, with proper equipment, and proper techniques. Polyester would be the only thermosetting resin that could be processed in this manner because of its fast gel and cure times.

Polyesters, properly formulated, are quite suitable for use in food and beverage packaging. The Food and Drug Administration has approved a number of applications where these materials must come in direct contact with food and beverages.

If a method were perfected whereby polyesters could be efficiently blow-molded, they could very well compete with glass bottles in soft drink use, beer bottling, and even perhaps in milk packaging. Because of the strength and resilience of polyesters, the bottles would be much more resistant to breakage than glass. The weight of a polyester bottle would be less than half that of a glass bottle, reducing shipping costs correspondingly. Polyester bottles can easily be tinted to any color for better appearance or for the protection of the contents of the bottles. Possibly polyesters could also be used in bottles for other products, such as fruit juices and syrups.

Blow-molding equipment has been highly perfected for vinyls, polyethylene, polypropylene, and other thermoplastics. Through slight modification of this equipment, such as changing the heat and cold cycles to a single heat cycle, there is no reason why this same equipment could not be used in polyesters. This equipment is highly automated. Often one man can oversee the operation of two or more machines. One machine is capable of producing up to 1,000 bottles per hr. A small amount of calculation will show this market to be very large indeed and worth investigating.

Consumer Goods: Decorator Items, Plaques, Lamps, and Trays

Such normal household items as floor lamps, table lamps, serving trays, and many others of these types of products may be the basis of very profitable manufacturing operations. Such decorative items as vases and plaques are smaller in volume but still may be manufactured and sold in quite substantial quantities.

Some of these items could be manufactured on a small scale, with relatively low investments. Small production could be done with flexible urethane or silicone-rubber molds. These molds would be particularly suitable where custom-designed products would be sold to a relatively small number of customers. The most intricate patterns and designs may be copied to the last fine detail with these types of molds.

Items that would be desirable to produce on a large scale could be injection-molded or compression-molded. Even casting can be an efficient method of producing many such articles when sufficient molds are used and production-line procedures are followed.

Two or three persons working in a small plant can make a profitable business by manufacturing such items for a limited market. There is always a demand for new designs in lamps, vases, plaques, and such household items. Good design will find a market, and if the costs of these items are high because of limited production, they still can be sold because in these articles price is usually governed by the simplicity or complicity of the design.

The Tooling Industry: Draw Dies, Vacuum Dies, and Drop-hammer Dies

This is a relatively new field for plastics. In past years, cast iron and steel were the principal materials used in tooling for forming other metals and plastics.

Draw dies, drop-hammer dies, vacuum dies, stretch dies, and many tools for the working of metals and thermoplastics may be made from highly filled polyester resins.

Metal body parts for automobiles and equipment are formed, for the most part, today with reinforced thermosetting plastic dies. Very large aircraft parts are also formed with these materials. Moreover, cabinets for washing machines, refrigerators, television sets, and many other metal parts are formed with these dies.

Thermoplastics are very often formed in such dies. Almost every type of shaping die can be manufactured from polyester resins, including the complex vacuum-forming dies.

These dies must be classed as temporary tooling. They are limited as to the number of formed parts they can turn out. Cast-iron and steel dies have an almost unlimited useful life but are much more expensive to make. The setting up of a model or prototype is the most expensive part of building these polyester dies. Once this prototype is set up, dozens of dies may be made from it. Dies are so fast and easy to build that the cost per set of dies is very low. Whatever the forming operation, a comparison between the metal and plastic forming tools must be made on the basis of several factors, as well as the complexity of the part to be formed: (1) If the tool is to be used in forming metals, polyester dies are most suitable for rather simple shapes where there will be much less wear and tear than in forming complex shapes. (2) The size of the formed parts—the larger the part to be formed, the more economical the polyester dies become in comparison to the metal dies. (3) The number of parts to be formed from the dies—in smaller parts, if over 5,000 parts are to be formed, the metal dies will usually be most economical.

In forming plastics, where the wear and tear on the dies are much less, polyester dies usually prove most economical regardless of the number of parts to be formed.

There are many methods of making polyester tools. Often, the highly reinforced polyester is merely used to face worn metal tools, that is, to renew the surface so that the tool can continue to be used. In other cases, the entire tool is built up from the polyester compound. In certain tools, often the face of the tool is a rather light metal, while the rest of the tool is polyester. The actual construction of the die depends greatly on its end use, the material which it will be forming, and the temperatures that may be involved in the forming.

In die making, the polyester resin forms a very small part of the compound, sometimes as little as 5% (by weight). The resin is used mostly as a binder for the fillers and aggregates. Sometimes a very heavy tool is desirable. In this case the majority of the compound will be made up of steel slag, steel filings, and sometimes steel shot, and even lead shot.

When very light tools are desirable, the face of the die will be polyester, highly reinforced with glass fiber and fabric, and backed up with either a foamed or honeycomb material for rigidity.

Many times, temporary tooling (tooling which will be used only a few times) will be made up with a very thin reinforced polyester face, and the rest of the tooling will be concrete, or molding plaster.

However the tool is to be made, and for the shaping of any material, the important thing is to design the tool so it can do the best job possible. A few factors which are of importance include: (1) Tolerances—since the polyester tool will have a shrinkage in approximate proportion to the percentage of resin in the compound, allowances must be made when the dimensional tolerances are critical. (2) Necessary strength— the tool must be made to withstand any stress exerted on it, whether flexural, compression, or impact.

The smoother the surface of the die, the better it will do the job and the better the parts formed. The tougher and more abrasion resistant the surface, the longer the polyester die will last. The die must be made with a resin that will withstand the temperatures to which it will be subjected. The fillers chosen for use in the die facing will determine to a large extent the durability of the die.

It is often advisable to apply a very thin coating over the surface of the model or prototype to assure a very smooth, slick surface. In this case, the gel coat should not be more than 2 to 3 mils in thickness, since the greater part of this will be worn off in the initial few uses of the die.

A good facing formulation for the die will be the following:

1. Polyester resin-monomer (carefully chosen).................. 15.00 lb
2. Promoter (mix before adding catalyst)...................... 0.03
3. Catalyst... 0.15
4. Aluminum oxide or boron carbide, 300 mesh................. 30.00
5. Aluminum oxide or boron carbide, 100 mesh................. 50.00
6. Carbon black, or acetylene black.......................... 5.00
7. Silica, 30–50 mesh.. 50.00
                                                            ———————
                                                            150.18 lb

This compound should be applied over the thin gel coat to a thickness of 3/16 to 1/4 in. and rolled or troweled out well to assure good compaction. A layer of glass fabric is layed out over this and rolled into the surface as much as possible. The glass fabric will not be wet out but merely partially imbedded into the compound. This is allowed to gel, and the following compound is placed over the facing material:

1. Polyester resin-monomer (same as above).................. 25.00 lb
2. Promoter.. 0.05
3. Catalyst.. 0.25
4. Crushed quartz, No. 00.................................. 75.00
5. Silica, 100 mesh.. 25.00
6. Silica, 200 mesh.. 10.00
7. Chopped glass fiber..................................... 10.00
                                                            ———————
                                                            145.30 lb

This compound is placed over the facing material and rolled and troweled out well to force the thorough wetting-out of the glass fabric below, and to force out all air from the compound.

The thickness can be whatever is necessary for rigidity, strength, and weight. This last compound can also be topped off with a layer of glass fabric if desired, and additional layers of glass fabric may be added.

If very thick castings are to be made over the facing material, then the fillers and aggregates may be much larger.

If the die is very large, it will have to be structurally reinforced with steel-, aluminum-, or glass-reinforced polyester members, or with rigid polyester foam if weight is critical and the stresses in use will permit it.

Many variations of the polyester mixes given can be used in the making of tooling. The important factor is to have a good, abrasive-resistant facing compound on the working face of the die. The aluminum oxides, boron carbides, and caborundum are excellent for this purpose. Tungsten carbide does not bond well to polyester resins as a rule.

On a tool facing such as this, normal lubricants used in metal forming can be used, and the tool will last for a very long time. Such a die face may be repaired and reworked when it is badly worn; however, usually it is better to make another new tool from the model or prototype because in the repairing of a die some of the perfection of the face is always lost.

Such dies may be used in metal forming or in thermoforming plastics. With the plastics, there is much less need for abrasion resistance of the face of the die. Less expensive fillers may be used in these applications.

Vacuum-forming of the thermoplastics is a very large segment of the plastics business. Many articles are formed from the vinyl plastics, polyethylene, polypropylene, and many other thermoplastic sheet materials by vacuum-forming. Cast-iron or steel vacuum dies are very expensive because of the multitude of tiny air ducts that must be either cast or drilled into the tool.

Vacuum-forming tools may be cast very inexpensively with polyester resins. A model or prototype is set up, and a form is built around it. A compound of polyester and fillers is selected of such sizing that there will be natural voids throughout the finished casting. These voids form the air ducts for the vacuum.

A good formulation for small vacuum dies is the following:

1. Polyester resin-monomers	10.00 lb
2. Promoter	0.02
3. Catalyst	0.12
4. Silica, 30–50 mesh	110.00
	120.14 lb

A mix such as this will be literally filled with tiny voids or air ducts. There is sufficient polyester resin to firmly bond the grains together, but there are no fine filler particles to fill the tiny voids between the larger particles. The compound will be approximately 20% voids when cured.

The mix is poured into the form around the model and pressed into place with a trowel. It must not be vibrated or troweled but merely pressed into place tightly. If the part being made is deep, then the compound must be pressed into place in layers of 3 to 4 in. to avoid large voids that could affect the strength of the tool.

When cured, the part is removed from the model, and the surface next to the model will be smooth but filled with tiny pores. Proper vacuum fittings are bonded to the tool, and the entire surface, except the face, is completely sealed with a coating of very thixotropic polyester. The thixotropy is to keep the resin from running down into the pores and perhaps sealing off a number of the air ducts. Polyester resin-monomer, promoter, and catalyst are mixed into about 5% colloidal silica and about 15% china clay. This will give a good mix for sealing the exterior of the dies.

In small vacuum tools, one vacuum fitting is sufficient, but in larger tooling, multiple vacuum fittings are required so the amount of vacuum will be the same over the entire surface of the working face of the tool. In general, one fitting is sufficient for a working surface of up to 200 to 250 sq in.

Such tools as these are most economical to make and may be utilized in almost every application calling for vacuum tools. If the model or prototype is set up properly, hundreds of tools may be made from the one model.

The same general system may be used in making very large vacuum tools. However, the larger the tool, the more strength will be required. Since this compound is rather weak in mechanical properties because of the percentage of voids, larger tooling will have to be reinforced. This may be accomplished in many ways. For medium-sized tools that must be round or rectangular, such as those for thermoforming flower-pots or planter pots, a wire mesh is excellent. It can be placed into the form around the model, and the compound placed around the mesh. For tools that are long and narrow, such as might be used to thermoform plastic boxes for long-stem roses, small bars of reinforcing steel may be placed into the compound to give it the necessary strength.

Besides tooling for forming metals and plastics, this type of tooling is ideal for manufacturing paper and papier-mâché products.

Most paper and papier-mâché products are manufactured by the suction of a liquid slurry, containing the fiber, onto a metal wire screen of some kind. When the proper amount of fiber has been deposited onto the screen, it is blown off, dried, and becomes a finished product. Minnow buckets, flowerpots, ceiling tile, and many other products are manufactured by this general method.

These fibrous slurries are often most corrosive, so only copper and stainless wire is usually utilized for these tools. These wire tools are very expensive because most of the work is done by hand fabrication, soldering, etc. They have a limited working life and must frequently be repaired. The important factor in tooling for the vacuum-slurry processes is that the ducts through the tool are designed so as not to clog. This is perhaps the most difficult part of slurry-forming products. The tools clog up and must be cleaned out, which impedes production.

Tooling of this type may be made, similar to the above vacuum-forming tools, with polyester resins and properly sized fillers or aggregates. Careful selection of the grains of filler material in a size that will leave the proper-sized ducts is most important. A study of the fiber being used in the process must be made to determine the sizing of the smallest and the largest fibers. The finer the fiber, the smaller the ducts or voids in the tool.

When compounded in this manner, the size of each duct or pore in the compound will be approximately 25% the size of the granular materials. Thus, if the filler were a granular silica sand of 20-mesh size, the pores would be approximately 80-mesh size or $\frac{1}{80}$ in. each. By careful selection of grain size, these tools can be made almost clogproof.

These polyester tools will be much more economical and durable than normal wire tools. The corrosive elements in the slurries will not affect either the polyester or the silicas used as fillers. They will be easy to clean as necessary. A blast of compressed air will free them of any fiber that becomes entrapped in the pores.

The tooling market is, to a large extent, a proprietary market. That is to say, for the most part the industry which uses these types of tools makes most of its own tooling. (Some companies contract this out, but this is the exception rather than the rule.) For this reason, the market may not seem at first glance to be very large. However, this is far from true. This type of tooling has a very large market in the metals-forming, thermoplastics, and paper industries.

Companies make their own tooling because there are so few plants set up to custom-make tooling of this type for the market. A very large industry could be formed to supply the other industries with the tooling so necessary for their plants. It could do a very large volume of business if located near a group of industries who utilize this type of tooling. For the most part, companies would be very glad to leave the tool-making business and contract this process to others.

The Coatings Field: Paint and Corrosion Control

Besides being used in the heavy industrial and marine coatings discussed in Chap. 7, polyester resins can be utilized in many more prevalent coatings materials. House paints, both interior and exterior, clear finishes for natural wood-grain paneling, furniture finishes, and baked coatings of all kinds for appliances, metal office furniture, and almost every application where such coatings are used today.

Polyesters can be manufactured that will cure in the presence of air without the waxes and paraffins of a few years ago. This makes them most suitable for every coating application where good appearance, good durability, and resistance to the elements are desirable.

These coatings can be formulated from polyester resins in high-gloss, semigloss, or matte finishes. Polyesters can replace many of the coatings polymers used today.

Portable Buildings: House Trailers, Campers, Portable Offices

Portable housing has become a very large industry in this country. House trailers have been used by a large segment of our population for many years. Recently small weekend campers have acquired a large market. Portable office buildings are used for construction sites. Portable schoolrooms are used extensively as temporary classrooms in our crowded schools. Complete homes of three and four rooms are premanufactured, carried out to the customer's property, and set up ready to be moved into in a matter of hours.

In house trailers and campers, considerable reinforced polyester sheet material is now used. It is used in much the same fashion that plywood, sheet aluminum, or other materials would be used. It is fastened or bonded together to form the shell over the frame members and is often used both on the interiors and exteriors of these units, with a foamed urethane or polystyrene in between for insulation.

In order for polyester compounds to realize their full potential in such applications, processes must be developed whereby these units may be entirely manufactured in the plant from raw materials, rather than be fabricated from sheet and panel materials.

Processes, equipment, and techniques must be developed whereby these units may be laid up with fast, efficient, high-volume glass-chopper and resin guns over molds. This will make a much stronger unit, and it will never be bothered with leaks or some of the other problems which beset the fabricated units. In this way, an integral unit can be achieved, with no seams or joints in the shells. Proper spaces and openings can be left in the walls for doors, windows, air-conditioning units, etc.

As with most processes of this nature, the molds present the one large problem. Here is an application where hundreds of units will be produced exactly the same, whether they be small campers or large house trailers. With one set of molds, one unit could be produced per day. Where several sizes are manufactured, there would have to be one set of molds for each size and model.

Recently much progress has been made with inflatable molds. These have been used with good success in the manufacture of tanks and vessels of considerable sizes.

A set of molds would consist of three basic parts: a plain flat mold for the lay-up of the floor; an inflatable mold for the lay-up of the interior shell; and a fixed metal mold for the lay-up of the exterior shell.

The floor could be laid up first, and the inflatable mold would be set in place on this. The interior shell would be laid up over the bag, adhering to the floor section at the same time so the floor and the interior shell would be all in one seamless part. At the same time this is being done, the compound would be applied to the interior of the female or exterior shell mold. Upon curing, the exterior shell would be placed over the interior shell and the space between filled with polyester foam, which would completely bond the two shells and the floor into one integral, seamless unit.

Equipment will have to be developed which will deposit large volumes of resin and chopped glass per minute to reduce labor costs and the total time required to finish each unit. This equipment can be developed along the same lines as present polyester-fiberglass guns. It will just have to be larger. The guns will have to be supported on a small boom, quite like a small crane, and the operator would position it by either manual or power controls.

Tooling up for such a process will be costly; equipment and molds will constitute a major investment. However, in the production of such units on a large scale, the investment will be easily amortized. The cost per finished trailer can possibly be reduced to half of present costs. Quality will be much better, and the unit will be stronger and more durable.

All types of portable units may be manufactured in this fashion, regardless of size. Complete houses with dividing partitions can be made with such a process. Temporary classrooms, portable offices, and many other such applications can be made from polyester compounds.

Luggage: Trunks, Suitcases, and Bags

A few manufacturers of luggage items have done some work with reinforced polyesters. The few pieces manufactured were more or less prototypes to see how the market would receive them. Thus far, these pieces have been less than successful on the market because they have been priced too high. The few pieces manufactured were made up in very small quantities, hence were not made on a high-production basis, which accounts for the high price of these articles.

The reception to the articles themselves was most enthusiastic. They were light in weight, very good in appearance, and very strong. They would withstand a large amount of punishment without damage.

These items of luggage can be manufactured and placed on the market at prices competitive with even the lowest-cost luggage. However, like most products manufactured with polyester compounds, they will have to be produced on a large scale with proper production-line methods, equipment, and tooling.

This is an item where thousands of one particular piece can be produced alike. A large luggage manufacturer may offer many shapes and sizes, but there are thousands of each produced.

Compression-molding would probably offer the most advantages in this type of production, where precision of each part would be of importance. The thin walls of such a product also lend themselves better to this process than to any other process.

Most pieces of luggage would consist of two parts. In some cases the two parts would be exactly alike and could be manufactured in the same set of dies, but in other articles the two parts would be different and would require two separate sets of dies.

The largest part of the investment would be in the dies if the assortment of luggage were to offer many styles and sizes. The rest of the equipment, such as presses and auxiliary equipment, would depend on the total production per day required.

A production line such as this could manufacture many pieces of luggage per day. One press with two pair of dies installed—two male and two female—can produce easily 400 pieces of luggage per 8-hr shift.

The installation of hinges, locks, and other accessories would be done right in the same production line, probably on a conveyor system between presses and packaging sectors. Much of the installation of the accessories can be done automatically. Drilling, fastening, and other operations of this nature are reasonably inexpensive with the equipment available today.

A large-scale production of this type is the only way this luggage can ever be competitive on the market. It cannot be done by hand-lay-up methods or in a small way and be marketed in competition with conventional luggage.

Street and Highway Signs and Signals

In driving down our streets, highways, and freeways today, we are beset by a large number of signs on every side. In high-speed traffic, the public must be informed of every intersection, turn-out, speed limit, and highway number.

The amount of these signs installed each year is staggering. A few states have tried plastics for these signs, but for the most part they are either painted or porcelanized metal. The porcelain signs are good and very durable, but they are very expensive. The painted-metal signs require constant maintenance, so in a few years have cost the taxpayer as much as the porcelainized signs.

The size of this market warrants the attention of any manufacturer of polyester products, especially one who is looking for new manufacturing opportunities. In each state, the total cost of such signs varies widely, but in any one state alone, the cost will be several million dollars per year.

Conditions and signs change somewhat in each state, but on an average, there are about 20 basic designs, of which about 10 are usually the same size, with different markings or lettering. The other 10 or so will usually be the same size, with different colors, and the lettering and numbering will change from sign to sign. The former are the curve signals, directional signals, arrows, and speed-limit signs. The latter are the large signs depicting the highway numbers, traffic-lane instructions, etc.

With about 10 fixed sets of dies and about another 10 sets of dies with interchangeable inserts, the entire market for highway signs can be filled by polyester compounds.

The dies can be designed so that the lettering may be raised, even with the surface, or indented. The lettering and numbers may be plain colors, or they may be luminescent.

These signs may be manufactured in a number of ways. For large-scale production, probably compression-molding would be most efficient and produce the parts at lower costs. In small production, until the market were fully established, it may be wise to manufacture in open molds and lay the signs up with the resin and glass-chopper guns available.

For small production, the lettering, numbers, and arrows could be precast separately. The molds would be gel-coated, the numbers, etc., laid into the gel coat, and the rest of the sign built up with the gun. For a production of 40 to 50 signs per day, this method would be very efficient. Costs would be somewhat higher than a large-scale production by compression-molding, but very probably would be quite in line with the present costs of such signs.

The differential in costs between this method and compression-molding is largely owing to labor costs and to the fact that with these lay-up guns no low-cost fillers can be used. In compression-molding, the compound used would be of much lower cost, consisting of silicas, clay, chopped fiber and resin.

This is a very large market for polyester products. Every state has a need for these signs. Many of the signs are of the same type and design, and so could be manufactured and shipped all over the nation. Sign-making could become a very large polyester industry.

The Container Field

A very large part of our economy is packaged in some kind of a container. There are tinned and aluminum cans of all sizes and all types of plastic containers, such as garbage cans, clothes hampers, wastebaskets, chemical containers for shipping all types of materials, and hundreds of others.

Everything from tobacco to paint is packaged in tinned cans. Foodstuffs and beverages are being packaged in aluminum cans. Motor oil, transmission fluids, and all such products are packaged in some type of can.

There are many types of containers that must be hermetically sealed; others use friction or pressure lids; and still others just use close-fitting tops. Many types of chemical containers have bolt-on closures and even locked types of closures.

Many types of these containers may be manufactured with polyester compounds. The hermetically sealed containers would be the most difficult to manufacture with these compounds because they would present some problems in the final sealing phase.

Containers such as garbage cans, wastebaskets, laundry hampers, etc., could be manufactured very easily by compression-molding. The lid and container would be manufactured separately in separate dies.

These products can compete very well on the market with the usual metal or thermoplastic products because the material would be highly filled and the raw-material cost would be low.

Friction- and pressure-type containers could be manufactured with polyester compounds, but the rim at the top of the present design would present some production problems. The basic design could perhaps be changed so as to be processed more easily, but it is doubtful that polyesters could compete in price with the tinned steel cans in this particular application.

Larger drums, such as 5-, 15-, 30-, and 55-gal drums would be much easier to process with polyester compounds. These can be rotation-molded without too many problems. This application may very well be worth consideration.

Drums for the packaging of many chemicals present a real problem to manufacturers. Steel drums must often be coated inside with special chemical-resistant materials, and in many cases a polyethylene drum liner must be used. Drum coatings and liners are never completely satisfactory. Often either the coating or the polyethylene liner are damaged, and the chemical is exposed to the steel drum. In many instances this is a hazard to human beings and to other materials.

Polyester drums can withstand a great majority of these chemicals, and the market for such drums could be a large one. Processing methods and techniques can certainly be developed whereby they may be made by a number of methods.

All types of containers should be considered as a possible market for polyester products.

Swimming Pools

In Chap. 7 mention was made of coatings that could be manufactured for use in concrete swimming pools to seal and to beautify. However, *entire* swimming pools can be manufactured most profitably with polyester resins. These can be premanufactured in plant, transported to the site, buried, and ready for use in a matter of hours.

In a product such as this, only one side has to be good. The side that goes into the ground is of no importance as far as appearance is concerned. The interior of the pool must be beautiful and able to withstand chlorinated water and exposure to the sun and other elements of nature.

In applications of this nature, polyesters can be placed on the market at much lower costs than any known type of material.

A concrete swimming pool is very expensive, whether it be formed and poured concrete or the gunnite type of concrete. A concrete pool must be painted at regular intervals or must have ceramic tile placed in it.

Prefabricated metal pools have been tried but have been very unsuccessful. No matter how they were coated for protection, they would either rust from the outside or from the inside in time. Small pools have been manufactured in one piece with reinforced plastic materials, but the larger pools (20 × 40 ft) have been manufactured in sections and later joined together. These sectional pools have been quite unsatisfactory. In time they leak, and the designs are not very good.

For the manufacture of such pools in one piece, the only great expense would be one male mold for each size and type of pool to be manufactured. These molds could be laid up in light-gauge sheet metal with good fabricating work and would be entirely satisfactory. The sheet metal could be fastened over either a wood or metal framework for support.

Molds could be quite simple (such as the above) or they could be quite complicated. If a manufacturer wished to produce a pool with an authentic ceramic-tile appearance, this would present no problems, although it would be more expensive to build the molds. The molds would have to have slightly raised ribs on 4-in. centers to simulate the grout joints of ceramic tile. (Inflatable molds may also be used efficiently.) In production, the tops of these ribs would be first roller-coated with a thixotropic white polyester compound. The entire exterior of the male mold would be gel-coated, and then the walls would be built up with the resin-glass-chopper gun.

When removed from the mold, the interior of the pool would be identical to the interior of a ceramic-tile-lined pool. Colors could be chosen to match exactly those of ceramic tile, so the authenticity would be more complete.

For large objects such as this, again we are in dire need of larger, high-production resin-glass-chopper guns that will lay up to 50 lb or more per min of the combination. These can be furnished by present equipment manufacturers as soon as there is a market for them.

When large products such as these are contemplated, means must be provided into the design for lifting, handling, and hauling. These parts may be easily removed from the molds by compressed-air jets which are built into the mold. Strong rings or bars can be built into a central location for lifting and handling.

If a proper design is made, the wall thickness of these pools need not be more than $\frac{1}{8}$ in., with a lip or projection around the top of about $\frac{3}{4}$ in. or more for rigidity in handling and placing. A pool that is $20 \times 40 \times 10$ ft deep at one end and 4 ft deep at the other would weigh approximately 1,800 lb, and plant costs should not exceed $1,000. Calculating the earth removal, backfilling, profits, and all hauling, these pools could be sold to the customer for around $2,000. This figure compares well with over $3,500 for an unlined concrete pool, and at least $6,000 for a ceramic-lined pool of like dimensions.

Instead of having his yard torn up for weeks, the customer could have the pool installed and ready for use in only 1 or 2 days.

The transportation of objects of this size should not present any unsurmountable obstacle. Most cities allow such hauling at certain hours when traffic is at its lowest volume.

A very large industry could be built around this product. Any large city can provide a sufficient market for such a manufacturer. A well-made pool with good design can be sold, not only to homeowners, but to schools, clubs, and other organizations.

Mortuary Products: Caskets and Headstones

There is at least one manufacturer who has a very good market established for reinforced polyester caskets. His business is growing rapidly, and he has expanded several times in less than 5 years.

A product such as this may be manufactured by any of several methods. For good appearance on both sides, it should be compression-molded in matched metal dies. If good appearance on the outside is sufficient, it can be laid up with the glass-chopper-resin guns inside a single female mold. In this case, the product would not have a good appearance inside, so would have to be lined with cloth or other material.

The lids or tops can be manufactured in this same fashion. Provisions can be made for a tongue-and-groove fit between top and bottom, or a gasket arrangement can be made. A product made with this material will be far more resistant to the elements of the soil than any but the most expensive bronze caskets. This product will be able to compete with even the wooden caskets in price.

A manufacturer should not overlook the possibilities of a market of this size. A good product can be manufactured and shipped all over the country from a central location.

Cemetary headstones can provide a very large market for polyester products. These stones can be made exactly like natural granite or marble stones, complete with names, dates, and other lettering cast right into them.

For this market, there are many advantages to this type of headstone. The cost will be a small fraction of that for a natural headstone. The weight will be also a small fraction of the natural stone.

The choice of designs would have very little effect on the process to be used in manufacturing these stones. They would be cast in rather inexpensive double molds. The exterior mold would be designed with a good interior finish, and the male inner mold would be designed with a good outer finish. Plywood could be used for mold construction, with one side lined with highly polished, high-pressure laminate of the phenolic type.

The space between the molds could be ¾ in., so the headstone would have a wall thickness of this amount, with the interior entirely hollow.

When in place, no one would ever know the stone were hollow. It will appear to be a natural headstone.

The two molds would be slightly tapered boxes, one fitting inside the other, at a distance of ¾ in. The outside or female mold would be upside down on a vibrating table for the filling position.

Either metal or polyester letters, numbers, etc., with a contact type of adhesive on one side, would be properly positioned in the female mold, and the entire interior would be gel-coated.

The interior or male mold would then be positioned inside the female, and the following compound should be poured and vibrated into place until the mold is filled:

1. Polyester resin-monomers .... 15.00 lb
2. Promoter (mix before adding catalyst) 0.03
3. Catalyst 0.15
4. Crushed granite, No. 2 .... 80.00
5. Crushed quartz, No. 0 .... 25.00
6. Crushed granite, No. 00 .... 15.00
7. Silica, 100 mesh 10.00
8. Silica 200 mesh 5.00

$$\overline{} \quad 150.18 \text{ lb}$$

The above compound would be approximately the proper amount to make a headstone which is 24 in. high, 36 in. wide, and 6 in. thick, with a slight taper from top to bottom. The total material cost, purchased in relatively moderate quantities, would be $7.00.

When cured the molds would be blown off with compressed air through fittings near the bottoms of the molds. The metal or plastic letters would be removed, and the headstone would be finished.

With the above compound, the finished product will be an exact replica of a natural granite headstone. Only by close examination would a knowledgeable person know the difference.

Each headstone will be in fact a custom-made product, with the necessary lettering right in the material. The same process would be followed to make synthetic marble headstones. One of the formulas in Chap. 5 would be quite suitable for the marble headstones. These will look completely authentic, as will the synthetic granite.

Here is a product that is entirely suitable for a small manufacturer, with perhaps two or three employees. The investment can be rather small, yet 12 to 15 headstones can be produced during each working shift.

An inventory of mold designs may include as many as 20 in different sizes and shapes. Made of plywood and faced with phenolic laminate, they should not cost more than $30.00 per pair to build. A small mortar mixer of 3 cu ft capacity and a vibrating table will suffice as far as equipment is concerned. With a modest inventory of resin, catalysts and promoters, fillers and aggregates, the small industry can begin work.

While with this modest-investment production is definitely limited, the small industry may grow and can supply several nearby cities with these products. The small plant can later install an oven so that cures can be obtained very fast, and metal molds may be built. Such equipment as a fork lift, larger mixer, and liquids blender may be installed as the business grows.

With the same number of employees, the same small plant can produce up to five or six times as many headstones as soon as the oven and other equipment is installed.

There are few products in polyester compounds that may be produced with such a low starting investment. The market price will permit rather inefficient production processes to still compete very well in this particular product. This is a very profitable small industry in any major city.

Art: Sculpture, Murals, Mosaics, and Synthetic Stained Glass

Other small industries that may be started with very limited capital are art items, reproductions of sculpture, wall mosaics, and synthetic stained-glass windows for churches.

Since these products do not lend themselves to mass production and the market is somewhat limited, they are good examples of small industries that can be set up with perhaps two men and very limited equipment; they may grow as the market expands.

Almost any object made of almost any material may be copied exactly with polyester compounds. If a model is available, it can be borrowed, purchased, or perhaps rented to be used as a prototype. If no model is available a copy may be made in modeling plaster and used as a prototype from which to make molds.

Products of this type will almost always have to be made in flexible molds because of undercuts and the kinds of forms and shapes that will be encountered. The mold materials most suitable for limited production are the room-temperature-curing silicone elastomers and the polyurethane elastomers. By careful choice of polyester resins, up to 100 parts may be taken from a set of these temporary molds.

There is no space here for a discussion of the making of these flexible molds. Any good mold and die maker knows the process, and, in addition, the companies supplying these flexible mold materials will furnish information and aid as to the process involved.

Sometimes the complicity of a certain design will dictate that a mold will have to be made in two or more pieces. This is not unusual and is easily done. Undercuts, indentations, and very complicated designs present few problems to an experienced worker with these materials.

The prototype or model is of the most urgent importance. If it is not perfect, the molds and subsequent production in them cannot be good. If a pattern must be laid up by hand, copying a mural or mosaic, or if an original prototype is laid up, it must be very good before the flexible molds are taken from it.

It might be wise for someone who is thinking of starting up a small industry of this type to associate himself with a decorator, artist, or person quite adept in this field so as to have a constant supply of original work from which to copy.

Any existing mural or mosaic may be copied by an artistic person by carefully measuring, sketching, and later duplicating as nearly as possible with almost any available material. The layout should be on plywood or other good level surface so that, after completion, the form may be placed around it to receive the liquid polymer.

In copying multicolored objects, it is often advisable to make multicolored molds, matching the colors in the art object. This is entirely possible by hand-painting the colored elastomer in a thin coat over the different parts, allowing them to partially cure, and then pouring the rest of the polymer over the entire object. When cured and demolded, the mold will show where each color is to be placed in the reproduction of the object.

Decorative Flower Pots, Planter Boxes, Birdbaths, and Fountains

Many products can be made to be sold for use in the interiors of houses or in gardens. Very decorative flowerpots, planter boxes, birdbaths, and fountains may be designed and manufactured from polyester resin compounds.

The best of the clay and concrete pots will not be comparable with polyester pots. The very nicest of the redwood or metal pots and boxes will not be comparable in appearance or in durability. Birdbaths and fountains, which are now mostly made from concrete and stone, can be made much more advantageously with polyester compounds. They will be much lighter in weight and much more attractive in design and appearance.

Large birdbaths can be made in several pieces or in one piece, whichever may be more convenient. These articles may be made with the gun-lay-up method over a single female mold.

The pots and planter boxes could very conveniently be compression-molded if the volumes involved were large enough. For small production, the gun lay-up would be quite suitable, as only one side of the article must be perfect. The inner side may be slightly rough and would be of no consequence.

Outdoor Advertising

We often hear considerable talk about abolishing outdoor billboards and signs along our streets and highways. Perhaps if they were more attractive, there would be less talk about doing away with them.

In recent years, there has been a new method used in outdoor advertising: portable signs and posters. These large billboards are mounted on small, light trailers and can be moved about and positioned wherever the largest amounts of people will see them.

For the most part, outdoor advertising is very unattractive. The huge sections of sheet metal, covered with paper posters, become pretty dirty and dingy after a few weeks exposure to the elements. However, these signs needn't be unattractive at all. Very attractive frames and signboards can be designed and made with reinforced polyester. Advertisements, lettering, etc., can be all done in attractive, three-dimensional polyester figures. Properly lighted, these can be most efficient advertising means for both day and night.

Such three-dimensional figures need not be expensive because they would be merely a formed, thin shell, perhaps $\frac{1}{32}$ in. in thickness. No matter how large, the cost would be very small. Here, again, only one mold—a female—would be necessary. The lay-up can be done with the chopper gun in one thin pass. The exposed, exterior side will be good, and the inner, rough surface will be against the billboard and so will not be seen.

Figures, letters, and significant parts of the advertising can be lighted from within the translucent parts, and the effect can be quite good.

For very little difference in costs, advertising in these outdoor locations can take on another, completely new dimension.

This market is very large. There are thousands of huge signboards in and around every city in the country. This can become a very large new industry for the polyester resins.

Safety and Sporting Equipment

Reinforced polyester has long been used in the manufacture of safety helmets for industrial workers and, to some degree, in sports equipment such as football helmets and baseball batters' hats. There is still much room for expansion in these markets. Football protective padding, safety shoe toes, and many other applications remain to be developed more fully. The aluminum safety hats are still commonplace. There is no comparison between the safety afforded by the aluminum helmet and by a reinforced fiberglass hat. A properly formulated polyester hat will be resilient to a blow from a heavy object dropped on it and will regain its former shape instantly. The aluminum helmet will bend, and should the object have somewhat of a point, the hat will be ruptured, probably along with the head under it.

PHOTO 17.   *Bowling-ball production, Columbia Industries, Inc.*

Shoe soles and heels for electrical workers all should be made with a polyester compound because of its high dielectric properties. The heel and the foresole can be made in separate parts. Attached to the normal leather or rubber boot and shoe by an adhesive, they would give much added protection from electrical shock. They may be made up with a ribbed bottom, for better traction and protection from slipping.

Polyester compounds have far better electrical properties when dry than when wet, but even when thoroughly wet, they have much better properties than the best rubber used in safety shoes and boots.

In sports equipment, weight is of major consequence. The wearer needs maximum protection, yet must have minimum weight. Reinforced polyester does this job better than any metal or plastic material known, combining resilience with strength.

There are thousands of applications for small products of this type that can be manufactured from polyester.

Polyester Fiber, Filaments, and Fabrics

Polyester fiber has been used extensively for over 15 years. This fiber has been used in shirts, wash-and-wear suits, curtains, and for many other uses. Recently, it has been used extensively in cord for tires, and has been found to be far superior to most of the nylon or rayon cord previously used.

Most synthetic fibers are somewhat more expensive than the natural fibers such as cotton and wool. All fiber, natural or synthetic, has one or more drawbacks. A perfect fiber for all applications has not been found so far, and probably will never be found. One fiber will serve best in one application, while another will be superior for still another use.

Today we have polyamide fiber (known as nylon), acrylic fiber, polypropylene fiber, rayon, cellulose acetate, and a number of other synthetics. All have one or more properties which make them useful for one or more particular applications.

Polyester fiber is one of the more recently developed synthetic fibers, yet it has already taken over a large percentage of this market. It is somewhat less expensive than nylon.

The polyester fiber used today is based in part on terephthalic acid resins. These polyesters give good results in fiber manufacture. They are easy to work and process, and the cost is comparable with the acrylic fibers.

Research work on fibers has continued in polyester development. Many companies are spending considerable sums of money in the development of these applications for this polymer. Some resins have been developed that are based in part on digallic acid. Resins of extremely high molecular weight yet low viscosity can be manufactured using this saturated acid. The mechanical properties of a fiber made with this resin are far superior to those of a fiber based on terephthalic acid.

Many completely new intermediates have recently been made available for the manufacture of polyesters. Other intermediates that have been on the market for many years are coming to the attention of resin manufacturers. Until recently, the polyesters have been thought of as being in roughly three categories: rigid, resilient, and flexible. Little or no thought has gone into the manufacture of a polyester elastomer. Today, this is completely possible, and there is a great need for it in the fiber industry.

The substitution of polybutadiene for some of the normal dihydric or polyhydric component in the resin and the use of some digallic acid in the saturated component can produce polyesters with very good elastomeric properties.

There is no reason why polyester fibers should not replace many synthetic and natural fibers for a great number of applications when a group of polymers such as this can have such widely varying properties. Polyester can be formulated to meet the needs of almost any application in the fiber field.

Almost all of the other polymers used in the manufacture of fiber are thermoplastics. The acrylics can have a rather wide range of properties, depending on the combinations of monomers used in their manufacture. The acrylics are noted for good resistance to ultraviolet light, good color stability, and ease of processing. The methacrylates are similar and have much the same desirable properties. The disadvantages of the acrylates and methacrylates include less tensile strength than most of the synthetic fibers and poor resistance to abrasion and wear.

Quite a group of the polyamides are now available for the manufacture of fiber. These nylons, as they are called, are considerably more expensive than either polyesters or the acrylics. Nylon has good tensile strength, good abrasion and wear resistance, and is relatively easy to process into fiber. Its disadvantages include very poor resistance to ultraviolet light, fading, oxidation, and inability to be exposed for prolonged periods to the outdoors. The nylons have very poor clarity, and when used without pigments, will darken rapidly. When pigmented, the colors tend to fade much more rapidly than any of the other fiber polymers.

The polypropylene fibers recently made available show excellent promise in a number of industries. They seem particularly suitable for use in carpets. Color retention is good, abrasion and wear resistance is good, and when properly compounded, ultraviolet light and oxidation have little effect. These fibers have been made into synthetic grass for baseball parks, putting greens, and patios. So far, results have been very good indeed. The costs of these fibers are still high, but prices should be reduced as production is increased. Polypropylene fibers have also made a good start into the reinforced plastics industries. They are available in strand, mat, and fabric form to use with epoxies and polyesters in place of glass fiber. Their much lower weight makes them most suitable for many applications.

Cellulosic fibers of many types have been used for a number of years. Rayon was our first synthetic fiber, and it has served well in many applications. However, other cellulose fibers which have been produced are much better than rayon and are swiftly replacing it in the market.

For use in fabrics, polyesters have a great advantage over the other polymers in that they can be formulated so easily to fit any specific need. Synthetic fibers are needed for different applications which can have these properties: tensile strength, for use in automobile, truck, and aircraft tires; abrasion and wear resistance, for use in clothing, upholstery, and other fabric applications. Fibers with low compression set are desperately needed for tires, to prevent "flat spots" after a vehicle has been parked for a time. The same low compression set is needed for wrinkle-free fabrics. Many different properties are important in any particular application for fiber. Since the properties necessary vary so widely in different applications, polyester fibers have a tremendous advantage.

Polyester polymers may be manufactured which are suitable for many specific fiber applications:

1. Stockings, clear, sheer
2. Stockings and socks, colored
3. Stockings and socks, support
4. Underwear
5. Shirts, blouses
6. Trousers, suits, dresses
7. Work clothes
8. Rainwear
9. Topcoats
10. Draperies
11. Upholstery materials and fabrics
12. Carpeting
13. Plastics reinforcing
14. Auto, truck, and aircraft tires
15. Insect screens
16. Filament winding
17. Fishing line, nets
18. Strings for tennis rackets
19. Sheets, pillowcases, tablecloths
20. Tents, tarpaulins, etc.

Chart 7 shows how the various polyester fibers compare to the other fibers, both synthetic and natural. Values are approximate because many of the synthetic fibers, in particular, change rather drastically from manufacturer to manufacturer as precise formulation changes. Untreated cotton is seldom used today, and there are so many methods of treating cotton, each of which imparts different properties to the base fiber.

In many applications for fiber, cost of the basic fiber is a relatively secondary consideration. A shirt that may have a total of 6 oz of fiber cannot be affected much by a differential in cost of a few cents per lb. A tire which may have 6 lb of fiber can be affected very little by cost. In so many applications, performance, durability, and strength are overriding factors. In others, beauty may be the primary objective.

The wide group of polymers in the polyester category can meet far

CHART 7. COMPARISONS IN FIBER PROPERTIES

L—low
M—medium
H—high
P—poor
F—fair
G—good
E—excellent

Fiber	Color (gardner)	Specific gravity	Color stability unpig.	Color stability pigm.	Ultraviolet resistance	Oxidation resistance	Tensile strength	Flexural strength	Flexural modulus	Flexural fatigue	Elongation	Abrasion (wear resist.)	Comp. set (wrinkling)	Heat resistance	Flame resistance	Water absorption	Static electricity	Organic acid	Inorganic acid	Alkalie	Chlorine	Alcohol	Acetone	Stain resistance, food	Iodine	Shoe polish	Cost
Terephthalic polyester	2	1.1	G	G	G	E	M	M	L	E	M	G	E	F	P	L	P	F	G	F	F	E	G	E	G	F	M
Digallic polyester	1	1.1	G	G	G	E	H	M	L	E	M	G	E	F	P	L	P	F	E	F	F	E	G	E	G	F	M
Chlorosuccinic polyester	2	1.1	G	E	E	G	M	M	M	E	M	G	E	G	G	L	P	F	G	E	E	E	G	E	G	F	M
Acrylic polyester	1	1.1	E	G	G	E	H	M	L	G	L	G	G	F	P	L	P	F	G	F	F	E	G	E	F	F	M
Cyclopentane polyester	1	1.1	G	F	P	E	H	M	L	E	M	E	E	F	P	L	P	F	P	F	F	P	P	E	G	F	M
Nylon 66	7	1.1	P	F	P	F	H	M	L	G	L	E	G	F	P	L	P	F	P	E	F	P	P	G	P	F	M
Nylon 610	7	1.1	P	F	P	F	H	H	L	G	L	E	G	F	P	L	P	F	P	E	F	P	P	G	P	F	M
Nylon 6	6	1.1	P	G	P	F	M	H	L	G	L	E	G	F	P	L	F	F	P	E	F	P	F	G	P	F	M
Polyurethane elastomer	2	1.1	P	G	P	G	H	H	M	E	H	E	E	P	P	L	F	F	G	E	L	F	G	F	P	F	M
Polyurethane semielast.	2	1.1	P	G	P	G	H	M	L	E	M	E	G	P	P	L	F	F	G	F	G	E	G	G	F	F	M
Polyurethane	2	1.1	F	G	G	F	M	L	L	G	L	P	F	P	P	M	P	P	G	G	G	F	F	G	G	F	M
Polypropylene	1	0.9	F	G	G	F	L	L	L	F	L	F	L	P	G	M	F	P	E	G	G	F	P	G	F	F	M
Chlorinated polypropylene	1	1.0	E	E	P	F	L	L	M	L	L	P	L	F	P	M	P	P	E	E	E	P	P	G	F	F	M
Polyethylene	1	0.9	E	E	E	E	L	L	M	L	L	P	L	F	P	M	F	P	E	F	E	P	P	G	P	P	L
Acrylic	1	1.1	P	F	E	E	L	L	M	F	L	P	P	F	P	H	F	E	F	F	E	P	P	G	P	P	M
Methacrylate	3	1.1	G	F	E	F	L	L	M	L	L	P	P	L	E	L	L	P	F	F	F	P	P	G	P	P	M
Acrylonitrile	3	1.1	E	G	P	F	L	L	H	L	L	P	P	F	P	M	L	P	F	F	F	P	P	F	P	F	L
Rayon	—	1.4	P	P	F	G	L	M	L	F	L	E	P	F	P	L	F	P	L	G	L	E	E	G	P	P	M
Acetate	2	1.0	P	F	P	P	H	L	L	L	L	L	P	F	P	L	F	P	P	G	F	F	G	G	P	P	L
PVAc	—	1.3	G	F	F	E	M	M	M	L	L	F	P	P	P	H	E	P	P	P	P	P	P	E	P	F	H
Glass	—	2.3	E	G	P	G	H	M	L	P	L	L	P	G	P	L	E	P	P	P	P	P	P	G	G	P	H
Cotton untreated	—	—	P	G	P	G	M	H	M	G	L	F	P	F	P	H	F	P	P	P	P	E	G	G	P	F	L
Silk untreated	—	—	G	G	G	G	H	M	L	G	L	F	P	F	P	H	P	F	P	P	P	P	G	F	P	P	H
Wool untreated	—	—	P	F	P	G	H	M	M	G	L	F	P	L	P	H	E	F	P	G	P	L	F	P	P	F	H
Linen untreated	—	—	G	G	G	G	H	M	L	G	L	F	P	L	P	H	F	P	P	P	P	P	L	P	P	F	H
Asbestos	—	2.2	G	G	G	G	H	H	M	P	L	P	P	E	E	H	G	F	F	G	G	G	G	P	P	P	M

more of the requisites than all the other fibers combined. Polyesters are easier to work with because of their low viscosity, and processing them into fibers is very economical. There are many additives that are compatible with the polyesters, which may be used to impart specific properties. In colors, they can be made completely flame-resistant by the addition of additives such as triammonium phosphate and antimony trioxide.

As newer and better polyesters are developed, more and more manufacturers will turn to polyesters for fibers. This market will become one of the largest single applications for these polymers.

In addition to the products described thus far, there are many thousands of manufactured products that can be made from polyester resins. These polymers have much to offer any manufacturing firm which is considering new products or looking for better means of manufacturing present products.

Some of the newer developments in polyester resins for fiber have included thermoplastic polyesters of polyethylene terephthalate and butadiene terephthalate. Work is progressing along these lines to develop other thermoplastic polyesters for use in fiber and fabric.

These resins, together with the thermosetting polyesters, offer a very wide range of basic polymers from which to process these products, with a broad selection of methods.

Eleven

GENERAL POLYESTER DATA FOR THE FORMULATOR

Resin Manufacture

The manufacture of polyester resins has changed very little in basic equipment requirements, but it is about the only aspect of resin manufacture that has not changed drastically.

The polymers have changed widely over just the past 2 or 3 years. New raw materials, intermediates, and monomers have been made available, and many other intermediates that have been with us for many years are now being used. Some of these materials have been previously used as curing agents for epoxies and as intermediates in other polymers for quite some time. Only recently have resin manufacturers been realizing their potential in polyester manufacture.

Industry has demanded better polyesters, and the resin manufacturers are striving to satisfy these demands. The days of the so-called general-purpose resin, the standard resilient resin, and the modifying flexible resin are gone forever.

Polyesters have long been regarded as polymers to be used in the manufacture of FRP only for small pleasure boats, water skiis, surfboards, transluscent roofing panels, serving trays, and a very few other end products. Only recently has the great potential of these polymers begun to be realized. They may be formulated so as to replace a great number of other polymers that are more expensive and harder to process into finished products, and that, in many cases, will not serve the purpose of the end product nearly as well as polyester resins.

The term polyester in many cases is misleading to people who work with them. This name or misnomer covers a very wide range of polymers that are loosely related to one another. So many different materials are available with which to manufacture these resins, that the end properties of one resin as compared to another are completely different.

We will not discuss here a large number of other resins, which are polyesters, but which are not the types which are the subject of this book. These include the vinyl polyesters, the epoxy-acrylics, and the oxiranes. Also excluded will be a discussion of the alkyds (or nonpolymerizing polyesters) and the new thermoplastic polyesters. All these materials have definite places in industry today and give excellent results in many applications. However, even a partial discussion of these would tend to complicate an already complex subject.

We will be concerned with polyesters that are manufactured with one or more hydroxyl-bearing compound—either di- or polyhydric, with one or more saturated dibasic or dicarboxylic acid or anhydride and one or more unsaturated acid or anhydride, together with one or more reactive monomer; these, in the presence of a catalyst, form a cross-linked polymer in the thermosetting category.

Today, it is not an easy matter to fully categorize all polymers as being definitely thermosetting or thermoplastic since it is possible to formulate such wide variations of some of the polymers. However, the type of polymer which we will be considering here is definitely a thermosetting plastic. It cross-links with itself and with a monomer, either at room temperature or at elevated temperatures; creating an exotherm heat in the process of curing. It is insoluble in its own monomer and in other monomers. It is insoluble in solvents of the aliphatic, aromatic, and ketone categories. It cannot be remelted with heat or postformed under the influence of heat and/or pressure once it has cured. This places it most definitely in the thermosetting category.

Equipment

The equipment used in the manufacture of polyester resins is approximately similar to that used in the manufacture of most polymers. The major piece of equipment is a reactor kettle for cooking the raw material which goes into the resin. This vessel can be from a very small laboratory size up to a 100,000-lb capacity. It will be stainless steel in many cases and glass-lined steel in other instances. It will be jacketed for either oil, steam, or other types of heating and cooling. It will be fitted for the extraction of water and other waste products by vacuum. It will have a means of agitation and will be suitably fitted with a means for blanketing the materials with an inert gas as they cook.

Other equipment will consist of a source of heat, a source of cooling fluid (usually water), and a blending tank where the polymer is placed after it has been cooked to cool and to be blended with the monomers and other additives when the temperature has lowered sufficiently. The rest of the equipment will depend largely on the size of the investment the manufacturer has made. Weighing and pumping equipment may be completely automatic, with highly complex electronic controls; in small plants these processes may be carried out largely by manual labor. Temperature controls can be completely automatic for heating and cooling cycles as needed, or a small plant may perform these functions by manpower.

However, with the keen competition in the industry, the small plant is hard pressed today. To be profitable a plant must have every possible automation device in order to keep labor costs down. In the most modern plants, many reactors with their respective equipment, are completely controlled by one man who sits in an air-conditioned office nearby. This person can keep a constant visual check on every phase of all pieces of equipment in the plant through the gauges, dials, and instruments on the walls of his office. A few workmen maintain the building, and one or two more are employed in receiving shipments of raw materials and shipping finished products. Almost all the raw materials are handled by pumps and conveyor systems and are placed into their respective storage containers without manual labor of any kind. The finished products, whether they be liquid polymers, with the monomers already added, paste polymers to which monomers are not added, or be crushed and ground, dry, powdered polymers, are all handled with very little manpower.

For this reason, the costs of polyester resins have remained low, and in many instances they have actually been reduced during the past few years. Automation has provided the means for mass production of very large quantities of resin with very low labor costs. This has been combined with the greater demand for the intermediates and raw materials, enabling them also to be produced on much larger scales. As the demand for any material increases, production increases, permitting lower costs. This is carried along the entire industry, from the crude hydrocarbon to the finished consumer product.

Process

The hydroxyl donors are placed in the reactor, and the temperature is raised to about 200°F. The saturated acids, carboxylic acids, or anhydrides are now added, and the temperature is slowly raised to around 400°F, while the reactor is being slowly agitated and the mixture is under a blanket of an inert gas (usually nitrogen). When these two materials are cooking, the water and waste products are being drawn off by vacuum, aided with an azeotrope (usually xylol). When this ester has reached a certain stage, usually determined by acid number, the unsaturated acid or anhydride is added, and the cooking continues, still under the blanket of gas, with agitation and the removal of water and waste products.

The cooking time and temperature will depend largely on the particular materials being cooked. Some components take considerably higher temperatures and longer cooking times than others. As a general rule, the temperatures are around 400°F, and the cooking time is around 4 hr.

Temperatures must be carefully controlled, particularly as the material nears its finishing point, or it will gel. Many times, a small amount of inhibitor is introduced sometime during the final stages to prevent polymerization.

Cooking is stopped when the polymer has reached its prescribed molecular weight. The acid number is an indicator as to the molecular weight and is usually used as a control. When the acid number is in the range of 12 to 20, the resin is discharged into the blending and cooling tank.

This is the time-accepted procedure. However, this is where the process must be changed in order to produce top-quality polymers. When the acid number has reached a point between 12 and 20, ethylene carbonate should be introduced into the reactor, on an equimolar ratio with the remaining carboxylic groups. Agitation must continue until the reaction between the two materials has reached a conclusion and the acid number reaches zero. This will take approximately an extra 15 min in the reactor.

Either ethylene carbonate or ethylene oxide may be used for this purpose, but because ethylene oxide is a gas and very hard to handle, ethylene carbonate is far superior.

The reduction of the acid is by chain termination and not by chain linkage. There is no increase in the molecular weight, hence there is no rise in the viscosity of the polymer.

The polymer may now be discharged into the cooling and blending tank. If it is to be a dry, powdered polymer and is to be shipped in this form to the purchaser, it is allowed to solidify and is crushed and ground into fine dust. The purchaser will blend it with monomers as he uses it. These are very high-molecular-weight polymers, such as the bisphenol polymers. The advantage here is that there is no limit to the shelf life of the resin, and no special precautions must be made for shipping and storage. Often the purchaser has a supply of monomers nearby, and thus he saves considerable sums on shipping the monomers long distances.

If the resin is intended to be a paste resin, without monomers, it is packaged while still fairly hot, and hence is fluid. Here, again, is a resin with much longer shelf stability. Fewer precautions as to the temperatures at which it must be shipped and stored are necessary, and the purchaser has the advantage of saving money on the monomers. The flexible isophhalic polymers are often shipped in this fashion. Often these are shipped in railway tank cars or in trucks that are fitted with internal heating coils. When the vehicle arrives at its desitnation, the paste is heated slightly for easier pumping into storage receptacles.

The polyesters that are to be blended with monomers are cooled to around 120°F or so in the blending tank. Then an inhibitor is added, and the monomers, already containing inhibitors, are added. These inhibitors will depend on the end use of the resin, and can vary widely in nature. Chart 13 gives a variety of inhibitors, together with the end purposes and process for which they should be used.

Sometimes other additives are blended into the resin at the blending-tank stage. If a polyester is to be used as a gel-coat resin, 1 or 2% (by weight) of cellulose acetate butyrate can be added when the resin is at about 200°F. If it is a coating resin, both the butyrate and a small amount of a special silicone resin are added at about the same time in many cases. The silicone would be a maximum of 0.5% (by weight) and is usually less. The silicone controls the surface tension of a coating and makes it smooth out well. The butyrate is a flow-control agent and will prevent sag and running in a gel coat or a coating on vertical surfaces. Many other additives may be desirable to include during this stage of resin manufacture, depending on the resin and its end purpose. Sometimes a stabilizer is added to keep the polymer from reacting with steel or tin containers. This is usually triphenyl phosphite in very small quantities. If a resin is to be used as a coating resin or in room-temperature-cure situations, often the promoter is added after the polymer has cooled completely. Sometimes a clarifying agent is also added.

The important thing, of course, is that every ingredient that goes into the polymer impart the properties which the purchaser needs for the particular product, and for the particular environment in which it is to be used.

The resin manufacturer and the purchaser must be in complete accord as to the designated use of the resin, the process by which it is to be used, and the environment in which the end product will be placed.

With these in mind, the resin can be custom-made for this particular application. This, of course, entails the demand for large quantities of one particular formulation. The resin manufacturer cannot custom-formulate a few hundred pounds of such a resin. The application must be large enough to be of value to both the resin manufacturer and the manufacturer of the end product.

However, many times an identical resin can be used by a number of purchasers, so the demand should be measured by the sum of these purchasers and quantities manufactured accordingly.

Formulating the Polyester Resin

Every detail about the end use of a polymer should be known before it is formulated. Following are the major points that should be considered:

1. The process should be determined by which the polymer will be manufactured into an end product—by casting, compression-molding, calendering, or other means. It will have to be known whether it is to be a gun-lay-up resin, a coating resin, or a gel-coat resin. It must be established exactly how it is to be used and by which process and at what temperature it is to be cured.

2. It must establish whether it is to be pigmented or used clear. Also the maximum color grade of the resin should be known, as established by the Gardner, platinum cobalt, or alpha methods.

3. The gel time desired should be determined. It may be formulated to fit almost any cycle time required by any process. This will depend greatly on the reactivity of the resin, as established by the raw materials and intermediates, monomers, inhibitors, and promoters, if used. The mole-weight percentages of saturated to unsaturated acids and particular combinations of hydroxyl components can all contribute greatly to the degree of reactivity of the polymer. The functionality of the ingredients also have a great effect on the reactivity of the finished resin. The higher the functionality of the intermediates, the higher the reactivity. The molecular weight of individual intermediates will also affect reactivity to a large extent. Higher-molecular-weight intermediates generally give more reactive resins. In general, the more rigid resins are more reactive with faster gel times, because of the higher ratio of unsaturated to saturated acids. In resilient and flexible resins, reactivity may be achieved through use of such hydroxyl components as pentaerythritol, sorbitol, and glycerol in small amounts.

4. The desired flexural modulus of the resin must be established. This is perhaps the most important point in the formulation. It must be closely coupled with all the other requirements of the resin. The modulus must be established mostly through the ratios of unsaturated to saturated acids. The higher the ratio of the unsaturated acid, the more rigid the resin. The hydroxyl components and the monomers will to some degree affect the modulus, but the acid ratios more closely govern this aspect.

5. It must be determined whether the resin is to cure tack-free in the presence of air. In matched dies, this is of no consequence, so the choice of hydroxyl components will be much wider. Dicyclopentadiene, neopentyl glycol, and others will give resins with good surface cures in the presence of air. Charts 5 and 8 give more details on this phase of resin formulation. Resins that must cure completely in the presence of air are somewhat more difficult to formulate in that they must possess this quality along with all the other requirements. When air cure must be combined with flexural modulus, reactivity, and the other properties required, a well-balanced formulation of all these properties must be carefully considered.

For demonstration purposes, a formula calling for a total of 4.2 moles will be used, excluding the monomers. (The hydroxyl components are set at 2.2 moles of the total to allow for the roughly 10% lost in water and waste. This will vary slightly with different hydroxyl components but to no great extent. So, with a total of one, two, or more hydroxyl components, totaling 2.2 moles, we will show how the acid components may be altered in percentage to control the final flexural modulus of the resin.)

Total Unsaturated Acids (Moles)				
1.0	0.7	0.5	0.3	0.2
Rigid	Resilient	Very resilient	Flexible	Very flexible
Total Saturated Acids (Moles)				
1.0	1.3	1.5	1.7	1.8
Rigid	Resilient	Very resilient	Flexible	Very flexible

The monomers must match the unsaturated acids, mole for mole, plus at least 5%. The nearer the monomers stay in stoichiometric amounts, the better the air-drying properties of the resin. Additional monomers may be used in many instances where a resin is not to be subjected to air-cure. In general, the higher the monomer content and the more combinations of monomers, the higher the flexural modulus will be. Many resins to be used in matched-molding operations may contain up to almost double the stoichiometric amount without undue effects to the finished product. For some end products, the properties may actually be enhanced by additional monomers.

In applications calling for curing in the presence of air, the best suited monomers are chlorostyrenes, diallyl chloride, diallyl phthalate, triallyl cyanaurate, and divinyl benzene. The methacrylates and styrene should be used sparingly if at all. If the application calls for matched dies, then any of the monomers may be used, subject to other requisites. The flexural modulus of the polymer is affected by both the monomer and the hydroxyl component to some extent. The longer the chain length of the hydroxyl component, the more flexible the polymer. The higher the molecular weight of the monomer, the more flexible the polymer if used at stoichiometric amounts plus some 5%. Above this, the flexural modulus will rise. Combining two or more monomers will also cause the modulus to rise slightly because of additional cross-linkage.

6. The acid resistance must be determined. If a polymer is designed for use in a highly acid environment, the saturated acid is of utmost importance. Phthalic anhydride, isophthalic acid, and the hydrophthalic acids will all give a very good saturated acid system. When two or more are combined, the resistance to acids will be increased somewhat. The choice of hydroxyl components and unsaturated acids will have little affect on acid resistance as long as the polymer is a rigid one. The higher the degree of rigidity, the higher the chemical resistance of a polyester. The choice of monomers can greatly affect acid resistance. Styrene, vinyl toluene, and divinyl benzene will serve best for this use.

7. The alkali resistance should be established. For maximum alkali resistance, the polyester should be by all means made with a hydroxyl component consisting mainly of bisphenol A. The saturated and unsaturated acids should be chlorinated. Such acids as chlorofumaric acid should be used for the unsaturated component, and either tetrachlorophalic or chlorendic anhydride should be used for the saturated component. Of the nonchlorinated acids, isophthalic acid will give best results in alkalies. If the application calls for a product that will be exposed to both heat and alkalies, then the saturated component should consist at least in part of HET acid. Here, again, the monomers chosen will affect the alkali resistance. They should be composed of either M-chlorostyrene, O-chlorostyrene, dichlorostyrene, or one of the allyl monomers. Again, the resistance of the polymer to alkalies will depend to a large degree on its flexural modulus. The more rigid the polymer, the higher its chemical resistance.

8. The resistance to chlorine (gas or liquid) should be established. Here, the extremely high modulus resin will give by far the best results. It should be very similar to the resin that resists alkalies, but the saturated acids should be made up of HET acid and either pyromellitic

dianhydride or trimellitic dianhydride. These will give extremely good chlorine resistance at temperatures well over 400°F. The resin should be designed to have a modulus well exceeding 800,000 psi.

9. Is the end product to be filled with low-cost fillers, or is it to be reinforced? If so, what are the mechanical properties desired in the finished product. Here, such factors as tensile strength, flexural strength, and modulus must first be considered, and the chemical resistance, electrical properties, etc., must be secondary. On the following pages are the effects of fillers and reinforcing materials on a polymer. From these the resin manufacturer can more or less judge the requirements for the mechanical properties of a resin in order to design it for specific mechanical properties in the end product. Resins should almost never be blended (two or more) together to attain specific mechanical properties. There are a few exceptions to this, but it is much easier to design one resin to meet the requirements than it is to try to blend several resins together and thus gain the necessary end mechanical properties. An isophthalic resin, blended into an orthophthalic resin, will greatly improve the impact strength of the orthophthalic resin, but here the improvement ends. Many times, a very flexible isophthalic resin, of the type known as "putty" resins, will be blended into a resilient orthophthalic to gain more flexibility. This does not work for a number of reasons. First, the average manufacturer will load the isophthalic with up to twice the stoichiometric quantity of styrene to reduce viscosity and price. The additional styrene also makes these resins more reactive, but it defeats the purpose in every way. The additional sytrene will cause the flexural modulus to rise tremendously, not only with the isophthalic resin, but also with the orthophthalic resin. Next, there is some molecular and crystalline change in both resins when they are used in combination, causing the higher modulus.

If a resilient orthophthalic resin, with a flexual modulus of 500,000 psi, is blended half-and-half with an isophthalic resin of 150,000 psi, the end result is a polymer with a modulus of about 600,000 psi. As stated earlier, it will have greatly improved impact strength, a very slight gain in tensile strength, but other properties do not change to any degree.

Thus, it may be seen why it is so necessary for the resin manufacturer to know every possible detail of the end properties of his customer's product—the kinds and amounts of reinforcing and fillers that are to be used. It is impossible to give even close values on every specific resin in combinations with every kind of filler and reinforcing fiber. It would take a full year of testing and a complete book to record all this. However, there are a few basic factors which will serve as a guide:

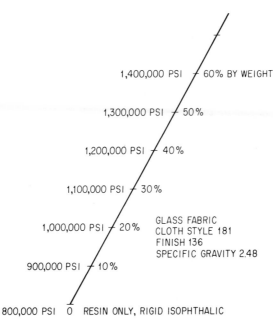

1,400,000 PSI — 60% BY WEIGHT

1,300,000 PSI — 50%

1,200,000 PSI — 40%

1,100,000 PSI — 30%

1,000,000 PSI — 20%   GLASS FABRIC
                       CLOTH STYLE 181
                       FINISH 136
                       SPECIFIC GRAVITY 2.48

900,000 PSI — 10%

800,000 PSI   0   RESIN ONLY, RIGID ISOPHTHALIC

GRAPH 1. *The effects of glass fiber on flexural modulus. Parts compression-molded 0.125 in.*

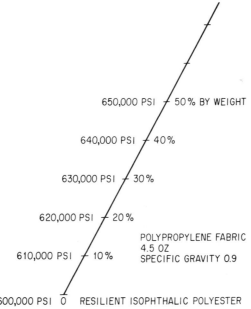

650,000 PSI — 50% BY WEIGHT

640,000 PSI — 40%

630,000 PSI — 30%

620,000 PSI — 20%

                       POLYPROPYLENE FABRIC
                       4.5 OZ
610,000 PSI — 10%   SPECIFIC GRAVITY 0.9

600,000 PSI   0   RESILIENT ISOPHTHALIC POLYESTER

GRAPH 2. *The effects of polypropylene fiber on flexural modulus. Parts compression-molded 0.125 in.*

a. The rigid isophthalic resins give higher tensile strengths than the orthophthalics and better impact strengths, whether used alone or with fibers and fillers. Better bond to fibers and fillers certainly can account for most of this. (This holds true as well for the resilient and the flexible resins.)

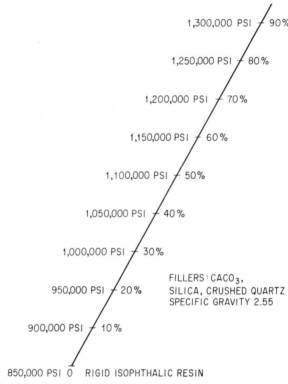

GRAPH 3.   *Effects of fillers on flexural modulus. Parts compression-molded 0.125 in. Thus, it is shown that the modulus is not affected by fillers to the degree it is with glass.*

b. Compression strengths will be nearly the same for resins of like flexural modulus. Flexural strengths for the isophthalics will be slightly above those of the orthophthalics.

c. Barcol hardness will vary only slightly from resin to resin of like flexural modulus. Fillers, aggregates, and fibers can change the hardness drastically, particularly in high percentages.

d. Every property of a resin is dependent on its ultimate flexural modulus. Mechanical properties, chemical resistance, electrical properties (to a lesser degree), water absorption, heat resistance, etc., all depend to a very large extent on their modulus.

e. The reinforcing fibers, fillers, and aggregates are of no lesser importance. Some of the properties of the end product may be drastically changed through proper selection of these materials. They must be matched to the resin to gain the properties desired in the finished product. All these factors must be considered by the resin manufacturer

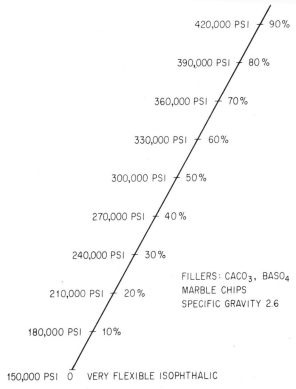

420,000 PSI — 90%

390,000 PSI — 80%

360,000 PSI — 70%

330,000 PSI — 60%

300,000 PSI — 50%

270,000 PSI — 40%

240,000 PSI — 30%

FILLERS: $CACO_3$, $BASO_4$
MARBLE CHIPS
SPECIFIC GRAVITY 2.6

210,000 PSI — 20%

180,000 PSI — 10%

150,000 PSI   0   VERY FLEXIBLE ISOPHTHALIC

GRAPH 4. *The effects of fillers on flexural modulus. Parts compression-molded 0.125 in.*

and the customer, and the resin should be designed to accomplish the desired end result.

10. The heat and flame resistance should be determined. This is best accomplished through the use of the higher molecular weight chlorinated component parts. These are available in all component parts except the hydroxyl donor. The higher the molecular weight of the saturated acids, the higher will be the heat distortion point. The higher the chlorine percentage in the intermediates and monomers, the more flame-resistant will be the product.

11. The weather resistance should be established. This is perhaps the

most difficult property to categorize in the individual components going into a resin. First, weather resistance takes in many factors. There is ultraviolet light, infrared rays, and oxidation to consider. All are distinct within themselves. Water absorption must be considered, and expansion and contraction must be calculated. All these factors and more must be carefully considered when a product is to be exposed to an outdoor

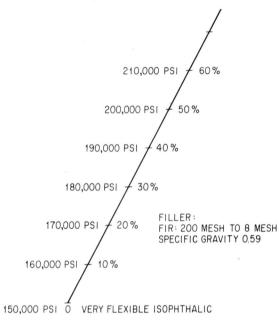

GRAPH 5. *Effects of wood flour on flexural modulus. Parts compression-molded 0.125 in. Note: This is as high a percentage of wood flour as may be used while still compression-molding in the 250–300 psi range. Up to 90% wood flour may be used, but press capacity would have to be around 1,000 psi.*

environment. Even the fillers and pigments that will go into the finished product are of utmost importance.

Again, the modulus of the resin enters into the picture. A rigid resin is more resistant to the elements than a polymer which consists of the same basic component parts but is more flexible. It is not completely clear whether the cause lies in the higher percentage of saturated acid or in the different molecular structure between the rigid and flexible resins. (This writer feels the latter factor to be the cause.)

Weather resistance can be greatly aided by avoiding hydroxyl components with excess oxygen bridges. Propylene glycol is excellent for use in resins for outdoor exposure. The new hydroxy acrylates are very good when used on a 50:50 basis with propylene glycol. The best results can be obtained with the use of proper monomers. Styrene should be used very sparingly, if at all. Chlorinated styrenes give good results when combined with acrylates or methacrylates. Allyl monomers are also helpful when used in proper proportions. Two or more monomers must always be used in a resin which is to be exposed to the elements.

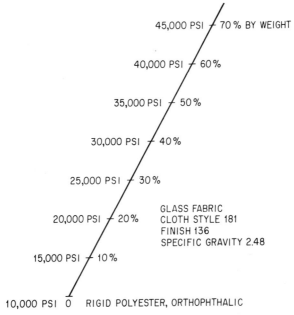

45,000 PSI   70 % BY WEIGHT

40,000 PSI   60%

35,000 PSI   50%

30,000 PSI   40%

25,000 PSI   30%

GLASS FABRIC
CLOTH STYLE 181
FINISH 136
SPECIFIC GRAVITY 2.48

20,000 PSI   20%

15,000 PSI   10%

10,000 PSI   0   RIGID POLYESTER, ORTHOPHTHALIC

GRAPH 6. *Effects of glass fiber on tensile strength. Compression-molded parts 0.125 in.*

The higher degree of cross-linking makes the finished product much more resistant to the sun, rain, and oxidation.

The saturated-acid component can be assisted with a percentage of acrylic acid, particularly if the resin is to be a rigid polymer. In a rigid exterior resin, half or more of the saturated component may be acrylic acid, but in more flexible resins the acrylic acid must be used in lesser proportions. When acrylic acid nears an equimolar ratio with the unsaturated-acid component, the resulting polymer will suffer too much loss in mechanical properties. Thus in a flexible resin, the acrylic acid used would amount to perhaps 20% of the total saturated components.

12. Tensile strength must be determined. Resins based on isophthalic acid give excellent tensile strength. Digallic acid also will give a resin with good strength because of its higher molecular weight. A resin based

on digallic acid may be cooked to a much higher molecular weight and still retain low viscosity. Sebacic acid will give good results in very flexible resins, close to the values of the isophthalic resin. Pyromellitic dianhydride gives very high tensile strength in very rigid resins but does not perform well in flexible resins. The tensile strengths of all resins are reduced in direct proportion to the lowering of the flexural modulus. As the modulus is decreased, the strength is reduced.

13. Compressive strength should be established. The compressive strength of a resin, unfilled or unreinforced, is also largely related to the flexual modulus but in a slightly different manner. A resin based on phthalic anhydride, for instance, with a flexural modulus of about 600,000 psi, will have the highest values for compressive strength. Above this, as the resin becomes more rigid, the compressive strength becomes reduced. As the modulus is reduced, the compressive strength is diminished considerably faster than when the modulus is raised. A curve showing this would be the following:

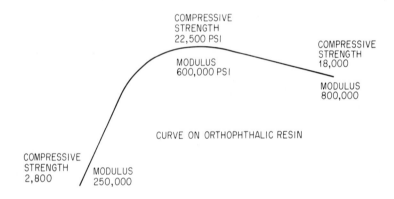

COMPRESSIVE STRENGTH 22,500 PSI

MODULUS 600,000 PSI

COMPRESSIVE STRENGTH 18,000

MODULUS 800,000

CURVE ON ORTHOPHTHALIC RESIN

COMPRESSIVE STRENGTH 2,800

MODULUS 250,000

This curve does not hold true for every type of polymer. In an isophthalic resin, the differential is far less but will still decline toward both ends of the curve.

14. Flexural strength must be established. The curve on the flexural strength of a given resin will fairly well parallel that of the compressive strength. The highest values will be found somewhere around 650,000 to 700,000 psi modulus and will decline somewhere above that and rather sharply below that. This is, of course, for unfilled resins. The flexural modulus can be greatly improved through proper use of reinforcing materials. A resin with a flexural strength of 14,000 psi can be elevated to well over 50,000 psi with glass, polypropylene, or polyester fiber.

15. The flexural modulus must be known. Since all the other mechanical properties and most of the other properties of a polymer are tied

so directly to the flexural modulus, it must be emphasized that this is the focal point in the manufacture of any resin.

As the line graph demonstrated earlier, the modulus depends almost entirely on the proportions of saturated to unsaturated acids. More flexibility can be obtained through the use of hydroxyl components with oxygen bridges and longer chain lengths, but this brings the undesired results of making a resin more hygroscopic.

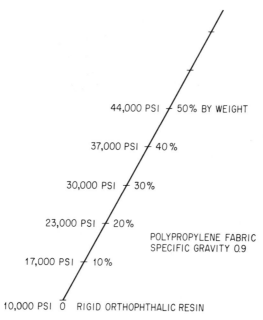

44,000 PSI — 50% BY WEIGHT

37,000 PSI — 40%

30,000 PSI — 30%

23,000 PSI — 20%

POLYPROPYLENE FABRIC
SPECIFIC GRAVITY 0.9

17,000 PSI — 10%

10,000 PSI 0   RIGID ORTHOPHTHALIC RESIN

GRAPH 7. *Effects of polypropylene fiber on tensile strength. Part compression-molded 0.125 in. Note: It is shown that the polypropylene fiber gives higher strength-to-weight ratios than does glass. However, less may be used. This is about the maximum that may be handled at low pressures.*

The use of a polymer such as hydroxy-terminated polybutadiene as a large part of the hyroxyl component can be a great aid in reducing modulus, without affecting too many of the other properties.

The flexural modulus is definitely affected by the monomers, not so much in the choice of monomers as in the quantity used. For flexible resins, stoichiometric amounts must be adhered to rather strictly.

The great need today in polyesters is the development of flexible polymers that also have the desirable mechanical properties—chemical resistance, etc.—of some of the more rigid polymers. This must be achieved through the use of the more recent developments in hydroxyl components—polymers such as polybutadiene, polyethers, polyactones, and perhaps some of the hydroxyl-bearing thio compounds. A number of the mercaptopropionic acid derivatives look very promising for this purpose. The price of these materials is still very high, but will decrease as they become more widely used. These HSOH groups may furnish the necessary properties to a polyester. To further this development, some of the very high-molecular-weight acids such as digallic, mellisic,

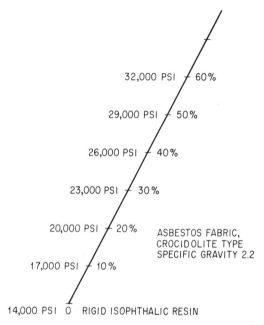

32,000 PSI   60%

29,000 PSI   50%

26,000 PSI   40%

23,000 PSI   30%

20,000 PSI   20%   ASBESTOS FABRIC,
                         CROCIDOLITE TYPE
                         SPECIFIC GRAVITY 2.2
17,000 PSI   10%

14,000 PSI   0   RIGID ISOPHTHALIC RESIN

GRAPH 8. *Effects of asbestos on tensile strength. Compression-molded 0.125 in.*

and benzophenone tetradianhydride acids seem to offer more promise than any of the more commonly used acids.

16. Elongation is directly tied to the flexural modulus of a given resin, as are most other properties. In the commonly known polymers today, elongation will range from up to 50% in a very flexible isophthalic to less than 4% in a very flexible orthophthalic. Rigid resins will elongate from 6% in an isophthalic, with a modulus of 600,000 psi, to less than 0.5% for a similar orthophthalic.

Thus far, a true elastomeric polyester has not been developed. There is a great need for such a resin for flooring and roofing materials. It can and will be developed along the same lines as the very flexible polyester with good chemical resistance and good mechanical properties. The resin manufacturers have been far too slow in going ahead with such work. The market has desperately needed such a polymer for a long time, and the market for it could be very large. It will not be an easy task to develop this resin, but it must be done without delay.

17. The hardness should be determined. Polyesters can range in hardness from 80 or more (Barcol), for a very rigid resin based on pyromellitic dianhydride, to a Shore D scale or 30 for a very flexible isophthalic. At a Shore D scale of 30, a person can indent the resin with a thumbnail.

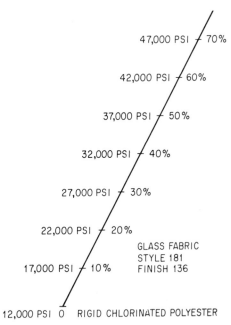

47,000 PSI ─ 70%

42,000 PSI ─ 60%

37,000 PSI ─ 50%

32,000 PSI ─ 40%

27,000 PSI ─ 30%

22,000 PSI ─ 20%

GLASS FABRIC
STYLE 181
17,000 PSI ─ 10%   FINISH 136

12,000 PSI 0   RIGID CHLORINATED POLYESTER

GRAPH 9. *Effects of glass fiber on flexural strength. Part compression-molded 0.125 in.*

The hardness of any given resin can be increased tremendously with the use of the proper fillers, reinforcing fibers, and aggregates. A resin with a Shore D reading of 30 can be increased to a Barcol reading of 35 to 40, with a formulation containing 10 parts resin to 90 parts fillers and aggregates.

The harder resins, with the Barcol readings above 60, are most desirable for use in coatings, gel coats, and other applications requiring good mar resistance.

18. The abrasion resistance must be established. Abrasion resistance is not parallel to the hardness of a resin, as is believed by many to be the case. Very often, a resin with a Barcol hardness of 30 will have better abrasion resistance than one reading 60 or more. Abrasion resistance is more related to toughness than to hardness. The two proper-

ties should not be confused. Abrasion resistance is very easy to acquire through use of proper fillers, but in clear, unfilled resins it presents more of a problem.

A polymer with a hydroxyl component made of dicyclopentadiene and polybutadiene will give very tough, abrasion-resistant resins. Hardness can be acquired at the same time through the use of some pyromellitic dianhydride in the saturated portion. The polybutadiene-hydroxyl donors and others will aid in obtaining the toughness required for good abrasion resistance. The monomers chosen can also affect considerably the abrasion resistance of the finished polymer. The acrylates, methacrylates, and styrenes must be used very sparingly. The allyl monomers will impart toughness and abrasion resistance. A combination of either diallyl phthalate or triallyl cyanaurate with allyl diglycol carbonate will help tremendously in the end polymer.

19. The water absorption must be determined. Water absorption is a property which has always been tied directly to the flexural modulus. The higher the modulus, the lower the water absorption. However, this thinking is swiftly changing now, with the advent of such hydroxyl components as polybutadiene and polymers of quite low modulus which have excellent resistance to water absorption. Of the more common hydroxyl compounds, propylene glycol will impart the best water resistance (as discussed in paragraph number 11, weather resistance).

Polyester has the lowest water absorption of any polymer known today. For this reason it is excellent in applications involving chemical resistance and corrosion-control problems. Polyester forms the dense, porefree surface so desirable where absorption resistance, gas permeability, and adsorption resistance are prerequisites.

20. The salt resistance must be established. Since polyesters are the polymers with lowest water absorption in existance and completely impervious to the effects of salt, they are extremely desirable in the protection of metals or other materials which are subject to salt attack. All polyesters have these properties, but those based in part on isophthalic and/or hexahydrophthalic acid will give particularly good service.

21. The sulfides resistance must be determined. The same types of polyesters that work well in salt environments will give excellent service in and around sulfides. Combining bisphenol A, as part of the hydroxyl component, with isophthalic acid in the saturated acid component will even further the resistance to sulfides of all types.

22. Resistance to solvents must be established. Polyesters withstand very well motor oil, gasoline, aliphatic and aromatic solvents, and keytones. The only solvents which attack polyesters badly are the chlorinated solvents: methylene chloride, carbon tetrachloride, and others of this type. The highly chlorinated polyesters withstand these solvents

better than any others but not for any length of time. With other solvents, the resistance of polyester is directly related to the flexural modulus. The more rigid the polyester, the more resistant it is to solvents. The isophthalics are more resistant than most polyesters to aromatic solvents and ketones.

Besides the important considerations outlined above, there are many other factors to be discussed between a resin manufacturer and the processor of manufactured goods:

1. Should the resin be shipped with or without monomer?
2. If it is shipped with monomer, then should be resin be inhibited for room-temperature or elevated-temperature cures?
3. Should the resin be promoted, and if so, with which promoters?
4. Should an internal mold release be added, and if so, which internal-release agent best fits the processors type of operation?
5. Should a flow-control agent be added? (This is more easily done by the resin manufacturer at his plant than at the processor's plant.)
6. Should a surface-active agent be added?
7. Should an ultraviolet blocking agent be added?
8. Is a clarifying agent necessary?
9. Would it be desirable to add a stabilizer in cases where the resin may be placed in steel drums for some time?

Each and every one of these factors is important. The additives are more easily added to the resin by the resin manufacturer in the cooling stage than added by the processor as aggregate to the formulation at the plant. Controls in the resin plant are often more adequate in these cases where perhaps a few parts per million are to be added. (See Chart 13, which gives additives that are most useful in polyester resins for obtaining certain end properties.)

Both the resin manufacturer and the product manufacturer can benefit greatly by being in complete accord in every phase of the resin production. The resin must be designed for its exact end purpose, even to the very last small ingredient. Many of the large plastic products manufacturers manufacture their own resins today because they could not get the complete cooperation of the resin manufacturers in formulating resins for their specific uses. Most of these manufacturers did not want to become resin producers, but it was necessary in order to survive. Resin manufacturers are now realizing this and becoming much more cooperative.

Charts 8 to 20 show a few of the many raw material, intermediates, monomers, catalysts, promoters, and additives that may be used in polyester resins. These charts do not, by any means, show all such materials,

CHART 8. HYDROXYL COMPONENTS: EFFECTS AND PROPERTIES IMPARTED TO POLYESTER RESINS

Legend:
L–low M–medium H–high P–poor F–fair G–good
X–not recommended E–excellent O–no known effect C–only in combination Blank–not known

Note: The columns Ultraviolet resistance, Infrared resistance, Oxidation resistance, Abrasion resistance and Shrinkage are marked **"No major effects"** (written three times down the chart for legibility); these cells are left blank below.

Component	Cost	Reactivity	Ambient-temp. cures	Medium-temp. cures	Elevated-temp. cures	Ultraviolet res.	Infrared res.	Oxidation res.	Abrasion res.	Shrinkage	Tensile strength	Compressive strength	Flexural modulus	Flexural strength	Impact strength	Elongation	Hardness (Barcol)	Dielectric strength	Dielectric constant	Water absorption	Gas permeability	Heat resistance	Flame resistance	Organic-acid res.	Inorganic-acid res.	Alkali res.	Salt res.	Sulfides res.	Solvents res.	Air-curing properties
Dicyclopentadiene	M	E	E	E	E						M	M	M	M	M	M	M	M	M	M	M	M		G	E	F	E	E	E	E
Ethylene carbonate	L	C	G	E	E						M	M	M	M	M	M	M	M	M	M	M	M		G	E	F	E	E	E	E
Neopentyl glycol	L	G																												G
Heptaethylene glycol	M	G	F	F	F						L	L	L	H	H	L	L	H	H	H	L	L		F	G	F	F	F	F	F
Sorbitol	H	C	G	G	G						H	H	H	L	L	H	H	L	L	L	H	H		F	G	F	G	G	G	G
Bisphenol A	M	E	F	G	G						H	H	H	L	L	H	H	L	L	L	H	H		F	G	F	G	G	G	F
Polyactone	M	E																												
Hydroxy acrylates	H	E	E	E	E						H	H	H	L	L	H	H	L	L	L	H	H		F	G	F	G	G	G	G
Polybutadiene	M	G	E	E	E						L	L	L	H	H	L	L	H	H	H	L	L		G	E	G	E	E	G	G
Polyether oxy prop.	M	G	G	G	G						L	L	L	H	H	L	L	H	H	H	L	L		F	G	F	G	G	G	G
Castor oil	M	C	F	F	P						M	M	M	M	M	M	M	M	M	M	M	M		F	G	F	G	G	G	F
Pentaerythritol	H	C	G	G	G						H	H	H	L	L	H	H	L	L	L	H	H		F	G	F	G	G	G	G
Thio diglycol	H	G												G																
Glycerine	M	C	G	G	G						H	H	H	L	L	H	H	L	L	L	H	H		F	G	F	G	G	G	G
Pentanediol	M	E	G	G	G						M	M	M	M	M	M	M	M	M	M	M	M		F	G	F	G	G	G	G
Hexanediol	M	E	G	G	G						M	M	M	M	M	M	M	M	M	M	M	M		F	G	F	G	G	G	G
Propanediol	M	E	G	G	G						M	M	M	M	M	M	M	M	M	M	M	M		F	G	F	G	G	G	G
Polypropylene glycol	M	E	G	G	G						L	L	L	H	H	L	L	H	H	H	L	L		G	E	F	E	E	G	G
Tetraethylene glycol	M	E	G	G	F						L	L	L	H	H	L	L	H	H	H	L	L		F	G	F	G	G	G	G
Dibutylene glycol	L	G	G	G	G						L	L	L	H	H	L	L	H	H	H	L	L		F	G	F	G	G	F	F
Butylene glycol	L	G	G	G	G						M	M	M	M	M	M	M	M	M	M	M	M		G	E	F	E	E	G	F
Tripropylene glycol	L	G	F	F	G						L	L	L	H	H	L	L	H	H	H	L	L		G	E	F	E	E	G	G
Dipropylene glycol	L	G	F	F	G						M	M	M	M	M	M	M	M	M	M	M	M		G	E	F	E	E	G	F
Propylene glycol	L	G	G	G	G						H	H	H	L	L	H	H	L	L	L	H	H		G	E	F	E	E	G	F
Triethylene glycol	L	G	F	F	F						L	L	L	H	H	L	L	H	H	H	L	L		F	G	P	G	G	P	F
Diethylene glycol	L	G	P	P	P						M	M	M	M	M	M	M	M	M	M	M	M		F	G	P	G	G	P	P
Ethylene glycol	L	G	F	F	P						H	H	H	L	L	H	H	L	L	L	H	H		F	G	P	G	G	P	P

nor do they show all the effects, purposes, and properties that these materials impart to polyester resins. In the instances where the imparted properties are known, they are given. In other cases, properties that may be imparted to a given resin by a particular material may not be known, and so the charts will indicate this also.

In many instances, these materials will be used in very small quantities or percentages, along with other, more conventional components.

The purpose of these charts is to make the industry aware of the great quantities of such materials that are available for use in polyester resins. These raw materials, intermediates, and monomers differ so widely in characteristics that there is almost no limit to the end properties that the finished polymer may have.

Every resin must be tailored to fit its end purpose, with every conceivable requirement taken into consideration. A resin designed with one environment in mind may be totally unsuitable for use in another application.

No contention is made that polyesters can be formulated to fill every need in the plastics industry. There are applications where polyesters would be entirely unsuitable. However, by very careful formulation, polyester resins can be manufactured that are more versatile and that can fulfill a far larger segment of the needs for organic polymers than was ever thought to be possible.

It is very difficult, if not impossible, to categorize these hydroxyl components as poor, fair, good, or excellent. It all depends exactly on the formulations in which they are used and the combinations with the other hydroxyl components.

Several points do stand out rather clearly, however, as a general rule. Propylene and many other hydroxyl components withstand weather better than the ethylene derivatives. The diethylene components seem lowest in resistance to outdoor exposure. As the ethylene derivatives become polyfunctional, the higher the functionality, the better they withstand outdoor exposure but still to a lesser degree than the polypropylenes and others. The higher the hydrocarbon content, the better the weather resistance in most cases. The longer the chain length of the hydroxyl component, the more flexible the resin may be. Excess oxygen bridges in this component tends toward water sensitivity. The higher the functionality of the hydroxyl component, the better the chemical resistance of the end resin, and the better the reactivity of the resin.

A great deal, however, depends on the other components in the resin. Hydroxyl components affect the end properties far less than unsaturated acids, saturated acids, and monomers. There are exceptions to all generalities, however, and one example would be bisphenol A, which imparts excellent alkali resistance to an end resin. Another notable example would be polybutadiene, which although producing very flexible resins, will also impart good chemical resistance. Very few very flexible resins can have such good resistance to chemicals, weather, etc.

It must be understood that many of these hydroxyl components would never be used as the sole component. Pentaetheritol, sorbitol, glycerine, and others would be utilized as a relatively small part of the total component. These materials are so highly reactive they must be used with care or the batch can easily gel in the reactor.

Other intermediates have specific characteristics which can be imparted to a finished polymer. Bisphenol A imparts the ability for better bonding to metal, glass, and other substrates. It should be at least a part of the hydroxyl component in any resin to be used in formulating a metal primer.

The isophthalic resins, in which bisphenol A is incorporated, give the very best of bonds to metal, glass, and other nonporous surfaces. By the same token, good mold releases—internal or external—are more difficult to find for them.

Besides thiodiglycol, listed here, there a number of derivatives of mercaptopropionic acids which should have extensive use in polyesters. These HSOH groups are very reactive and may impart very desirable properties to the resin.

Other relatively untried materials are the polyactones and neopentyl glycol. Their characteristics make them ideal for use in polyesters.

The hydroxyl component does not seem to affect such factors as shrinkage, abrasion resistance, or resistance to solvents to any degree. The type of cure and the process by which the end product is manufactured also do not to appear to be affected by the exact hydroxyl component. The more reactive the resin, the faster and better it will cure.

It is very difficult to classify a given saturated acid as imparting low, medium, or high mechanical properties. In most cases, it relates directly to the flexural modulus.

Isophthalic acid is perhaps the most difficult to classify. With this saturated acid, the finished resin can range from very flexible to very rigid, according to the molar ratio of saturated to unsaturated acid. Its end properties, however, will be higher than most other resins of like modulus.

Such acids as adipic, sebacic, and succinic acids will given resins of low modulus, and all other mechanical properties will be correspondingly low, regardless of the molar ratios of saturated to unsaturated acids.

Intermediates such as chlorendic anhydride, HET acid (hexachlorendomethylene tetrahydrophthalic acid), pyromellitic dianhydride, and trimellitic acid will give resins of very high modulus, even when used

Legend:
L—low, X—not recommended
M—medium, E—excellent
H—high, O—no known effect
P—poor, C—only in combination
F—fair, Blank—not known
G—good

Property	Phthalic anhydride	Isophthalic acid	Terephthalic anh.	Tetrahydrophthalic	Hexahydrophthalic	Tetrachlorophthalic	Adipic acid	Sebacic acid	Succinic acid	Chlorendic anh.	Pyromellitic dianh.	Dodecylsuccinic anh.	Methyl (nadic) anh.	Chlorophthalic	Chlorosuccinic	Acrylic acid	Methacrylic acid	Ascorbic acid	Mellisic acid	Naphoic acid	Benzophenone t-dianh.	Digallic acid	HET acid	Cyclopentane dianh.	Trimellitic anh.	Diphenic acid	Formic acid
Cost	L	M	M	M	M	H	H	H	H	H	H	H	M	H	H	M	M	M	M	M					H		
Reactivity	O	G	G	E	E	G	O	O	O	O	E	E	E	O	O	E	E		E			G		E	E		
Ambient-temp. cures	G	G	E	E	E	G	F	F	F	G	E	O	E	G	G	E	E		E			E	E	E	E		
Medium-temp. cures	F	O	O	O	O	G	F	F	F	G	E	F	E	G	G	E	E		E			E	E	E	E		
Elevated temp. cures	P	F	F	F	F	G	P	F	F	F	E	F	E	F	F	P	P		F			G	F	G	G		
Ultraviolet resistance	M	H	M	M	M	H	L	M	M	H	H	M	H	H	M	M	M	M	M			M	H	M	H		
Infrared resistance	M	H	M	M	M	M	L	L	L	H	H	M	H	M	M	M	M	M	M			M	H	M	H		
Oxidation resistance	L	L	L	M	M	M	L	L	L	H	H	L	H	H	L	L	L		L			L	H	H	H		
Abrasion resistance	M	H	M	M	M	H	L	M	M	H	H	M	H	H	M	M	M		M			M	H	H	H		
Shrinkage	H	H	H	H	H	M	H	H	H	H	H	H	H	H	H	H	H		H			H	H	H	H		
Tensile strength	L	H	L	M	M	M	H	L	L	L	L	L	L	L	L	L	L		L			L	L	L	L		
Compressive strength	L	H	H	M	M	M	L	M	M	M	M	M	H	M	M	M	M		M			M	L	L	L		
Flexural modulus	M	H	H	M	M	M	M	M	M	M	M	M	M	M	M	M	M		M			M	L	L	L		
Flexural strength	H	H	H	M	M	M	M	M	M	M	M	M	M	M	M	M	M		M			M	L	L	L		
Impact strength	H	H	H	H	H	M	M	M	M	M	M	M	M	M	M	M	M		M			M	L	L	L		
Elongation	L	L	L	L	L	L	M	M	M	L	L	M	L	M	M	L	L		L			L	L	L	L		
Hardness (Barcol)	M	H	M	H	H	M	M	M	M	M	M	M	M	M	M	M	M		M			M	M	M	M		
Dielectric strength	L	H	H	H	H	M	M	M	M	L	L	M	L	L	L	M	M		M			M	L	L	L		
Dielectric constant	L	H	H	H	H	L	M	M	M	L	L	M	L	L	L	M	M		M			M	L	L	L		
Water absorption	F	L	L	L	L	L	P	P	P	L	L	P	L	L	L	P	P		P			P	L	L	L		
Gas permeability	P	L	F	L	L	O	P	P	P	L	L	P	L	L	L	P	P		P			P	L	L	L		
Heat resistance	P	F	P	F	F	O	P	P	P	P	P	P	F	F	F	P	P		P			P	F	F	P		
Flame resistance	G	P	P	O	O	G	O	G	G	O	G	O	O	G	O	G	O		O			G	O	G	G		
Organic-acid resistance	O	F	F	F	F	F	G	G	G	F	G	F	G	F	P	P	P		P			P	F	F	P		
Inorganic-acid resistance	P	F	F	F	F	L	G	G	G	F	F	F	F	L	L	L	L		L			L	F	F	P		
Alkali resistance	G	E	O	O	O	O	O	O	O	O	O	O	O	O	O	O	O		O			O	O	O	O		
Salt resistance	P	E	F	F	F	O	G	G	G	E	E	F	E	F	F	P	P		F			F	F	F	P		
Sulfides resistance	G	E	E	E	E	G	G	G	G	E	E	G	E	E	G	G	G		E			E	E	E	E		
Solvents resistance	O	E	E	E	E	O	G	G	G	E	E	O	E	E	G	G	G		E			E	E	E	E		
Air cure	P	F	E	E	E	G	P	G	G	G	G	P	G	G	F	F	F		G			P	G	G	G		

No major effects (noted over the Succinic acid and Methyl (nadic) anh. column groups)

All except chlorinated (noted over the right-hand column group near HET acid / Cyclopentane dianh.)

in rather high molar ratios with unsaturated acids. In these materials, usually used in applications calling for very high heat-distortion points, it is very difficult to attain anything except a rather high modulus resin.

The chlorinated saturated acids give good result in any environments, except acid environments, for which there are other intermediates far more 'suited. They do give good results in alkaline environments, especially when combined with bisphenol A in the same formulation. The higher the chlorine content, the better will be the finished resin for flame resistance.

Little difference can be noted in resistance to solvents, except that the more rigid the polymer, the higher the resistance.

Shrinkage seems to be dependent entirely on the choice of monomers and the molar ratio of monomers used. Little or no difference in shrinkage can be seen between highly flexible and very rigid resins.

The choice of the saturated acid does not affect the process in which a resin is to be used or the curing system that is to be used. The more reactive a resin, the faster and better it will cure in any given process at any given temperature.

Reactivity depends to a great extent on the molar ratio of saturated to unsaturated acids. However, in a highly flexible resin containing a very low molar ratio of unsaturated acid, much or all of the difference in reactivity can be compensated for in the hydroxyl component by utilizing more polyfunctional components. Also, much of the lack of reactivity in a resin containing very high molar ratios of saturated acids can be made up in the monomer and catalyst-promoter systems.

A few of these saturated acids are much more reactive than others, regardless of molar ratios. Chart 9 shows the most and least reactive acids. Some of them are so reactive that only small percentages of the saturated component may consist of these. They must be balanced with other, less reactive acids.

Some of the saturated-acid components combine well with other acids and some do not. Isophthalic does not combine well with other saturated acids in a formulation; too many of the desirable properties of the isophthalic acid are lost. However, in cases where impact strength and flexibility are not of consequence, it may be done.

The unsaturated acid components are the least known of all the component parts of polyester resins. Almost all work has been done so far with maleic anhydride because of low cost. Recently, some work was done with fumaric acid when it was found to be most suitable for use in resins for certain applications. Even more recently, work has been done with the chlorofumaric and chloromaleic acids in order to achieve maximum flame resistance and alkali resistance.

Beyond this, a small amount of research has been done with methyl maleic, mesaconic, and itaconic acids. However, here work has stopped. The resin manufacturers felt their products were good enough and did not need to be improved through unsaturated acids. Properties were far easier to change through the hydroxyl component and the saturated acids, so why try to improve on already good unsaturated components?

It is in these unsaturated components, however, where perhaps the greatest improvements in polyesters can be made. Chart 10 gives many acids which are suitable for use in polyesters even if they are only a relatively small percentage of the unsaturated component.

Recently it has been found that crotonic-acid derivatives are most useful as ultraviolet screening agents. Why not use crotonic acid as part of the resin itself? Perhaps in this manner a resin can be formulated which is completely impervious to ultraviolet and infrared light, etc.

Coumaric acid is also a readily available acid which might be used to good advantage in polyesters. Work by at least one of the leading manufacturers of additives has shown that coumaric-acid derivatives are excellent clarifiers for polyesters, epoxies, and polyamides. Perhaps the word "clarifiers" is not the precise term that should be used. Many of the derivatives of coumaric acid are fluorescent and cause the polymers to appear lighter in color. "Brightener" is probably a better term for them. Certain fluorescent compounds have shown that in some plastics they can reduce the darkening from outdoor exposure. Used in small percentages, coumaric acid may be a most valuable component for polyesters.

Thioglycolic and mercaptopropionic acids should be most useful as part of the unsaturated component. The thio group has shown excellent results in imparting flexibility to plastics.

Acids such as benzoyl benzoic, stearic, salicylic acid, and many others may prove very useful in polyesters. Some of the amino acids may be able to impart some very distinctive properties to polyesters.

Polyester-resin manufacturers have always been very limited as to the amount of properties that could be designed into a resin through the unsaturated acids. Maleic anhydride and fumaric acid give rigid resins when used on an equimolar ratio with the saturated acids. The resin cannot be modified through maleic and fumaric acids, except by lowering the molar ratio and increasing the molar content of the saturated acid. When the molar ratio of these acids is lowered, the resin becomes less reactive, especially when it is lowered from an equimolar level by 75% or more. Thus, to regain reactivity the resin must be modified with pentaerythritol and other highly reactive hydroxyl components.

Why not develop an unsaturated acid that can impart resiliency or flexibility on its own accord, without lowering ratios and thus lowering the reactivity of the resin? The thio acids seem most likely to be able

CHART 10. UNSATURATED ACIDS AND ANHYDRIDES: EFFECTS AND PROPERTIES IMPARTED TO POLYESTERS

L-low E-excellent M-medium X-not recommended H-high O-no known effect P-poor C-only in combination F-fair G-good Blank-not known	Maleic anhydride	Fumaric acid	Chloromaleic acid	Methyl maleic acid	Mesaconic acid	Chlorofumaric acid	Itaconic acid	Stearic acid	Aceitic acid	Amino butyric acid	Amino caproic acid	Caproic acid	Cinnamic acid	Citric acid	Crotonic acid	Crotonic anhydride	Coumaric acid	Hydratropic acid	Myristic acid	Thioglycolic acid	Mercaptopropionic acid	Lactoic acid	Tartaric acid	Glyceric acid	Benzoyl benzoic acid	Teraconic acid
Cost	L	M	H	M	M	H	H	M	M			M	M	M	M	M	M			H	H					
Reactivity	E	E	E	G	G	E	E																			
Ambient-temp. cures																										
Medium-temp. cures									No apparent effects																	
Elevated-temp. cures																										
Ultraviolet resistance	G	E	E	G	G	E	G																			
Infrared resistance	G	G	G	G	G	G	G																			
Oxidation resistance	E	E	E	E	E	E	E																			
Ambrasion resistance									Apparently no effect																	
Shrinkage									No effects known																	
Tensile strength	H	H	H	H	H	H	H																			
Compressive strength	H	H	H	H	H	H	H																			
Flexural modulus	H	H	H	H	H	H	M																			
Flexural strength	H	H	H	H	H	H	M																			
Impact strength	M	M	H	M	M	H	H																			
Elongation	L	L	L	L	L	L	L																			
Hardness (Barcol)	H	H	H	H	H	H	H																			
Dielectric strength	E	E	G	E	E	G	E																			
Dielectric constant	E	E	G	E	E	G	E																			
Water absorption	L	L	L	L	L	L	L																			
Gas permeability	L	L	L	L	L	L	L																			
Heat resistance	F	F	G	F	F	G	F																			
Flame resistance	F	F	E	F	F	E	F																			
Organic-acid resistance	F	F	F	F	F	F	F																			
Inorganic-acid resistance	E	E	F	E	E	F	E																			
Alkali resistance	F	F	G	F	F	G	F																			
Salt resistance	E	E	E	E	E	E	E																			
Sulfides resistance	E	E	E	E	E	E	E																			
Solvents resistance									All except chlorinated																	
Air cure	F	G	E	F	F	E	F																			

to do this. There are a number to choose from. The prices are rather high mostly because these acids are seldom used, and the price is reflected from the relatively small production. If and when large volumes of these acids are marketed, the price will decrease.

The values for the well-known acids are given for when they are used at equimolar ratio with the saturated acids. No values could be assessed for the lesser-known acids since no data on their use in polyesters is available.

There is truly little difference in the properties these commonly used acids impart to polyesters, except that the chlorinated acids impart excellent flame resistance, considerably better alkali resistance, and better air-curing properties. The chlorinated acids detract somewhat from the electrical properties of a resin, as compared to maleic and fumaric acids. The chlorinated acids also impart slightly better resistance to ultraviolet light than the fumaric and maleic acids. Resins manufactured with these will also resist the chlorinated solvents slightly better than the other acids, but not well enough for the resins to be used in or around these solvents.

Research is overdue on new and untried unsaturated acids. There is a real need for these components, which can impart properties differing from the standard maleic and fumaric acids. Perhaps only very small percentages of some of these other acids can be of great value to the resin manufacturer and the processor of finished products.

As seen in Chart 11, monomers can vary the properties of the resin considerably. Those in the reactivity column C must never be used alone in polyesters. They must always be used with at least one other monomer.

All monomers are best used in combination with others in order to gain maximum cross-linking between polymer and monomers. By careful combination of two or more, properties can be improved quite drastically.

Some of the monomers are marked with an X to show that they should not be used under certain cure conditions. Some of them do not react well at ambient temperatures, and others have low boiling points which make them unsuitable for elevated temperature cures.

The acrylic monomers are perhaps the most difficult to work with because of their widely varying boiling points and properties. All the acrylics and methacrylates are most useful for resin clarity and good resistance to outdoor exposure. They have undesirable properties in that they detract from the abrasion resistance of the polymer, and they increase the shrinkage somewhat, particularly in the lower-boiling monomers. They have low heat resistance, except for 2-cyanoethyl acrylate, which is rather good.

CHART 11. MONOMERS: EFFECTS AND PROPERTIES IMPARTED TO POLYESTER RESINS

Legend:

L–low E–excellent
M–medium X–not recommended
H–high O–no known effects
P–poor C–only in combination
F–fair Blank–not known
G–good

Property	Styrene	m & o chlorostyrene	Dichlorostyrene	Methyl styrene	Ethyl acrylate	Methyl acrylate	2-Ethyl hexylacrylate	Butyl acrylate	Isodecyl acrylate	2-Cyanoethyl acrylate	Methylmethacrylate	Ethylmethacrylate	Vinyl toluene	Divinyl benzene	Vinyl chloride	Vinyl acetate	Vinylidene chloride	Acrylonitrile	Butadiene	Allyl chloride	Diallyl phthalate	Triallyl cyanaurate	Allyl diglycol carbonate	1,4, Dichlorobutane	Dibutyl fumarate	Hydroxy ethyl acrylate	Hydroxy methyl acrylate
Cost	L	M	M	M	M	M	M	M	H	H	M	M	M	M	M	M	M	M	M	H	H	H	H	M	M	H	H
Reactivity	G	E	F	F	C	C	C	C	C	C	C	C	G	G	C	C	C	C	C	F	G	G	C	F	G	C	C
Ambient-temp. cures	O	G	P	P	F	F	X	X	X	X	G	G	F	F	P	P	P	P	P	P	G	G	X	X	F	P	P
Medium-temp. cures	O	G	P	P	O	O	O	O	O	O	O	O	O	O	O	O	O	O	O	F	G	G	X	O	G	X	X
Elevated-temp. cures	O	O	F	F	O	X	O	O	O	O	X	X	O	O	O	O	O	O	O	O	G	G	X	O	G	X	X
Ultraviolet resistance	P	G	O	G	G	G	E	E	E	E	E	E	E	E	G	F	G	F	E	G	E	E	E	O	E	E	E
Infrared resistance	P	E	G	L	L	L	L	L	L	L	L	L	L	L	L	L	L	L	L	L	L	L	E	G	L	L	L
Oxidation resistance	F	M	G	F	L	L	L	L	L	L	L	L	L	L	L	L	L	L	L	L	H	H	L	G	L	L	L
Abrasion resistance	M	M	M	G	L	L	L	L	L	L	L	L	L	L	L	L	L	L	L	L	L	L	L	M	M	L	L
Shrinkage	H	M	M	M	H	H	H	H	H	H	H	H	M	M	H	M	M	M	H	M	H	H	H	M	M	L	L
Tensile strength	H	H	M	M	L	L	L	L	L	M	H	M	M	M	M	M	M	M	M	M	M	H	M	M	M	L	L
Compressive strength	H	H	M	M	L	L	L	L	L	M	M	M	M	M	L	L	L	M	M	M	H	H	H	M	M	L	L
Flexural modulus	H	H	M	M	L	L	L	L	L	L	L	L	L	L	L	L	L	L	L	H	M	M	H	M	M	L	L
Flexural strength	L	H	M	M	H	L	M	M	L	M	M	M	M	M	M	M	M	M	H	H	H	H	H	M	M	L	L
Impact strength	L	H	M	M	L	L	L	L	L	L	L	L	L	L	L	L	L	L	L	L	L	L	H	M	M	L	L
Elongation	L	L	L	L	L	M	H	M	M	M	M	M	M	M	M	M	M	M	H	M	L	L	L	L	M	L	L
Hardness (Barcol)	M	M	M	M	M	M	L	L	L	M	M	M	M	M	M	M	M	M	M	H	M	H	M	M	M	M	M
Dielectric strength	H	H	M	H	M	M	M	M	M	M	M	M	M	M	M	M	M	M	M	M	M	M	M	L	M	L	L
Dielectric constant	H	H	M	H	L	L	L	L	L	M	M	M	M	M	M	M	M	M	M	M	M	M	M	L	M	L	L
Water absorption	H	L	M	L	L	L	L	L	L	M	M	M	L	L	L	L	L	L	L	L	L	L	L	L	L	M	M
Gas permeability	L	H	L	L	L	L	L	L	L	L	L	L	H	H	L	M	M	M	H	L	L	L	L	L	L	L	L
Heat resistance	L	L	M	L	M	M	M	M	M	M	M	M	M	M	M	M	M	M	H	M	H	H	M	M	M	M	M
Flame resistance	L	M	M	L	L	L	L	L	L	L	L	L	L	L	M	L	M	L	L	M	L	M	L	H	L	L	L
Organic-acid resistance	M	H	H	H	M	M	M	M	M	M	M	M	M	M	M	M	M	M	M	M	M	H	M	M	M	M	M
Inorganic-acid resistance	H	L	L	L	L	L	L	L	L	L	L	L	L	L	L	L	L	L	L	L	L	L	L	L	L	L	L
Alkali resistance	L	M	M	L	M	M	M	M	M	M	M	M	M	M	M	M	M	M	M	M	H	H	M	M	M	M	M
Salt resistance	H	H	M	L	L	L	L	L	L	L	L	L	L	L	L	L	L	L	L	L	L	L	L	H	M	M	M
Sulfides resistance	L	H	H	H	M	M	M	M	M	M	M	M	M	M	M	M	M	M	M	H	H	H	H	H	H	M	M
Solvents resistance	H	H	H	H	L	L	L	L	L	L	L	L	H	H	L	L	L	M	H	H	H	H	H	H	H	M	M
Air cure	P	G	F	P	P	P	P	P	P	P	P	P	P	P	P	P	P	P	F	F	G	G	P	P	P	P	P

280

The acrylic and methacrylate monomers are used best at one-third to one-half the molar ratio of the total monomer content. At this level, they will improve the color of the resin and greatly improve exterior exposure propreties.

With some monomers, the acrylics react very slowly. This is particularly true when they are combined with a vinyl monomer, butadiene, or dichlorobutane. A very small amount [approximately 0.1% (by weight)] of the total polymer and monomers of either dodecyl mercaptan or lauroyl mercaptan will cause the two monomers to cross-link rapidly and completely when they are catalyzed. This is true whether the cure system is at ambient or other temperatures at which the acrylic can be used. These mercaptans are also promoters when used with hydroperoxide catalysts, so this must be taken into consideration. They do not have any promoting or accelerating effect with any other type of peroxide.

The mercaptans will also cause some of the rather sluggish monomers, such as methylstyrene, dichlorostyrene, and the vinyl monomers, to react more readily with other monomers. A mercaptan can be incorporated into the resin at the plant or added by the end user of the resin, always keeping in mind that it will cause acceleration if it comes in contact with hydroperoxides.

In polyesters that must surface-cure in the presence of air, the field is rather limited to M- or O-chlorostyrene and the allyl monomers. When used at the proper molar ratio in a resin, with the proper components and an acid number of 0, these will give good surface-cures.

In matched-die molding and many other types of processing, the ability to cure in the presence of air is not required, so that the field of monomers from which to choose is very large.

The monomers listed in the chart are but a few of those available. There are many more monomeric and polymeric intermediates that will cross-link well with polyesters.

The two hydroxy acrylates listed in the chart are not true monomers. They are listed because they present some very interesting possibilities with polyesters in that each is a hydroxyl component and a monomer at the same time. They could well be considered as part of the hydroxyl component when the resin is cooked in the reactor and would replace a part of the monomer at the same time. They could be especially useful in reacting with acrylic acid and then fumaric acid perhaps to produce an extremely clear resin for use in cell-casting clear panels and for gel coats, etc. Care must be taken to have a good inhibitor in the cooking process, once the fumaric acid is added, to prevent gelation.

In electrical applications, the allyl and vinyl monomers are the best choices. In applications involving high heats, triallyl cyanaurate gives excellent service.

Careful consideration of these monomers can greatly improve the end properties of any resin. When formulating for optimum properties, the price of the total formulation must often be a last consideration because the best formulation is most often obtained with the more expensive monomers.

Styrene remains by far the lowest in cost of all the monomers. Because of the pressure of competition, resin manufacturers are too prone to use styrene, even knowing that it will not give the best polymer. In some cases, entirely too much styrene is used, which lowers the costs still more.

Styrene is a good monomer in many applications, but it is far from an ideal cross-linking agent in others. It can be used in exterior applications only when combined with one of the acrylics or perhaps an allyl. Styrene can be used in many applications where the optimum properties are necessary but always in combination with other monomers. It reacts well with most monomers when it forms at least $\frac{2}{3}$ the entire monomer system. Below this, it can be sluggish when used with the acrylates, allyl diglycol carbonate, and some of the vinyl monomers. The same amount of the mercaptan compounds (mentioned earlier) will hasten the cross-linking to a great extent.

The base resin, of course, has much to do with the reactivity of the entire system. In highly reactive resins, often the mercaptan compounds will not be necessary or advisable.

In premix compounds that may be exposed to the open air for as many as 4 or 5 hr before being used up, styrene should be used sparingly. Styrene has a high evaporation rate, as do most of the acrylics and methacrylates. If not sealed well, a compound can lose enough of these monomers through evaporation to affect the proper cross-linking. Complete polymerization cannot take place if the monomer level falls below the stoichiometric amount. The open compound will lose monomer from the outer surface of the compound (from which it is being used); this can cause sticking because of undercured parts and a very high rejection rate of parts.

The monomers with higher boiling points are far better for use in such compounds. Vinyl toluene, the allyls, and the higher-boiling acrylates are ideal in these situations.

Monomers form a very important part of the finished polymer. They must be used to best advantage, dictated by a consideration of the exact process in which the resin will be used and the environment to which the finished product will be exposed.

The formulas in Chart 12 are examples of the proper polyester resins

CHART 12. RESIN FORMULAS

Based on:
Total hydroxyl – 2.2 moles
acids – 2.0 moles
monomers as shown

	F1	F2	F3	F4	F5	F6	F7	F8	F9	F10	F11	F12	F13	F14	F15	F16	F17	F18	F19	F20	F21	F22	F23	F24	F25	F26	F27
Hydroxyl components:																											
Propylene glycol	1.1	1.7	1.5	1.5	0.7		2.2	1.1		1.1	1.1	1.1	1.1	2.2		2.2	2.2	2.2	2.2	1.1	1.1	1.1	2.2	2.2	2.2	2.2	1.1
Diethylene glycol					1.5	1.1			1.1											1.1	1.1						
Dicyclopentadiene															1.2												1.1
Bisphenol A			0.7	0.7		1.1		1.1	1.1	1.1	1.1	1.1	1.1									1.1					
Neopentyl glycol															1.0										1.0		
Polybutadiene	1.1	0.5																									
Saturated acids:																											
Phthalic anhydride	1.6	1.3	1.3	1.3						1.2													0.5				
Isophthalic acid					1.1	0.3	1.0		0.5			0.8	0.5		1.4		1.1			1.0		0.4					
Hexahydrophthalic								0.5	0.3							0.9								0.5		0.6	
Tetrahydrophthalic								0.5								0.2								0.5		0.4	
Acrylic acid											1.0										1.0						
Chlorendic anhydride																		0.4	0.7								
HET acid													0.5					0.7	0.4								
Digallic acid									0.2			0.8		1.0								1.0	0.5				
Trimellitic anhydride																	0.9										
Pyromellitic dianhydride																											
Unsaturated acids:																											
Maleic anhydride	0.4			0.7	0.9	0.8	1.0	1.0	1.0	0.8	1.0	0.4	1.0	1.0	0.6	0.9	0.8	0.9	0.9	1.0	1.0	0.6	1.0	1.0	1.0	1.0	1.5
Fumaric acid		0.7																									
Chlorofumaric acid																											
Monomers:																											
Styrene	0.4	0.2	0.5	0.5	0.6	0.6	0.7	0.2	0.2	0.6	0.6	0.2	0.6	0.8	0.5	0.8		0.6	0.6	0.3	0.5	0.4	0.4	0.2	0.3	0.2	0.5
Chlorostyrene						0.6														0.7					0.7	0.6	0.6
Acrylates, Methacrylates								0.4	0.6	0.3	0.5	0.4		0.3	0.3	0.2	0.2	0.4	0.4					0.4	0.2	0.4	0.1
Vinyl toluene	0.2	0.7	0.4	0.4	0.4	0.3	0.4																				
Diallyl phthalate								0.5					0.5							0.1	0.5	0.6	0.8	0.6			
Triallyl cyanaurate									0.3												0.1						

Note: All quantities expressed in moles

for certain applications and certain processes. The characteristics and properties of these basic resins may be altered as outlined in Charts 8, 9, 10, 11, 13, 14, 15, and 16.

Formula 1: For compression-molded floor tile, flexible

Formula 2: For pressure-cast flooring, large patterns, resilient

Formula 3: For compression-molded floor tile, industrial type, resilient

Formula 4: For terrazzo-type floor tile, poured in place, room temperature

Formula 5: For industrial flooring, poured in place, room temperature

Formula 6: For protective concrete toppings, poured in place, ambient temperature

Formula 7: Gel coat, for interior use, wall paneling synthetic ceramic tile, etc.

Formula 8: Gel coat, exterior use, synthetic marble, granite, etc.

Formula 9: Gel coat, vanity tops, bathroom fixtures, bar tops, etc.

Formula 10: For exterior synthetic brick, synthetic dimension stone, rustic panels, and exterior marble and granite panels

Formula 11: For rigid roofing materials

Formula 12: For flexible, rolled roofing materials

Formula 13: For high-pressure pipe, filament-wound

Formula 14: For polyester foam

Formula 15: For coatings, steel primer

Formula 16: Air-cure coatings, exterior environment

Formula 17: Air-cure coatings, interior

Formula 18: Air-cure coatings, heat resistant

Formula 19: Air-cure coatings, flame resistant

Formula 20: Air-cure coatings, acid resistant

Formula 21: Air-cure coatings, alkali resistant

Formula 22: Polyester for electrical-wiring insulation

Formula 23: Polyester for high dielectric strength, rigid

Formula 24: Polyester, extremely clear, for optical use

Formula 25: Polyester for marine use—boats, ships, barges, high salt resistance, high strength

Formula 26: Polyester for use in automobiles, aircraft, swimming pools, etc., weather resistant

Formula 27: Polyester resin for fiber, fabric, clothing, plastics reinforcement, etc.

Note: All monomers are given at near stoichiometric amounts. These may be increased 5 to 10% in some cases, but it should be done with extreme care, particularly in resins for coatings that must air-cure, and always with the knowledge in mind that any changes in monomer content will affect end properties. The environment must be uppermost in considering additional monomers.

Additives are materials that are usually employed in very small quantities. Some of them are used at levels of a few parts per million (by weight) of the polymer. Others are used at levels of 5% or more in certain applications. They form a very important part of the finished poly-

CHART 13. ADDITIVES: PROPERTIES AND EFFECTS IMPARTED TO POLYESTERS

Legend:
L-low M-medium H-high P-poor F-fair G-good
E-excellent X-not recommended O-no known effect A-asset D-detriment

Additive	Cost	Ultraviolet absorption	Ultraviolet blocking	Infrared blocking	Oxidation resistance	Clarifiers	Color stabilizers	Thixotrophy flow control	Surface appearance	Surface tension	Glass retention	Flatting agent	Mold release internal	Heat resistance	Flame resistance	Water resistance	Static electricity resist.	Air-cure aid	Inhibitors, manuf.	Inhibitors, resin	Plasticizers	Promoters	Open molds	Matched dies	Ambient-temp. cures	Medium-temp. cures	Elevated-temp. cures
Benzophenones	H	G		P	P																						X
Crotonic acid der.	H	G		F	G																						
Coumarin compounds	H		F	F	P																						X
Zirconium compounds	M		G	G	G																						
Salicilates	M	F	F	P	P																				G	G	F
Colloidal silicas	H		F	F	G	F		G	G		E	G											G		G	G	F
Silica aerogels	H			F	G			G	G		E	E															
1/2 sec. butyrate	M			G				E								F		G					G	F			
1/10 sec. butyrate	M			G				E								F		G					G	F			
Triphenyl phosphite	M																										
Copper naphenate	M																										
Triammonium phosphate	H														G						F						
Diallyl chlorendate	L													G	G						F		G				
Chlorinated biphenyls	H	G													G						G						
Chlorinated polyphenyls	H	G								F					G						G						
Silicone (special)									E	E	E			G		G					F			X			
Organic semiconductors					E												E										
Hydroquinone																				G							
Tert-Butyl catechol																				G							
Quarternary ammonium																				G							
Pyrogallol																				G					G		X
D.m. amino m. phenol																			G						F	X	F
Promoters, Charts 14, 15																										G	G
Mold release, Chart 17																									X	X	G
Copper salts																									X	X	G
Biocides, fungacides																									X	X	G

For use in marine and certain environments

mer, giving it specific properties and characteristics and performing vital functions in the end application.

The additives used in light stabilization are perhaps the most controversial of all. Polyesters, like most organic polymers, will darken somewhat with age when given complete outdoor exposure for long periods of time. This is most noticeable in the clear, unpigmented gel coats. Polyesters, properly manufactured for specific outdoor exposure do not darken nearly as badly as do many other organic polymers. They will become slightly darker than the straight acrylics, methacrylates, allyls, and polycarbonates. For this reason it is important to incorporate some of the characteristics and properties of these polymers into the polyesters by selecting the monomers of these materials.

A tremendous amount of research has been done on the causes and cures of organic polymer discoloration and degradation when exposed to the weather. This work has taken many routes, following many theories as to the causes. Many researchers have felt they had the answers and proceeded to use additives that gave the most promising results. Some of these additives have given excellent temporary results, some have aided permanently, and some have aided permanently but have given very undesirable side effects.

We know there are several causes for the darkening and deterioration of polyesters and other polymers. We suspect a great variety of other causes and co-causes. We have considerable tangible proof for much of this evidence, yet a great deal must be learned before the final answers are found for many of the problems involved.

We know that ultraviolet light from the sun or artificial lighting causes some of the discoloration of clear plastics. We even know the wavelength which causes this in many of the polymers. In polyesters, the wavelength most harmful is from 275,000 to 400,000 mμ.

Many additives are available that will either absorb, block, or screen the ultraviolet rays at this wavelength. There are hundreds of benzophenone compounds that are quite effective for varying periods of time. Some of the new, recently developed crotonic-acid derivatives are extremely effective. A few zirconium and coumarin compounds show great promise in alleviating this particular problem. A limited number of salicilate compounds have proven quite effective. It has been shown that these will change, or partially convert, to benzophenones during the reaction of the polymer.

There are additional effective ways of overcoming the harm done by ultraviolet light. In some extremely clear polyesters, the best protection is found without artificial blocking or screening agents. Because of their high rate of light transmission, the rays are allowed to pass through the clear material to the pigmented substrate, with very little, if any, effects. The higher the degree of light transmission, the less the polyester suffers from the ultraviolet rays.

The crystalline structure of a given polyester has also been shown to have definite effects on the ability to withstand the effects of ultraviolet light. The more crystalline polyesters have the highest degree of branching and cross-linkage. These are much more resistant to the wavelengths which most affect the polymer. This is the reason for having highly reactive polymers, with two or more monomers, in any system to be used in applications involving extreme outdoor exposure.

Oxidation is the second most important cause of the discoloration and degradation of polyesters in outdoor exposure. Some researchers rate it first and ultraviolet light second. All materials, whether concrete, stainless steel, copper, or plastic, are subject to oxidation to some degree.

In polyesters, oxidation is accelerated in any polymer that has not reached its optimum degree of polymerization. Any unreacted groups, whether they be any residual carboxylic molecules or undercured monomer groups because of air inhibition, are subject to oxidation at very fast rates.

In molded parts, where the exposed side of the product is the side that cures next to the mold or die, there is little danger of oxidation in a properly formulated polymer. The problem arises on the side that cures in contact with the air. For this reason it is important to reduce the acid number of any resin to 0 and to have the monomer content very close to the stoichiometric amounts. In addition, in coatings resins and other resins where maximum weather resistance is desired, the raw materials and intermediates must be chosen for their air-curing properties.

We know that oxidation and ultraviolet light are responsible in part for much of the discoloration and degradation of polyesters and other plastics. This is fully evidence by yellowing or discoloration, loss of gloss, and, in time, complete deterioration. However, in all this what part is played by infrared light? What part is played by water, by hydrogen, and by nitrogen? What part is played by ozone?

The theories are many and complicated, depending on the individual researcher and the exact phase he is investigating. Unfortunately, research is too often directed toward the sale of a product, rather than toward solving an overall problem. Solving one of the causes of exterior degradation is, of course, helped to some degree when one of the causes can be eliminated, but far too little work is being done on the total picture, with all the possible factors firmly in mind. It is helpful to delay the discoloration of the polymer, or to increase its expected useful life in a given environment, but all these problems must be solved before it can be said that the life expectancy of a polyester product is unlimited.

Recent work by this writer has shown that the infrared rays at the edge of the visable spectrum are equally as harmful to the polyesters as the ultraviolet light rays, if not more so. In a cabinet setup, excluding all other factors, tests were run for a period of 180 days. It was shown that both ultraviolet light and infrared rays will cause darkening of polyesters and most other polymers but will not cause loss of gloss on the surface. Loss of gloss on the surface is almost entirely a factor of oxidation. In polyesters that were purposely undercured, oxidation also caused darkening of the polymer at a much faster rate than either ultraviolet light or infrared.

On properly formulated, fully polymerized polyesters, containing one monomer (styrene), discoloration in the ultraviolet cabinet was considerably less than in the infrared cabinet. Samples in the oxidation cabinet showed only very slight loss of gloss and no discoloration, showing the relation of oxidation to loss of gloss.

On samples containing two monomers and three monomers, the results were in exact parallel—no discoloration from the effects of ultraviolet light, very slight darkening from infrared, and no loss of gloss whatever.

All these tests were run without additives of any kind, but with polyester resins, monomers, and catalysts only. They were heat-cured, and the degree of polymerization was judged by the Barcol hardness of each sample.

Exactly the same tests were run on samples containing the various ultraviolet blocking agents. Twenty-seven samples were made, using benzophenones, crotonic-acid derivatives, salicylates, zirconium compounds, and coumarin compounds. Again, they were heat-cured, without promoters or other additives of any kind. The results of 180 days under the intensive tests were somewhat enlightening, if not totally conclusive.

The formulated samples containing benzophenones and salicylates showed no signs of either ultraviolet or infrared discoloration. Oxidation was not apparent for 90 days, but at 120 and 150 days the rate of oxidation had increased very rapidly. At the end of the 180 days, the samples were oxidized badly, with no gloss and considerable yellowing. The samples containing the coumarin compounds also showed good results in the ultraviolet and infrared cabinets but very poor results in the oxidation cabinet, even slightly worse than the benzophenones. The samples containing the zirconium compounds showed the best results of all three cabinets.

These results, although they are far from conclusive, show that the benzophenones and salicylates, while affording good temporary protection from ultraviolet and infrared, actually accelerate oxidation after a certain period. The same thing is true of the coumarin compounds. It could be that these materials decompose into materials which are highly subject to oxidation.

The samples containing the crotonic-acid derivatives showed very good resistance to ultraviolet light but only fair resistance to infrared. No oxidation whatsoever was apparent in these samples.

Although they were far too short and inadequate, these tests do show a definite trend. What they cannot show are the specific parts played by such factors as ozone, hydrogen, and nitrogen. What part, if any, was played by moisture? It seems reasonable to conclude that ozone and water will definitely increase the rate of oxidation. The parts played by hydrogen and nitrogen are not easily calculated.

This area of research must be more fully investigated before any concrete conclusions may be reached. The results of such research can be very rewarding because a polyester that will have an unlimited life expectancy in outdoor exposure could be produced.

The possible effects imparted by catalysts and promoters to polyesters exposed to exterior environments were also investigated, using the same three cabinets described above.

The catalysts that gave the best results were of the perether type, such as di-t-butyl peroxide, di-t-butyl perbenzoate, and di-t-butyl diperphthalate. Much better values were obtained with these in the tests for ultraviolet, infrared, and oxidation than with the oxidizing catalysts such as benzoyl peroxide and the hydroperoxides. (More information about this phase will be given in the discussion of Chart 15.)

The promoters that were used to promote samples cured at room temperature are listed in Chart 14. In the cabinet tests, stannous octoate, manganese, and mercaptan promoters showed superior results for weather resistance. (Chart 14 discusses this phase more completely.)

These tests, as far as they went, did not show any specific damage done by hydrogen. Nitrogen, however, was another matter. Certain aspects of the tests indicated that there was a factor which entered into the discoloration and deterioration other than ultraviolet, infrared, and oxidation.

Thus, a series of tests were run, in which nitrogen was introduced into the formulation through the use of diethyl and dimethyl analine promoters. Although in very small quantities [0.15% (by weight) of the resin], there were definite signs of additional oxidation when these NH groups were present. Samples, containing no promoters of any kind, that were heat-cured were then placed in a container, filled with pure nitrogen, and sealed. These clear-glass containers were placed in each of the three cabinets and checked every 30 days. At the end of 180 days, there were no signs of damage whatever. Thus, nitrogen alone did not cause any darkening or deterioration.

Again, samples were made up, catalyzed without promoters, and heat-cured. These were placed in clear bottles, containing air and a small amount of nitrogen gas.

At the end of 60 days, all samples were unchanged. At the end of 90 days, the sample in the infrared cabinet had begun to darken, while the samples in the ultraviolet and dark cabinets had not begun to change. At the end of 120 days, the sample in the infrared chamber had darkened from a Gardner color of 1, when it was placed into the chamber, to a Gardner color of 4. The sample in the ultraviolet cabinet had just very slightly darkened. No change was apparent in the sample in the dark chamber.

At the end of the 180-day test, the sample in the infrared cabinet had become Gardner 7 in color, the sample in the ultraviolet cabinet was Gardner 3, and the sample in the dark cabinet was completely unchanged.

Thus it was indicated that nitrogen could cause much of the deterioration of plastics when other elements were present. Both infrared and ultraviolet light were contributers, but the infrared was worse than the ultraviolet. Air (or possibly oxygen in the air) and probably moisture were the other elements necessary for these changes.

The exact same three tests were run once again. Unpromoted polyester samples introduced into three clear bottles, each containing air, a small amount of bottled nitrogen, and one small sponge, saturated with water.

The changes that occurred were on the same order as above, except that they were much more pronounced in the ultraviolet and infrared cabinets. At the end of 180 days, both samples were too dark to measure on the Gardner scale. The sample in the dark cabinet had not changed in any way whatever.

It is thus concluded that a combination of oxygen in the air, nitrogen from any source, and direct sunlight all have a very direct effect on the color stability of clear polyesters. Hydrogen may play a small part in all this, but there is no proof of this from these tests.

At this time the principal reaction appears to be that nitric oxide is formed in minute quantities; the nitric oxide then reacts with oxygen to form nitrogen peroxide, which in turn reacts with present moisture to form nitric acid, which attacks the polyester.

It is also possible that nitrogen trioxide is formed, which combines with moisture to form nitrous acid. Another possibility is that hydrogen in the air in some way combines directly with nitrogen to form a weak ammonia on the surface of the polymer.

All these possibilities must be checked further with proper laboratory facilities before any completely satisfactory conclusions may be drawn. They must be tested a number of times, utilizing different base resins and different catalysts, with and without promoters.

Many other factors must enter into the picture. Ozone, and even the different wavelengths of ultraviolet and infrared light must be checked out. There are many possible contributing factors, and all of them must be checked thoroughly.

A few of the answers are available, however, until we know every phase of the problem. Completely cured compounds resist both the effects of infrared and ultraviolet and the effects of oxidation far better than a compound which has an undercured surface. Certain additives (outlined here) greatly aid the yellowing and deterioration of polyesters. Highly cross-linked and branched polymer withstand the ravages of weather far better than the more linear polyesters. The acrylic monomers, the allyl monomers, and others, when used in combinations, aid greatly in any given polyester exposed to this type of environment.

The silicas, both the colloidal and aerogel types, also aid in such an application. Cellulose acetate butyrates and special silicones for polyesters also are an asset to any polyester exposed to outdoor environment.

As outlined more fully in Charts 14 and 15, the choice of catalyst and promoter also can make a great difference in the durability under these conditions.

The entire formulation, from the basic resin to the monomer system, additives, catalyst, and promoters, must be tailored to fit the end use of the polymer. Each phase is equally as important as the next. Each ingredient must be carefully considered from all aspects before being incorporated into the formulation.

Among the other additives, the chart explains the end purpose of each. The inhibitors, of which there are many, are each intended for a certain specific process, whether it calls for an ambient-, moderate-, or elevated-temperature cure.

There are additives which aid thixotropy and flow-control, additives which aid in surface tension, and additives, such as triphenyl phosphite, which stabilize the clarity of the resin when packaged in steel containers. Others aid in making the polymer more scorch and flame resistant.

There are additives which make polyester more resistant to static electricity, clarify the darker resins, and render them impervious to marine-life attack.

When the total necessities of the resin are throughly discussed by both the purchaser and the resin manufacturer, each additive must be discussed, and as many of them should be incorporated into the resin at the plant as is possible. Each additive must be selected to perform an exact function in the finished product.

Besides the promoters listed in Chart 14, there are dozens of other promoters that may be used with some of the catalyst systems. Some of them are of the metallic-salts type, and others are organic.

Most compounds that are to be cured at elevated temperatures should

CHART 14. PROMOTERS

Legend

All promoters at 0.15%	
All catalysts at 1.0%	
X	not recommended
C	in combination only
S	slow
M	medium
F	fast
Y	yes
N	no
R. T.	room temperature
M. T.	moderate temperature
E. T.	elevated temperature

Spanning annotations (across all compounds):
- **Benzoin** — Highly sensitive to ultraviolet and infrared
- **USP-245 (trade name)** — Sensitive only to heat
- **Acidic fillers, pig.** — Accelerate
- **Alkaline fillers, pig.** — Inhibit

Compound	Reactivity	Exterior exposure, curel	Benzoyl peroxide	M.E.K. peroxide	Lauroyl peroxide	Chloro benzoyl per.	Wet benzoyl per.	Dichloro benzoyl per.	Hydroheptyl per.	Succinic acid per.	t-Butyl peroctoate	Di-t-butyl peroxide	Di-t-butyl perbenzoate	Isoprofyl percarbonate	t-Butyl perbenzoate	Acetyl peroxides	t-Butyl peracetate	t-Butyl hydroperoxide	Di-t-butyl Di-perphthalate	Affects clarity
Stannous octoate R. T.	S	Y	S	S	S	S	S	S	S	X	X	X	X	X	X	X	X	X	X	Z
Stannous octoate M. T.	M	Y	S	M	S	S	S	S	M	X	M	X	X	X	M	F	M	M	X	Z
Stannous octoate E. T.	F	Y	M	F	M	M	M	M	F	X	F	F	F	X	F	X	F	F	F	Z
Dimethyl analine R. T.	M	Z	M	X	M	M	M	M	X	S	X	X	X	S	X	X	X	X	X	Y
Dimethyl analine M. T.	F	Z	F	X	F	F	F	F	X	M	M	X	X	M	M	X	M	X	X	Y
Dimethyl analine E. T.	F	Z	F	X	F	F	F	F	X	F	F	X	X	X	F	X	F	X	X	Y
Diethyl analine R. T.	F	Z	M	X	M	M	M	M	X	S	X	X	X	S	X	X	X	X	X	Y
Diethyl analine M. T.	F	Z	F	X	F	F	F	F	X	M	M	X	X	M	M	X	M	X	X	Y
Diethyl analine E. T.	F	Z	F	X	F	F	F	F	X	F	F	X	X	X	F	X	F	X	X	Y
Lauroyl mercaptan R. T.	S	Y	X	S	X	X	X	X	S	U	U	U	U	U	U	U	U	U	U	Z
Lauroyl mercaptan M. T.	M	Y	X	M	X	X	X	X	M	U	U	U	U	U	U	U	U	U	U	Z
Lauroyl mercaptan E. T.	S	Y	X	F	X	X	X	X	F	U	U	U	U	U	U	U	U	U	U	Z
Dodecyl mercaptan R. T.	S	Y	X	S	X	X	X	X	S	U	U	U	U	U	U	U	U	U	U	Z
Dodecyl mercaptan M. T.	S	Y	X	M	X	X	X	X	M	U	U	U	U	U	U	U	U	U	U	Z
Dodecyl mercaptan E. T.	M	Y	X	F	X	X	X	X	F	U	U	U	U	U	U	U	U	U	U	Z
Cobalt napth. R. T.	F	Z	X	S	X	X	X	X	S	X	X	X	X	X	X	M	X	X	X	Z
Cobalt napth. M. T.	F	Z	X	M	X	X	X	X	M	X	X	X	X	X	X	F	X	X	X	Y
Cobalt napth. E. T.	S	Z	X	F	X	X	X	X	F	X	X	X	X	X	X	X	X	X	X	Y
Cobalt octoate R. T.	M	Z	X	S	X	X	X	X	S	X	X	X	X	X	X	M	X	X	X	Y
Cobalt octoate M. T.	F	Z	X	M	X	X	X	X	M	X	X	X	X	X	X	F	X	X	X	Y
Cobalt octoate E. T.	S	Z	X	F	X	X	X	X	F	X	X	X	X	X	X	X	X	X	X	Y
Manganese octoate R. T.	M	Y	X	S	X	X	X	X	S	X	M	X	X	X	X	M	X	X	X	Y
Manganese octoate M. T.	F	Y	X	M	X	X	X	X	M	X	F	X	X	X	X	F	X	X	X	Y
Manganese octoate E. T.	F	Y	X	F	X	X	X	X	F	X	F	X	X	X	X	X	X	X	X	Y
Zirconium napth. R. T.	C	Y	C	C	C	C	C	C	C	C	C	C	C	C	C	C	C	C	C	Z
Zirconium napth. M. T.	C	Y	C	C	C	C	C	C	C	C	C	C	C	C	C	C	C	C	C	Z
Zirconium napth. E. T.	C	Y	C	C	C	C	C	C	C	C	C	C	C	C	C	C	C	C	C	Z

not be promoted. In these cases, promoters are neither desirable nor necessary. There are exceptions to this, however. With catalysts such as *t*-butyl peroctoate, a compound can be made, with a promoter such as dimethyl analine, which still has a mixed pot life of four to 5 hr at ambient temperature. When the compound is placed in the dies, it can be cured in as little as 10 sec at 350°F.

For some catalysts, no known promoter will affect either pot life or cure time. Such a catalyst is United States Peroxygen's 245. This catalyst reacts only to heat.

Promoters must be used with extreme care because they can affect the weatherability of the cured polymer. The cobalt promoters should never be used in exterior applications. The metal is retained in the polyester in sufficient quantities to cause a continued reaction for long periods of time. A polyester promoted with the cobalts will continue to get harder and harder as time progresses. A cured resin, after 7 days at ambient temperature, may register a hardness of 55 on the Barcol imperssor. After 6 months, the hardness will increase to 60, and, after 5 years, will increase to 70. This is not desirable since a point will be reached when the polyester will become brittle and check-crack.

There is some evidence also that the aniline promoters, dimethyl and diethyl, are also harmful to polyesters that are to be used in outdoor exposure. Here, discoloration is the problem. There is some evidence that the NH group in these analines reacts with the catalyst and leaves the nitrogen radical unreacted, which in turn can cause darkening of the polymer through the reaction of ultraviolet, infrared, and oxidation. The quantity would be so small that there seems to be little basis for this theory, but it should be further explored.

The mercaptan promoters, while not nearly so reactive as most other promoters, perform several functions. They act as promoters with the hydroperoxides and as fluxes or cross-linking agents with almost all peroxides in the cross-linking and branching of the different monomer systems with each other and with the resins. Polymerization is more complete in any compound containing small quantities of these mercaptan compounds. They may be used in many instances with combinations of other promoters, and in this provide their most useful function.

There are a number of zirconium compounds available. These are rather new, however, and little is known about their exact function. Enough work has been done with them to know that they are very poor promoters with any of the known catalyst systems. The reaction between a catalyst and a zirconium compound is so slight that it can hardly be classed as a promoter at all. Its function seems best described as a copromoter, particularly in conjunction with the metallic promoters. Zirconium has a synergistic effect on these promoters that causes them to react more completely with a given catalyst. Although the reaction is only preceptably accelerated in the length of time required, the polymerization of the resin is more complete. Since optimum cure of any polymer is of primary importance, the zirconium compounds must be considered as a copromoter in any catalyst-promoter system.

There are evidences of even further benefits in a system which utilizes zirconium compounds. The polymer has far better weathering properties when small amounts of these compounds are added to any system.

Stannous promoters, mercaptans, and zirconium are highly recommended in outdoor applications. For the most part, the mercaptans will be used in combination systems and the zirconiums will always be used in combination with other promoters.

The exact nature of the polyester resin will sometimes dictate the type of promoter system that must be used. In all cases, the processing system will dictate the promoter and the particular catalyst that will be used. Cure times may be adjusted from 72 hr to 10 sec by proper selection and amounts of these promoters. Gel times may be adjusted from 24 hr to 3 sec, depending entirely on the temperature of the dies, the reactivity of the resin, and other factors.

The mercaptans are particularly useful in the B staging of polyesters and in prepreg applications. By proper selection of catalysts and copromoters, a compound may be placed in a soft, partially gelled stage at which it can be kept indefinitely at room temperature or lower, yet can be cured in seconds at elevated temperatures.

Formulating the Compound

All the materials discussed heretofore can be incorporated into the polyester resin at the time it is manufactured and cooled before it is shipped to the consumer. The only other ingredient that sometimes may be added at the plant is the internal mold release. Both the internal and external types of mold releases are discussed later in this chapter (Chart 17).

In formulating the polyester compound for any purpose and process, the first thing that must be considered is the catalyst system. It must conform to the promoter (if a promoter is to be used) and to the basic resin. Also, it must conform to the type of process in which it is to be used, at given temperatures, and under specific conditions.

Chart 15 gives the better-known catalysts and their reactions at different temperatures, without promoters and with promoters. It gives the sensitivity of the catalyst itself to the effects of ultraviolet light and infrared rays. Some catalysts can be activated when the compound is exposed to these elements. Polyester resins, with some of the catalysts incorporated, may be entirely cured (unpromoted) by being exposed to sunlight. With other catalysts, the potlife of the mixed compound may be shortened greatly if it is exposed to a bare lightbulb or to the sun's rays. With still other catalysts, a process may call for curing the compound by artificial ultraviolet light or the combined rays and heat of infrared curing systems.

The gel times noted in Chart 15 are only intended as a general guide and will vary widely with different resins and promoters.

The resin used in this compilation of data was a rigid orthophthalic resin of a medium-reactive type. The promoters used were those recommended in Chart 14 for the given catalyst, and the promoter level in all cases was 0.15%. No combinations of promoters were used in any case.

The catalyst was used in all cases at 1% (by weight of the resin). The tests were made in all cases with 20-g batches in standard test tubes. Up to 175°F, all tests were run in a water bath. From 200°F and higher, all tests were run in an oil bath.

It must be understood that with any given resin, repeated tests must be run with all additives present to obtain true gel and cure times. Every resin will differ greatly in gel and cure times, peak exotherm, and the exotherm curve.

After all tests have been run on the resin and its additives and promoters (if they are to be used), then tests must be run with all pigments, fillers, aggregates, and other materials present before calculations may be made as to the true cycle times that may be expected with a complete compound.

Gel tests, exotherm tests, and cure tests can be very deceiving when run in small-test-tube batches. Every factor in these small batches will change in large batches. The pot life in large batches will be much shorter than in small batches. Gel and cure times will inevitably be longer in the test tube than in matched-metal molds under pressure.

Calculations only may be made from SPI gel tests. They are useful in determining the reactivity of a particular system, and, with experience, fairly close calculations may be made as to the probable cycle time of a given system after fillers, pigments, and other ingredients have been added.

A very useful result of these tests is to constantly check the reactivity of resins, monomers, and catalysts. After prolonged storage, these tests must be run quite often to be sure of the condition of these materials.

These tests also serve a good purpose when testing the gel times of compounds with high filler content. In general, any fillers, pigments, and aggregates that are alkaline will retard the reaction to some degree and slow down gel and cure times. Acidic materials will speed up the reaction in almost every case. Many times a compound with very high alkaline filler contents will require additional catalyst content to compensate for the differential; conversely, highly acid systems will require somewhat less catalyst content.

As a general rule, in systems that are close to neutral in pH, a 1% catalyst concentration is recommended. When a process requires very fast cycle times, this is best accomplished through the use of promoters or higher molding temperatures, not through additional catalyst.

The catalysts in the chart will vary rather widely in active oxygen content. Some catalysts, such as lauroyl peroxide, are very low in oxygen content and will require higher concentrations (as much as 2% in some systems). However, in most cases, the catalyst concentration should be kept close to 1% (by weight of the resin) for optimum properties.

There are many catalysts besides the ones listed in the chart. There are a wide variety of hydroperoxides, such as cumene hydroperoxide, and a great variety of combinations of two or more hydroperoxides. The large catalyst manufacturers have long lists of these combined catalysts from which to choose. Most of them are formulated for specific applications, and a processor would do well to consult with the catalyst manufacturer as to a recommended catalyst or blend of catalysts for his needs.

In addition, there are many other different types of peroxides available. Dicumyl peroxide is a medium-to-high-temperature peroxide which gives good results in some applications. In these solid peroxides, many catalyst manufacturers also furnish blends and combinations of two or more, dispersed in some compatible medium. As a rule, these are either phosphate or phthalate esters, and they are usually furnished in a paste form at 50% concentration of the catalyst, so this will have to be taken into consideration in formulating.

The dry, powdered forms of catalysts will all dissolve well in monomers, but the processor must make up very small batches and keep them in a cold room or use them immediately. Many technical people prefer the paste forms of catalysts, and they will do a good job where matched molds or dies are to be used; however, they should never be used in a process calling for air-cure because a small percentage of the plasticizer can migrate to the surface, causing tackiness at the surface and a soft, easily abraded film.

For almost every process, liquid peroxides are available that will do the job very well. Some of these peroxides are monofunctional, and others are difunctional. The difunctional peroxides will usually give best results at the higher temperatures, with better polymerization and fewer reject parts. This is highly important in high-speed, automated production, where a few reject parts can interrupt the production cycles.

A particular inhibitor system can affect certain catalysts to a rather large degree. Hydroquinone has a far greater inhibiting effect when used with catalysts such as dicumyl peroxide than when used with a hydroperoxide. The promoter system can also be affected, but to a lesser degree, by the inhibitor system.

Each and every factor must be thoroughly checked out repeatedly before final selection of these materials is made for a given application.

Peak exotherm temperatures and exotherm curves are mostly a factor of the polymer itself, governed to a large degree by the reactivity of the resin. However, here, again, there is no hard and fast rule. The inhibitor, promoter, and catalyst can all affect these factors.

A given resin, with varying inhibitors, promoters, and catalysts, can have peak exotherms varying as much as 35°. This can be particularly important in applications such as encapsulation and potting of electrical component parts, where high exotherm temperatures can damage or ruin expensive electrical and electronic components.

The monofunctional catalysts will usually give the highest exotherm temperatures, and benzoyl peroxide will give the highest exotherm temperature of all (by as much as 10% in many systems).

Chart 15 attempts to show approximately the affects of temperature, in rises of 25°F with both promoted and unpromoted resins, on the different catalysts.

In many ways, the chart can be misleading in that the catalysts do not react at an even rate as the temperature rises. Some catalysts have a definite kickoff point, at which the reaction of polymerization becomes much faster—a point with perhaps as little as 3° differential. Only by careful gel tests, run repeatedly on a given resin, can these temperatures be established accurately. Usually, an average value taken from three tests run identically will be close enough for most purposes.

In addition, the chart does not show the differences of gel times with different promoters. The differential can be as much as 75% or more, either way, by changing the promoter or the amount of promoter.

There is absolutely no way to show—graphically or otherwise—many factors concerning the reactions between resin, catalyst, and promoter. These factors can only be deduced from individual testing. They include peak exotherm, time to peak, and curve length of the exotherm. These factors may be established on the resin without pigments, fillers, and other additives as a guideline. But the only way in which they may be established on a compound is to run tests on the total compound, using exactly the same process that will be utilized. Die surface temperature, pressures per square inch, and other factors enter into determining the cycle time that can be expected.

CHART 15. CATALYSTS

Legend:

- All promoters at 0.15%
- All catalysts at 1.0%
- X—not recommended
- Y—yes
- N—no
- R—recommended

Catalyst	Exterior exposure, cured	Ultraviolet sensitive	Infrared-sensitive	Gel, unpromoted 75°F, days	100°F, days	125°F, hr	150°F, hr	175°F, min	200°F, min	225°F, sec	250°F, sec	275°F, sec	300°F, sec	325°F, sec	350°F, sec	Gel, promoted 75°F, hr	100°F, hr	125°F, min	150°F, sec	175°F, sec	200°F, sec	225°F, sec	250°F, sec	275°F, sec	300°F, sec	325°F, sec	350°F, sec
Benzoyl peroxide (dry)		Y	Y	5	1	24	4	45	20	90	75	60	40	20	10	3	3	70	65	40	30	16	X	X	X	X	X
Benzoyl peroxide (wet)				6	1	30	4	50	25	95	75	60	40	20	10	3	3	80	70	42	31	17					
M.E.K. peroxide				4	2	20	2	20	5	60	X	30	X	X	X	2	2	55	40	31	14	6					
Lauroyl peroxide				6	2	30	4	60	35	95	85	70	60	30	15												
Chlorobenzoyl peroxide	R	Y	Y	5	1	24	4	55	25	90	75	60	40	20	10									X	X	X	X
Dichlorobenzoyl peroxide	R	Y	Y	5	1	24	4	55	25	90	75	60	40	20	10								X	X	X	X	X
Hydroheptyl peroxide				5	1	24	4	20	–	95	80	80	40	20	10	5	3	90	70	40	25	15	10	5			
Succinic acid peroxide				9	3	48	7	90	40	–	90	80	40	20	10	2	2	50	35	26	11	7	12	7			
t-Butyl peroctoate	R			5	1	24	–	25	15	–	90	80	40	20	10	5	4	95	65	45	30	17	X	X	X	X	X
Di-t-butyl peroxide				5	1	24	–	25	10	35	10	5	X	X	X	X	X	X	X	X	X	X	X	X	X	X	X
Di-t-butyl perbenzoate				5	1	24	90	40	25	–	90	70	40	20	35												
Isopropyl percarbonate				4	0.7	18	–	10	5	90	90	5	X	X	X												
t-Butyl perbenzoate				9	2	36	4	40	15	95	80	80	40	20	10												
Acetyl peroxides				5	1	24	4	45	20	90	85	75	40	20	10												
t-Butyl peracetate				5	1	24	4	25	10	–	80	70	40	20	10												
t-Butyl hydroperoxides		Y	Y	6	1	24	–	45	15	90	90	70	40	30	10												
Di-t-butyl Diperphthalate	R	Y	Y	6	1	24	–	45	20	95	90	60	30	15	10												
Benzoin				9	2	72	90	90	35	–	90	60	30	15	10												
USP-245 (trade name)				15	4	72	6	40	10	70	45	30	20	10	5												
Acidic fillers, pigments																											
Alkaline fillers, pigments																											
Affects clarity																											
In molecular sieve																											

Annotations:

- Accelerate reaction
- Inhibit reaction
- No promoters react
- All liquid peroxides may be absorbed easily

Note: All tests run with a rigid orthophthalic resin, no fillers or additives, in 20-gram batches.

298

Every ingredient that goes into the compound will affect exotherm temperatures, peaks, and time, if only to a very small extent in some cases. Pigments, fillers, aggregates, and reinforcing materials can all greatly influence these factors by virtue of their thermal conductivity.

A particular unfilled resin system that reaches a peak exotherm of 375°F may peak out at 225°F when used in a compound containing 90% fillers. The same resin system alone may gel in 20 sec at 300°F in the test tube, but when used at 10% (by weight) resin to 90% fillers, the gel time can be reduced drastically if thermally conductive fillers are utilized. All the filler materials that are normally used will be better thermal conductors than the resin itself. Much will depend on the thickness of the parts being produced. The thicker the part, the more conductive the fillers will be in order to attain fast cycles.

In some processes, such as autoclaving parts of large volumes of compounds, resins, catalysts, and fillers must be selected for minimum exotherm temperatures in order to prevent the buildup of excessive heat stresses in the part. The larger the volume of compound being cured, the higher the exotherm temperatures will be in the center.

Apart from using catalysts that are selected merely for exacting cure schedules, catalysts may be used that will affect other aspects of a finished product. There is some rather convincing evidence that shows that the nonoxidizing catalysts, such as perethers, give better service in compounds which are exposed to exterior environments. This phase of formulating needs further study and research.

Alloys. Many other materials are compatible with polyester resins in one form or another. Many polymerize directly with the hydroxyl-terminated polyesters. The diisocyanates are an example, and the combination is known as polyurethanes.

There are many types of epoxies, and most of them are compatible with polyesters. The liquid, unmodified epoxies of the epichlorohydrin-bisphenol type are compatible and combine through their mutual hydroxyls. The oxirane types of epoxies are also completely compatible and work well in combinations with polyesters. The epichlorohydrin-butadiene epoxies also combine very well with all types of polyesters. The Novolak type of epoxies do not combine, except at elevated temperatures.

A compound can gain some fine properties by incorporating differing quantities of epoxy resins. The curing system must be carried out at moderate to elevated temperatures to reach optimum cures. The system must be a two-component system, with the peroxide catalyst in the epoxy and the acid or anhydride hardening agent in the polyester. When the two components are then mixed together, all components polymerize very completely.

These resins are sometimes used in compression-molding compounds for products that are to be subjected to extreme alkaline conditions. The percentages of polyester to epoxy can vary widely; however, the higher the percentage of epoxy, the longer the molding cycle.

These alloys form very highly cross-linked polymers that are very resistant to alkalies, acids, and most extreme environments.

The melamine resins in the mono and dimethylol stages will combine very well with polyesters in applications calling for good surface-cures. While they do not cross-link well at ambient temperatures, they will polymerize very well at moderate to elevated temperatures. The inclusion of 10 to 15% of melamine in polyesters can result in excellent finishes for wall paneling, or applications with good abrasion resistance, and coatings that may be applied in thin films or baked on appliances, furniture, etc.

Polyamides form a strange combination with polyesters. They are very useful in B staging and prepreg applications. They should be used sparingly, however, and some resin systems will take far higher percentages of polyamides than others. When the maximum point is reached, the result is instant gellation into a soft pregel that can later be worked, molded, and cured. Certain patients exist on this combination of resins, and this should not be overlooked.

Polymercaptans, discussed previously as epoxy curing agents, are very useful in polyesters in B staging and prepreg applications. They also may be used in combination epoxy-polyester applications for good room-temperature cures.

The polyacrylates, polymethacrylates, and polystyrenes may be used in polyesters in many applications where a solvent would not be objectionable. These polymers may be predissolved in solvents such as acetone-toluene (70:30) and incorporated into polyester resins to replace a like amount of monomer. These polymers will cross-link the polyester in place of the normal monomers, and the material will surface-cure in the presence of air much better than with monomers.

These materials are particularly suitable for coating formulations, where relatively thin films are to be applied. They may be fully cured at ambient or moderate temperatures very quickly.

The same holds true for many other polymers. The polycarbonates, allyls, acetal, polychloroether, and others are very useful in polyester coating formulations, introduced in solvent solution. All these polymers will replace like amounts of monomers, based on the solids portion of the solvent solution, with the exception of acetal. With this polymer, no monomer is replaced.

Excellent properties may be built into polyester coatings with the use of some of these polymers. They should not be overlooked in any

Key:
L-low · G-good
M-medium · E-excellent
H-high · X-not recommended
P-poor · O-no known effect
F-fair

Property	Diisocyanates	Epoxies	Melamines	Polyamides	Polymercaptans	Polyacrylates	Polymethacrylates	Polystyrenes	Polycarbonates	Allyl polymers	Acetal polymers	Silicones	Polybutadienes	Ketone polymers	Polysulfides	Butyrates (CAB)	Furanes	Alkyds (many types)	Polyvinyl formal	Abietic acid resins	Chlorinated biphenyls	Chlorinated polyphenyls	Polychloroethers	Refined asphalts	Refined coal tars
Cost	M	M	M	H	H	M	M	L	H	H	H	H	M	M	H	M	M	L	M	M	M	M	H	L	L
Reactivity in polyesters	E	F	F	F	E	E	E	L	F	E	L	O	O	O	P	G	P	P	F	O	O	O	O	O	O
Ambient-temp. cures	E	P	X	P	E	E	E	E	F	E	P	F	P	F	P	E	P		F	G	E	E	P	F	F
Medium-temp. cures	E	F	F	G	G	E	E	E	G	E	P	L	F	F	X	E	P		F	X	E	E	P	X	X
Elevated-temp. cures	P	G	E	P	G	E	E	P	G	E	F	P	G	F	X	X	P		F	X	E	E	P	X	X
Ultraviolet resistance	G	G	E	P	G	E	E	P	E	G	F	G	F	P	P	G	O		L	O	O	O	P	O	O
Infrared resistance	E	G	E	P	G	E	E	P	E	G	F	G	F	P	P	G	O		F	O	O	O	F	O	O
Oxidation resistance	G	G	E	P	G	E	E	P	E	G	G	G	F	F	P	E	O		P	O	O	O	G	O	O
Abrasion resistance	E	G	G	G	O	P	P	P	E	G	G	G	F	F	P	L	O		P	O	P	P	G	P	P
Shrinkage	G	G	G	G	O	O	O	O	O	O	O	O	O	O	O	O	O		P	O	O	O	O	O	O
Tensile strength	L	G	G	F	F	G	G	P	G	G	O	O	L	O	P	F	O		L	O	P	O	O	P	P
Compressive strength	L	G	G	F	F	G	G	P	G	G	G	O	L	O	P	F	O		O	O	P	O	O	P	P
Flexural modulus	E	L	H	L	L	L	L	H	M	H	G	O	L	H	L	M	O		F	O	L	L	L	L	L
Impact strength	L	H	L	G	L	M	M	L	L	L	H	O	L	F	O	G	O		O	O	O	O	G	H	L
Flexural strength	M	H	M	L	L	M	M	H	H	H	E	O	H	P	P	F	O		H	O	P	P	G	L	P
Elongation	L	H	L	L	L	M	M	M	L	L	E	O	L	L	H	L	O		L	O	L	L	G	M	M
Hardness (Barcol)	L	L	L	L	L	L	L	M	L	L	L	O	M	M	L	M	O		O	L	L	O	M	L	L
Dielectric strength	M	H	H	M	L	M	M	H	M	H	H	O	L	L	M	M	O		M	L	L	L	H	M	M
Dielectric constant	M	H	M	L	L	M	M	M	H	H	H	O	L	L	M	L	O		L	L	L	L	H	M	M
Water absorption	L	L	L	L	L	P	P	P	L	L	L	H	P	M	H	L	O		M	L	L	L	L	M	M
Gas permeability	L	L	O	O	L	P	P	P	O	O	H	H	P	M	H	F	O		M	L	O	O	O	M	M
Heat resistance	P	P	L	O	L	P	P	P	L	L	H	L	F	P	P	P	O		P	P	E	F	F	X	X
Flame resistance	P	F	O	F	L	P	P	P	F	L	L	L	O	P	P	P	O		P	P	P	F	F	X	X
Organic-acid resistance	P	P	F	P	P	P	P	P	F	G	L	G	O	F	P	G	O		P	P	F	F	F	P	F
Inorganic-acid resistance	F	E	F	P	F	F	F	O	F	F	G	O	E	F	P	G	O		F	F	O	O	O	F	G
Alkali resistance	G	G	G	G	F	F	F	O	F	F	F	G	E	O	F	G	O		O	G	O	O	O	G	G
Salt resistance	O	G	G	G	G	F	F	G	F	F	F	O	E	G	G	G	O		P	P	P	O	E	G	G
Sulfides resistance	G	G	G	O	G	F	F	G	F	F	G	E	O	F	F	P	O		O	P	P	P	E	G	G
Solvent resistance	O	G	G	G	G	L	L	G	L	L	E	E	O	G	P	G	O		O	P	P	P	O	P	P
Air curing	E	G	G	O	F	G	G	F	F	O	O	F	F	G	O	O	O		O	O	O	O	M	O	O

application where solvents are not objectionable. The limit in thickness of an application containing solvent is about 0.010 in. per coat. Beyond this, there is danger of trapping unwanted solvent into the material, which will greatly reduce its resistance and expected life.

Where extremely high viscosity polymers are not objectionable, some of these polymers can be dissolved in such monomers as styrene, methyl methacrylate, and allyls, and introduced into the polyester polymer without solvents of any kind. The resulting polymer will have a very high viscosity, but when properly formulated it can be utilized in many molding and coating applications.

The special silicones used in polyesters are used in such minute quantities that they have little or no effects. The same applies to the butyrates. Butyrates may be introduced into polyester in higher quantities if used in solvent solution. It has no function as a cross-linking agent, but it does alloy very well with polyester at any percentage level. It aids greatly in obtaining good surface-cures in the presence of air. It raises the abrasion resistance of polyesters somewhat in coatings for appliances, equipment, and similar applications.

Many of the other polymers are compatible to some degree with polyesters, depending on the particular polyester polymer used. Ketone polymers, polybutadienes, polysulfides, and furane resins are all compatible to some degree. They should be tested very carefully for the resulting properties of the alloys thus formed.

Abeitic acids, the refined wood rosins, are useful in polyesters in certain applications such as adhesives. These materials will give a polyester the tack that it needs to be used in such applications. The liquid form of these materials also acts as a plasticizer for polyesters, imparting better elongation and lower modulus.

Chlorinated biphenyls and polyphenyls are extremely useful in polyesters in that they impart flame resistance. They are used in proportions of up to about 15% of the polymer. The liquid biphenyls also act as plasticizers, reducing modulus, Barcol hardness, etc. The polyphenyls have little effect on properties, apart from imparting flame resistance.

There is evidence that the chlorinated biphenyls and polyphenyls also aid in the adhesion of polyesters to certain substrates. This should be carefully checked on any given substrate with conditions under which the formula will be utilized.

There are applications in which refined coal tars and asphalts may be used to advantage in polyester resins. The requirements for the coal tar or asphalt are low moisture content, low phenol (free) content, and low sulfur content. Any of these materials which meet these requisites will alloy very well with the more rigid and reactive polyesters for applications such as road patching, pipeline protection, and sheet piling for use in saltwater. These materials may also be used in many saltwater and freshwater environments where more expensive protective coatings or shields would be too costly.

Percentages can range to 50:50, without losing too many of the properties of the polyester. This half-and-half liquid can be further reduced in cost through the use of low-absorption fillers and aggregates. It can be applied by troweling, casting, or in many other ways. It will bond well to steel, concrete, wood and other substrates.

Mold releases are very difficult materials to chart because the types of molds or dies, temperatures, and conditions can vary so widely.

Chart 17 gives a few specific applications of both internal and external mold releases and certain mold and die materials. In general, any type of closed mold or die process is suitable for an internal mold release. The die material itself determines the temperature at which the process can be carried out.

In open dies, where casting or contact molding is being done, an external mold release is generally required. The temperatures at which the product will be cured determine which external mold releases are most suitable. Many of the external mold releases give good service to 300° or higher temperatures, but these are very few and must be thoroughly checked for use at such temperatures. The fluorocarbons are one of the few mold releases that may be used above 300°F in external applications.

Generalities are very dangerous in the polyester industry, and the values set down in this chart are intended as guidelines only. Each application can be very different, and the mold release to be used must be checked at the exact temperatures in the dies under the exact processing conditions which will be used, before a conclusion may be drawn.

Much will depend on the end product. If it must be bonded to another surface, the mold releases that may be used—internal or external—are limited. Some mold releases leave a very thin film on the surface of the part, which, unless completely removed, will prevent bonding with any known adhesive. The internal mold releases that contain stearates are particularly inferior in this respect. The external mold releases must be carefully checked.

If the part is a finished product when it emerges from the dies, then surface appearance is of utmost importance. Mold releases—both internal and external—can affect surface appearance to large extents. Of the internal mold releases, stearic acid and zinc stearate can reduce the gloss of the finished part. Calcium stearate does not do this, nor do most of the commercial mold release preparations.

In external mold releases, the application of the material to the dies or molds is of utmost importance. If applied according to the manufac-

CHART 17. MOLD RELEASES

P-poor F-fair G-good E-excellent X-not recommended	Ambient temp., 100°F	Medium temp., 250°F	Elevated temp., 250-350°F	Open, contact molds	Closed, matched molds	Internal mold release:	Zinc stearate	Stearic acid	Calcium stearate	Zelac (DuPont)	Mildgard-x (RAM)	Mold Wiz 54 (AXEL)	Mold Wiz 20-E (AXEL)	External mold release:	Fluordcarbons	5727 (Mitchell-Rand)	804-071 (Brulin)	512-B (RAM)	605 (RAM)	Silicones	Polyvinyl alcohol	Parfilm (Driscoll)	Kant Stik (Specialty Prod.)	N (Specialty Prod.)	3060 (Crown)	F57-AZN (AXEL)	Carnauba wax
Mold or die type:																											
Mild steel - - - - - - - - - -	V	V	V	V	V										G	E	E	E	E	X	E	E	E	G	E	E	E
Hardened steel - - - - - - -	V	V	V	V	V		F	F	G	E	E	E	E				G	E	G	X	E	G					G
Stainless steel - - - - - - - -	V	V	V	V	V		F	F	G	E	E	E	E				G	E	G	X	E	G					G
Chrome plate - - - - - - - -	V	V	V	V	V		F	F	G	E	E	E	E				G	E	G	X	E	G					G
Cast iron, unplated - - - - -	V	V	V	V	V					F	F	F			G		G	E	G	X	E	G					G
Cast iron, chromed - - - - -	V	V	V	V	V		F	F	G	E	E	E	E				G	E	G	X	E	G					G
Cast aluminum - - - - - - - -	V	V	V	V	V				G	F	F	F			G		G	E	G	X	E	G					G
Aluminum plate or sheet - -	V	V	V	V	V			G	G	F	F	F			G	E	E	E	E	X	E	E	E	E	E	E	E
Cast babbitt metals - - - - -	V	V	X	V	V			G	G	F	F	F			G	E	E	E	E	X	E	E	E	E	E	E	E
Cast lead - - - - - - - - - -	V	V	X	V	V			G	G	G	G	G			G	E	E	E	E	X	E	E	E	E	E	E	E
High-press. phenolic lam. - -	V	V	V	V	V				E	E	E	E	G		G	E	E	E	E	X	E	E	E	E	E	E	E
High-press. melamine lam. -	V	V	X	V	V				G	G	G	G	G		G	E	E	E	E	X	E	E	E	E	E	E	E
Phenolic tooling - - - - - -	V	V	V	V	V				E	E	E	E			G	E	E	E	E	X	E	E	E	E	E	E	E
Epoxy-phenolic tooling - - -	V	V	V	V	V				E	E	E	E			G	E	E	E	E	X	E	E	E	E	E	E	E
Epoxy-amine tooling - - - -	V	V	X	V	V				G	G	G	G			G	E	E	E	E	X	E	E	E	E	E	E	E
Epoxy-anhydride tooling - -	V	V	V	V	V				E	E	E	E			G	E	E	E	E	X	E	E	E	E	E	E	E
Polyester tooling - - - - - -	V	V	X	V	V				F	F	F	F			G	E	E	E	E	X	E	E	E	E	E	E	E
Urethane elastomer - - - - -	V	X	X	V	V										G	X	X	E	X	X	E	X	E	X	X	X	X
Silicone elastomer - - - - -	V	V	V	V			No mold release required													X							
Latex elastomer - - - - - - -	V	X	X	V	V										G	X	X	E	X	X	E	X	E	X	X	X	X
Porcelainized metal - - - -	V	V	V	V	V				E	E	E	E			G	E	E	E	E	X	E	E	E	E	E	E	E
Plate glass (Crown) - - - - -	V	V	X	V	V				E	E	E	E								X							
High-temp. glass - - - - - -	V	V	V	V	V				E	E	E	E								X							
Plaster dies (sealed) - - - - -	V	V	X	V	V										G	E	E	E	E	X	E	E	E	E	E	E	E
Fluorocarbon tooling TFE - -	V	V	V	V	V		No mold release required																				
Fluorocarbon tooling FEP - -	V	V	V	V	V		No mold release required																				
Polyethylene - - - - - - - -	V	X	X				No mold release required													X							
Polypropylene - - - - - - - -	V	X	X	V	V										G	X	X	E	X	X	F	X	E	X	X	X	X

turer's directions, there will seldom be a problem as to defective surfaces.

To a large extent, the surface appearance of the finished part is wholly dependent on the mold surface. If the mold surface is not good, no mold release can give perfect parts.

Internal mold releases may be used in quantities ranging from 0.25 to 1% (by weight of the resin). This will depend largely on the mold or die material, its porosity, and its finish. The more perfect the finish of the dies, the less internal mold release is required to give good clean releases.

In temporary dies of polymeric nature, the temperature of the process will be the most limiting factor in choosing a good mold release. The manufacturer of the mold release will know the limits to which his product will give good results. The processor must know the heat limitations of his molds.

For the most part, silicone-containing mold releases are very unsatisfactory for use with polyesters. Among the materials not listed, which may be used in many applications as good mold releases, are some of the highly refined soya oils and the alginates, such as sodium and potassium alginates. Many waxes may be used as external mold releases at low temperatures and in thin applications where the exotherm temperatures do not exceed the melting point of the wax.

In polyester processing, mold releases form a most important part of the overall picture. They must be chosen with extreme care, bearing all factors in mind. Good releases may be obtained from any surface at any temperature by proper selection.

Some polyesters are harder to release cleanly than others. An isophthalic polyester and the bisphenol A polyesters are the most difficult to release. These will take the maximum 1% of internal mold release in most processes. In any process utilizing o- or m-chlorostyrene as the sole monomer, the release may be difficult also. This monomer is never recommended as a sole monomer in any matched-die process for this reason. When it forms up to 70% of the monomer, no problems are encountered.

The isophthalic polyesters should never be used in silicone-elastomer dies. Orthophthalic resins, containing high contents of acrylic or methacrylate monomers, will do fairly well, but polyesters which are based in part on acrylic acids will give better and many more parts during the life of the dies.

Since pigments are usually used in relatively small quantities, the physical and mechanical properties of the polyester is little changed by the addition of up to 10% (by weight of the resin) of these materials.

The areas where they can become important are in dielectric properties, flame resistance, and chemical resistance. Even in small quantities,

CHART 18. PIGMENTS: PROPERTIES AND EFFECTS IMPARTED TO POLYESTERS

L—low   E—excellent
M—medium   X—not recommended
H—high   O—no known effect
P—poor   A—asset
F—fair   D—detriment
G—good

Pigment	Cost	Specific gravity	Resin absorption	Reactivity	Exterior exposure	Abrasion resistance	Shrinkage	Tensile strength	Compressive strength	Flexural modulus	Flexural strength	Impact strength	Elongation	Hardness (Barcol)	Dielectric properties	Electrical conductivity	Water resistance	Heat resistance	Flame resistance	Organic-acid resistance	Inorganic-acid resistance	Alkali resistance	Salt resistance	Sulfides resistance	Thermal conductivity	Thixotrophy to resin	Pigmenting effect
Iron oxides	L	H	L		V	G		A	A		A	D		A	D	G	G	A	G	D	D	D	D	D	A	L	E
Chrome oxides	H	M	L		V	G		A	A		A	D		A	D	G	E	A	G	D	A	A	A	A	A	L	E
Cadmium colors	H	M	L			G		A	A		A	D		A	D	F	E	A	F	D	D	A	A	A	A	L	E
Phthalocyanines	H	L	L			P		D	D		D	D		A	A	P	E	A	G	A	A	D	A	A	A	L	E
Titanium dioxide (R)	H	M	L			P		D	D		D	D		D	D	F	G	A	F	D	D	D	D	D	A	L	E
Titanium dioxide (A)	H	L	L		V			A	A		A	A		A	D	G	E	A	E	A	A	A	A	A	A	M	E
Carbon black	L	L	L		V	G		A	A		A	D		A	D	E	E	A	E	D	D	A	A	A	A	M	E
Acetylene black	M	M	L	Depends on pH	V	G	All reduce shrinkage	A	A	All raise modulus	A	D	All reduce elongation	A	D	F	E	A	G	D	D	A	A	A	A	L	G
Zirconium dioxide	L	H	L		V	G		A	A		A	D		A	D	F	E	A	E	A	A	A	A	A	A	L	E
Antimony trioxide	H	M	L		V	F		D	A		D	D		A	A	F	E	A	P	D	D	D	D	D	A	L	F
Lead carbonate	L	L	L			F		D	A		A	D		A	D	P	E	A	P	D	D	A	A	A	A	L	F
Zinc oxide	L	L	L			F		A	D		D	A		A	D	F	E	A	P	D	D	A	A	A	A	L	P
Magnesium dioxide	L	L	L			F		D	A		A	D		A	D	F	E	D	G	D	D	D	A	A	A	L	E
Colored ground marble	H	M	M		X	F		A	D		D	D		A	A	O	F	A	G	D	D	A	A	A	A	L	E
Organic dyes	L	L	L			P		D	A		A	D		D	D	P	G	D	P	D	D	D	D	D	A	L	P
Chromium colors	M	L	L			G		D	D		D	D		A	D	F	E	A	G	D	D	D	A	A	A	L	F
Fluorescent pigments	H	H	L			P		A	A		D	D		D	D	P	E	A	P	A	A	A	A	A	A	L	F
Ultramarine blue	M	H	L		V	F		A	A		D	D		A	D	F	G	D	P	A	D	D	A	A	A	L	P
Lead Chromate	M	L	L			F		D	D		D	D		A	D	F	G	A	P	D	D	D	D	D	A	L	F
Zinc chromate	H	M	L			F		D	D		D	D		A	D	F	G	A	F	D	D	D	D	D	A	L	G
Stainless-steel powder	H	M	L		V	P		D	D		D	D		A	D	F	G	A	F	D	D	D	D	D	A	L	G
Synthetic pearl	M	L	L		V	F		D	D		D	D		A	D	P	G	A	G	D	D	A	A	A	A	L	G
Synthetic copper	H	H	L		V	P		D	D		D	D		A	D	P	G	A	G	D	D	A	A	A	A	L	G
Synthetic gold	H	H	L		V	P		D	D		D	D		A	D	P	G	A	G	D	D	A	A	A	A	L	G
Venetian reds	H	L	M			P		D	D		D	D		A	D	P	G	A	G	D	D	A	A	A	A	L	G
Siennas	L	M	M		V	P		D	D		D	D		A	D	P	G	A	G	D	D	A	A	A	A	L	G
Umbers	L	L	L		V	P		D	D		D	D		A	D	P	G	A	G	D	D	A	A	A	A	L	G
Ocher	L	L	L		V	P		D	D		D	D		A	D	P	G	A	G	D	D	A	A	A	A	L	G
Leafing aluminum	M	L	L			P		D	D		D	A		A	D	G	G	A	G	D	D	D	D	D	A	L	G

they may impart or detract important properties from the basic polymer.

In the overall picture, pigments can have quite dramatic effects on gel time and cure and cycle times required for a given formulation. The alkaline pigments may inhibit and can lengthen these times. The acid pigments usually have the reverse effect—they shorten cure cycles.

The most notable of these are the iron colors, which are almost always alkaline, and which lengthen cure cycles. The carbon blacks are almost always acid, and they shorten such cycle times. In formulations requiring high percentages of iron oxides, it is usually advisable to increase the catalyst content very slightly to compensate, and in carbon-black formulations the catalyst may be reduced very slightly.

Synthetic-pearl pigments and some of the umbers, siennas, and ochers can inhibit a formulation. Fine-ground colored calcium carbonates also have a slight inhibiting effect. Some zinc oxides inhibit slightly, while others accelerate a formulation. Inhibition is mostly dependent on the pH, moisture content, and impurities present.

Many formulators prefer paste colors to dry pigments for ease of dispersion and for greater pigmenting value. All aspects should be considered before making a decision on this important phase of the formulation of any compound.

Predispersed colors, ground to very fine particle sizes, do have much greater pigmenting value. This is particularly true in hard-to-disperse pigments such as titanium dioxide. One pound of predispersed titanium will have as much pigmenting value as 3 lb of dry pigment mixed into a compound.

Some automated systems, requiring completely automatic dispensing of the pigment into the mixer, will be forced to use proportioning pumps, and thus will have to use predispersed pigments at a viscosity which enables the equipment to handle them.

In some operations where pigment is to be manually handled and weighed, the dry pigments are far easier to handle. Weighing containers may be emptied completely into the mixer, without any of the color adhering to the walls of the container. So, in manually weighed processes, the dry colors are far better and more accurate.

Dry colors are best in processes calling for partial blending, such as synthetic marble manufacture. They can be premixed into a compound, contrasting with the matrix, and will blend in to a lesser degree, giving more natural appearing marble than the paste colors.

Both methods have certain applications at which they are best. Normal paste colors, when used, should never be purchased from pigment manufacturers without determining exactly the medium in which the pigments are to be dispersed.

Pigments in phthalate and phosphate esters should never be used with polyester resins. They all act as plasticizers and reduce modulus, hardness, etc., to the degree with which they are used. Some of these materials are very slightly incompatible with some polyesters and will partially exude to the surface as the resin compound cures, particularly at higher temperatures. The surface can be left tacky, soft, and under-cured. In open-mold processes, considerable pigment will come to the surface, exposed to air, and will remain as a sticky surface that will rub off when touched.

If predispersed pigments are to be used, by all means they should be predispersed in the same resin in which they are to be utilized. In this way, there is no problem of compatibility, exudation, or tacky surfaces. There will be no change whatever in the mechanical properties of the finished part.

A processor is usually wise in purchasing dry pigments and dispersing them himself. The high-shear mixer in which his liquids are to be mixed will serve the purpose very well. Pigments may be purchased in very fine particle size when required, so will not need grinding for the average end use. In some coatings application for automobiles, aircraft, and equipment, it will be necessary to grind the pigments, along with the other fillers, so such an application will require a grinder.

In the use of organic dyes, careful tests must be run. Some of these materials are just slightly incompatible with certain resin systems, and others inhibit the cure considerably. Each separate dye must be tested with the resin to be used.

Fillers and aggregates are very important in a compound in that in many compounds they form a very large part of the total ingredients. They may be used to 90% or more (by weight) of the entire compound in many applications.

Fillers and aggregates can be an asset or a detriment, depending on the selection for the particular application. The environment of the end product will have much to do with this. The proper fillers can make the compound flame resistant and heat resistant, and can contribute greatly to chemical resistance, water resistance, resistance to sulfides, etc.

The proper materials can make a product very abrasion resistant. They can increase tensile strength, flexural strength, and impact resistance. All fillers, used in any quantities, will increase the flexural modulus of a given resin. The highly absorptive fillers increase the modulus less than other materials simply because less of them may be used in a compound. The graphs presented earlier in this chapter illustrate the effects of fillers and reinforcing materials on polyester resins.

Polyesters may become semiconductors, with proper choice of fillers, suitable for use in areas where static electricity may be a hazard.

CHART 19. FILLERS AND AGGREGATES: PROPERTIES AND EFFECTS IMPARTED TO POLYESTERS

Legend: L–low · M–medium · H–high · P–poor · F–fair · G–good · E–excellent · X–not recommended · O–no known effect · A–asset · D–detriment

Notes: Shrinkage column — "All reduce shrinkage, in relation to absorption and %." Flexural modulus / Flexural strength columns — "All reduce flexural modulus, in relation to absorption and %." Elongation column — "All reduce elongation."

Filler	Cost	Specific gravity	Resin absorption	Reactivity	Exterior exposure	Abrasion resistance	Shrinkage	Tensile strength	Compressive strength	Flexural modulus	Flexural strength	Impact strength	Elongation	Hardness (Barcol)	Dielectric properties	Electrical conductivity	Water resistance	Heat resistance	Flame resistance	Organic-acid resistance	Inorganic-acid resistance	Alkali resistance	Salt resistance	Sulfides resistance	Thermal conductivity	Thixotrophy to resin	Pigmenting effect
Ground marble CACO₃	L	M	M	L	G	F		F	F			F		F	F		F	G	G	P	P	G	G	G	M	M	M
Marble chips	L	M	L	L	G	F		F	F			F		F	F		F	G	G	P	P	G	G	G	M	M	L
Dolomite	L	M	M	L	G	F		F	F			F		F	F		F	G	G	P	P	G	G	G	M	M	L
Treated silicas	M	L	H	O	E	E		F	E			E		E	F		F	E	E	E	E	G	G	G	L	H	O
Pearlite	L	M	L	O	E	P		P	E			P		P	F		P	E	E	E	E	E	E	E	H	H	O
Ground silicas 400-20 mesh	L	M	L	O	E	E		E	E			E		E	E		E	E	E	E	E	E	E	E	H	L	O
Quartz, crushed	L	M	L	O	E	E		E	E			E		E	E		E	E	E	E	E	E	E	E	H	L	O
Granite, crushed	M	M	L	O	E	E		E	E			E		E	E		E	E	F	E	E	G	G	P	M	L	O
Mica, muscovite	H	M	L	O	G	F		G	E			F		F	G		E	F	F	E	E	G	G	P	M	L	O
Mica, biotite	L	M	L	O	G	F		G	F			G		F	P		G	G	F	P	P	G	G	P	L	L	L
Mica, synthetic	L	M	M	O	G	F		F	F			G		F	E		G	G	F	P	P	F	G	G	L	L	O
Talc	L	H	H	O	G	P		F	F			E		F	F		G	E	F	P	P	F	G	G	L	M	L
Asbestine	M	M	H	O	G	P		F	F			E		F	F		F	E	F	P	P	G	G	G	M	H	L
China clay (kaolin)	M	M	L	L	G	P		F	F			G		F	F		F	E	F	P	P	G	G	G	L	L	L
BASO₄ (barytes)	L	H	H	O	G	F		G	F			E		F	F		F	E	F	P	P	G	G	G	M	H	M
Asbestos, shorts	H	M	L	O	E	P		F	F			E		F	F		G	E	F	P	P	G	G	G	L	L	L
Graphite	H	L	H	O	G	E		F	F			G		F	X	G	F	G	G	P	P	G	E	G	H	H	H
Bentonite	L	H	L	L	G	P		G	F			G		F	F		E	E	E	P	P	G	G	G	H	L	L
Aluminum oxide	M	H	L	O	G	P		F	G			E		F	X	G	E	E	E			G	F	G	L	L	O
Boron carbide	M	M	H	O	G	P		F	E			E		F	X	G	E	E	E	P	P	F	G	F	H	H	O
Wood flour	M	L	L	O	G	F		G	E			F		F	P		E	G	E	P	P	F	G	F	H	L	O
Zinc dust	L	L	L	O	G	E		E	E			F		F	X	F	E	E	P	F	F	G	P	G	L	L	H
Magnetite	L	H	L	O	G	F		E	F			F		F	X	G	F	G	E	P	P	F	G	G	H	H	H
Zirconium silicate	L	M	H	O	G	F		E	F			F		F	X	F	G	E	E	F	F	F	G	G	H	L	L
Diatomaceous earth	L	L	L	L	E	F		E	F			G		F	F		G	E	E	P	P	F	F	G	L	L	M
Rice hulls, ground	L	L	M	O	G	F		F	F			E		F	P		F	P	P	F	F	F	G	F	L	M	L
Bagasse, ground	L	L	L	O	G	F		F	F			E		F	P		F	P	P	F	F	F	G	F	L	M	L
Nut hulls, ground	L	L	L	O	G	F		G	G			E		F	P		F	P	P	F	F	F	G	F	L	M	L
Hydrated alumina	H	M	L	O	E	G		G	E			E		G	X	G	E	E	E	P	P	F	F	G	H	L	M

309

They may be excellent nonconductors for use in electrical applications. Polyesters have excellent dielectric strength in themselves, and this property may be greatly increased by use of fillers such as silicas, micas, and other nonconductors.

Polyester alone is not a good thermal conductor, so cycle times would be somewhat longer without the proper selection of fillers. The use of highly conductive thermal fillers can reduce cycle times tremendously.

Fillers and aggregates must be carefully selected for the desirable properties they can impart to the finished product, with the environment firmly in mind. No single filler or aggregate can be used that will in any way detract from those properties. Each must, if even in a small way, be an asset to the finished product.

There is such a wide selection of these materials to choose from that there is no problem in selecting one or more that will serve a specific purpose. Most of these materials are very low in cost as compared to the cost per pound of the resin. Only a very few cost as much or more than the resin.

The resin absorption of each filler must be carefully considered. Fillers and aggregates from different suppliers and different areas of the country can vary widely in resin absorption. Figures given for water or oil absorption cannot be used because they are completely different than for polyester resin.

The higher the content of fillers, the lower the cost of the finished product in almost every instance. By the selection of the least absorptive of these materials, resin content (and thus cost) of the product can be reduced.

The finer the filler material is ground, the higher the resin content must be. Therefore, in most compounds for molding, few fillers under 200 mesh should be used. In coatings and other applications, very fine fillers must be employed in order to get smooth finishes.

Ground marble and clays will vary most in absorption. Each of these materials to be used will have to be checked out with the resin at the processing temperatures to be sure of final absorption qualities.

Clays, wood flours, bagasse, and asbestos shorts are more absorptive fillers. They can be used sparingly to reduce overall costs, or they may be employed in large amounts to achieve flexibility in an end product.

Silicas, barium sulfate, crushed granite and quartz, and other materials of this type are the least absorptive of all fillers and aggregates. By proper selection of particle sizes in these materials, compounds may be made with as little as 5 or 6% (by weight) resin content. The larger the particle sizes that can be used, the lower the resin content may be. A compound of this nature must be calculated quite in the same manner that concrete is calculated. Take the largest aggregate size, and calculate 35% voids. With the next smaller-sized aggregate, calculate 30% voids, etc., to 200-mesh size, where the resin itself coats all particles and fills the smallest voids. When the largest-size stone can be ½ in. or greater, the resin content may be very low.

The materials that are commonly thought of as fillers and aggregates are only a small part of the wide range of materials that may be used to good advantage is polyester compounds. Rice hulls, so plentiful in some parts of our country, are the cheapest of any possible fillers. Very good products can be based on this material and polyester resin.

In cane-producing areas, bagasse is a waste product. It can be most useful in polyester products. Nut hulls, wood flour, sawdust, and even tree bark can be utilized in many products. Almost any of our natural stones can be crushed and used in polyester compounds. Calcium sulfate is one of the few common minerals that will not work in polyesters. Almost any of the low-cost ores and mineral products can be used to some extent.

If a final product must be ground (such as in a terrazzo-type floor tile), then the fillers and aggregates must be chosen for their ability to be ground. Silicas, quartz, granite, and other such materials must be avoided because of the high cost of grinding such hard materials.

The impurities that must be avoided in filler materials are iron, to some extent, and sulfur. Also, copper impurities must be avoided in all instances. Fillers and aggregates should be as clean as possible and free of dust, dirt, and moisture.

The moisture content of all fillers and aggregates must be very closely controlled. This is particularly important in compounds that may be 90% filler content or more.

In a compound with 10% (by weight) resin and 90% fillers and aggregates, these materials must be very dry. If these materials were to average 1% in moisture content, then the total moisture of the compound would be 9% (by weight of the resin). This is not permissible in polyester resins. It is very difficult to set a definite limit on the permissible moisture content of a compound, but it must be in the vicinity of a maximum of 0.5% (by weight) of the resin.

A lot will depend also on the process by which the compound will be turned into a finished product. Moisture will have very different effects in a compression-molding process than in a casting process.

In addition, much will depend on such factors as the acid number of the resin and the pH of the fillers used in the compound. The type of resin, catalyst, promoter system, and all such factors enter into the exact effects of water on a compound. The end effects of excessive moisture content will be defective products, rejects, partially polymerized polymers, and, in such processes as casting, pinholes and pores.

A considerable amount of research has been done on the exact effects of moisture on a polyester resin. Most of this work has been done without the presence of fillers and aggregates but with regard to gel times, cure cycles, exotherm temperatures, and exotherm curves, with catalyzed resin in more or less conventional SPI gel tests.

An excellent article was written by J. D. Malkemus of Reichold Chemicals and presented in the Annual Conference of the Reinforced Plastics Division of the Society of the Plastics Industry in 1966. This article is certainly good reading for anyone interested in this phase of the polyester industry. It does not take into consideration fillers of any kind, but it thoroughly explores the effects of water on resins, catalysts, and promoters.

Others have done extensive work along these lines. Dick Holtzendorf of Alpha Chemical has done a great amount of work on the effects of water on polyester formulations; all researchers agree that it is a very important factor to be considered.

This writer's work has been done along these lines, with emphasis on the effects of moisture on different filler materials and on different processing methods employed to use these compounds.

First, tests to check moisture content were run on some 30 different fillers as they arrived from the supplier. Quite complicated equipment was employed in order to show moisture content as accurately as possible.

The moisture content of the fillers ran as high as 3.5% in some of the clays, bentonite, wood flour, and asbestos shorts. The lowest moisture content was registered in silicas, barytes, very dense aluminum oxide, boron carbide, and other more dense fillers. The moisture content in these ran as low as 0.2%. One sample of ground marble that the supplier had taken particular care to dry had a moisture content of 0.02%. Most of the marble chips and ground marble had around 0.8% moisture content.

Next, a series of tests were run to see what the practical limits of moisture levels could be in these different materials. To be practical, as far as processing costs were concerned, the dryer had to be something feasible when used by a filler supplier. A small, rotating drum-type dryer was set up, quite like a small cement oven. These rotary-drum dryers are the most commonplace for an application such as this.

Quantities of all the materials were run through the dryer once and checked. All were well below 0.2%, with the exception of the clays, bentonite, and wood flour. The marble chips and ground marble were all well below 0.1%. Talc, asbestine, and most of the others were between 0.1 and 0.2%. The silicas and the barytes were in the range of 0.02%, which at the time was considered a very safe level.

All materials that were above 0.02% were run through the dryer a second time and rechecked. All except the clays and wood flour were in the range of 0.02% after the second trip through the dryer. The clays and the wood flour were sent through the dryer a third time and still did not prove satisfactory. The clay was at a 0.15% moisture level, and the wood flour contained 0.4% moisture. This was considered the maximum amount of drying that was possible while still having low-cost fillers.

The length of the small oven and the time the material was inside it were calculated and compared to a large kiln 60 ft in length. Approximately the same amount of drying time would be involved in the three trips through the small dryer as would be obtained in one trip in the 60-ft kiln.

All fillers can be reduced to moisture levels well under 0.02%, except wood flour and the clays. Since fortunately these fillers would be used in smaller quantities, perhaps this level can be adequate for most purposes.

In a system containing only resin, catalyst, and promoter, the effects of moisture are the following: (1) The gel time of the mix is shortened in almost direct proportion to the moisture content. Moisture of 1% will shorten gel time by approximately 20%, 2% moisture by close to 30%, and 3% moisture will shorten gel time by 40%. Somewhere between the 2 and 3% levels, the resin will lose a tremendous amount of its optimum cure. The polymer will be cheesy and will break apart very easily. Further tests show this level to be very near the 2% level. (2) The polyester will shrink, again in direct proportion to the percentage of moisture. At water levels of 0.5%, shrinkage on a rigid orthophthalic was 2.65%. At 1% moisture, shrinkage was 3.25%, and at 2%, it was 3.80%. (3) At moisture levels above 0.5%, parts can be expected to give poor release from the molds. (4) When moisture levels approach 0.5%, the surface of the parts will be inferior. (5) All properties—mechanical, electrical, and resistance to chemicals, weather, etc.—are detracted from by a great extent at moisture levels of as much as 0.5%. When moisture levels rise above 1%, the resulting polymer has very poor weather and chemical resistance, and the mechanical properties are reduced by as much as 40%.

The above tests show the effects of moisture on a rigid polymer. Similar tests were run on a flexible isophthalic resin, with even more detrimental results. The effects are more pronounced because the polymer is reduced in flexural modulus. Subsequent tests run with four different polymers—rigid and flexible—bore this out. There seemed to be no relationship to the type of resin. The orthophthalic, isophthalic, and bisphenol resins gave very similar results.

In the choice of catalysts, some difference was noted. Moisture definitely affects difunctional catalysts more than monofunctional catalysts. The difference was slight but noticeable.

Choice of promoters did not seem to make any difference. The time a resin was allowed to set after mixing was a factor. In mixes where no promoter was present and the mix, containing 1% water, was placed immediately in the oil bath to gel, the polymerization was much more complete than with an equal sample allowed to set 1 hr before being placed in the bath.

Next, work was begun with fillers. Small quantities of silica, clay, calcium carbonate, barytes, talc, and wood flour were baked in an oven until they were virtually free of moisture and then packed in air-tight bags immediately to prevent moisture pickup from the air.

Small 200-g batches were first made up, containing a combination of these fillers. Batch 1 contained silica, clay, and barytes. Batch 2 contained silica, calcium carbonate, and talc. Both were 85% fillers and 15% resin.

These were placed in an open mold, vibrated thoroughly, and placed in the oven at 250°F. After being allowed to cure and cool, these two samples were cut with an abrasive blade and studied under a microscope. The castings were both good, the mechanical properties were good, and there were very few tiny pores in the castings.

Exactly the same formulations were used in two other batches, and 0.5% moisture was added (by weight of the resin). These were cured and observed. Considerably more pores were present, and they were much larger than in the previous samples. One great difference was noticeable. The sample containing the calcium carbonate had many more pores than the other sample, and the pores were roughly twice as large.

The same process was carried out again, with 1% moisture. The pores got larger, and the pores in the sample containing calcium carbonate were very much larger and more plentiful than in the other sample. The mechanical properties were less than half those of the samples containing no moisture.

Next five batches were made up, each containing only one filler, to be sure that the trouble was caused by the calcium carbonate. Because of the thixotroping effect of clay, this sample was made at a 50:50 level with resin. To be certain of results, all other samples were made at the same level.

These samples were mixed with 1% water (by weight of the resin). Half of each batch was gelled immediately in the oven, and half was allowed to stand 1 hr before being placed in the oven.

The five batches that were placed in the oven immediately after mixing were cured, cooled, cut in half, and examined. The sample containing silica had no pores of any kind, and the mechanical properties were good. The sample containing barium sulfate was also free of pinholes, and had good properties. The sample containing clay had a few pinholes very near the top of the casting. The mechanical properties were just slightly lower than the other two samples. The sample containing talc had no visable pinholes, and the mechanical properties were equal to those of the two first samples. The casting containing calcium carbonate had an average of 8 rather large pinholes per sq in. About half of the pinholes had broken through the upper surface, and about half were under the surface. All were in the top $\frac{1}{16}$ in. of the casting. The mechanical properties of this sample were less than half those of the samples with silica and barytes.

After 1 hr, at approximately 75°F, the other five samples were placed in the oven to cure. There were no pinholes of any kind in the four samples that did not contain calcium carbonate. The sample containing calcium carbonate had many more pinholes and larger ones than the calcium carbonate sample that had been gelled and cured immediately after mixing. The properties were very poor, and the sample could be broken easily.

This indicated definitely that the trouble was caused by the calcium carbonate. The lack of pinholes in the second sample with the clay filler indicated that the holes in the first sample were air bubbles, caused by the very high viscosity of the mix, and that these air bubbles had time to escape in the hour during which the second sample had set before curing.

The fact that the calcium carbonate sample that had been allowed to set was much worse than the sample that had been gelled and cured immediately indicated that during the time that the mix was allowed to set a chemical reaction was taking place, causing the additional pinholing.

Next, four small batches were mixed, with resin, catalyst, and calcium carbonate, at a level of 70:30 (filler to resin). Batch 1 was virtually free of water. Batch 2 had 0.5% water added, batch 3 had 1% water added, and batch 4 had 1.5% water blended in. Each of the four batches was divided into two parts.

The eight parts were each placed in open molds, vibrated thoroughly, and allowed to stand. After 1 hr, four were placed in the oven for cure and then examined. The results were the same as in previous batches containing calcium carbonate. The higher the water content, the higher was the content of pinholes and the lower were the properties of the compound. The samples containing 1 and 1.5% would have to be. classed as totally unacceptable.

The four remaining batches were allowed to stand for 4 hr at 75°F before being placed in the oven. These were examined, and the difference was greatly accentuated by the 4-hr delay in curing. Even the sample containing 0.5% water was totally unacceptable, and the samples with 1 and 1.5% were cheesy and crumbled apart very easily.

The problem was fairly well established to be a chemical reaction between the calcium carbonate and the acids of the resin, catalyst, and perhaps others in the presence of water.

One hundred grams of resin were checked for acid number. The reading was 22. The catalyst being used was established to have a pH of 6.1. Promoters and internal mold releases were checked. The analine promoters were highly alkaline, and the metallic promoters were either neutral or very nearly neutral. Every internal mold release checked was highly acidic. The calcium carbonate being used was checked and found to have a pH of 8.3, with 1% water (by weight) present. As water was increased, the pH increased. At 3% water present, the pH reading was 8.7.

Resin, catalyst, and calcium carbonate were mixed at the same levels as above (70:30, fillers to resin), and 1% water was added. The mix was placed in a sealed container and allowed to stand 1 hr. Tests were run, and it was established that the mix was giving off quantities of carbon dioxide. The mix was allowed to stand 4 hr and then was poured out into an open mold and placed in the oven for cure. The results were the same as had been previously observed. The casting was totally unacceptable for any purpose. The pinholes averaged 9 per sq in. on the surface, and these were large, open pinholes. The sample was ground about $\frac{1}{16}$ in., and under the surface there were even more pinholes than on the surface.

To see what effect the oven heat had on the mix, one batch was mixed exactly like the batch above, except that promoter was added to this compound. The mix was placed into the mold, vibrated, and placed to gel and cure at 75°F.

Gel occurred in 1 hr and 20 min. The surface had an average of 7 pinholes per sq in. After 24 hr the sample was ground $\frac{1}{16}$ in. and observed. Here, again, there were more pinholes than on the surface but still slightly less than in the heat-cured samples. Thus the heat did affect the reaction of the carbon dioxide formation to some extent, but this sample still was totally unacceptable for any purpose.

Now, 15 200-g samples were made up, 3 with each of the 5 filler materials. The resin was catalyzed and promoted and used on a 50:50 (by weight) basis with the fillers.

One each of the fillers was used totally dry. One each had 0.5% water added, and the third had 1% water added (by weight of the total mix).

Each of the 15 samples was divided into 2 equal parts. One part went into open molds and was vibrated and allowed to set at 75°F. Each of the other 15 samples was placed into open-top containers, with a thermometer placed in it in order to check temperatures as the batches progressed.

The results were rather conclusive as to the effects of water on the resin and on the fillers. At the zero level of water, the slight difference in peak exotherm temperatures can be attributed to the difference in thermal conduction of the different fillers. This is normal and expected. All else in the tests must be attributed directly to the effects of the water, with the different filler materials.

The resin, catalyst, and promoter were exactly the same in all instances. Rigid orthophthalic resin, with acid number of 22, was used for the resin. The catalyst was benzoyl peroxide, and the promoter was dimethyl analine. All containers and thermometers used were exactly alike. No covers of any kind were used, and the room temperature was very close to 75°F.

	H_2O (%)	Silica	Talc	BaSO$_4$	Clay	CaCO$_3$
Time to gel	0	2 hr, 20 min	2 hr, 20 min	2 hr, 20 min	2 hr, 30 min	2 hr, 35 min
	0.5	1 hr, 50 min	1 hr, 50 min	1 hr, 50 min	1 hr, 55 min	1 hr, 10 min
	1.0	1 hr, .05 min	1 hr, .05 min	1 hr, .05 min	1 hr, 10 min	45 min
Peak exo-therm	0	235°	245°	240°	250°	245°
	0.5	220°	225°	222°	228°	195°
	1.0	190°	194°	192°	195°	160°
Time to peak	0	2 hr, 35 min	2 hr, 35 min	2 hr, 35 min	2 hr, 50 min	2 hr, 50 min
	0.5	2 hr	2 hr	2 hr	2 hr, .05 min	1 hr, 20 min
	1.0	1 hr, 15 min	1 hr, 15 min	1 hr, 15 min	1 hr, 20 min	50 min

It becomes obvious that water alone is not the problem. The calcium-carbonate, with the carbon dioxide given off, also has a great influence on gel times and peak exotherm temperatures.

The Barcol impressor was used on the samples left to cure in the open molds to get an idea as to degree of polymerization. These were checked 48 hr after the molds were filled.

	H_2O %	Silica	Talc	BaSO$_4$	Clay	CaCO$_3$
Barcol	0	56	54	54	53	54
	0.5	51	49	49	49	44
	1.0	45	43	43	43	31

The samples were then placed in an oven and postcured for 20 min at 250°F to see if the degree of polymerization could be improved in any way.

The hardness of all the samples that were free of water increased by two to three points on the Barcol scale. The hardness of the samples containing either the 0.5% or 1.0% of water did not increase in any way.

It was thus quite obvious that in open-mold casting at any temperature either calcium carbonate had to be very dry or it could not be used. It was apparent that the water content of any filler had to be very low or the finished product would be less than satisfactory.

Next more or less the same types of tests were run to see what effects moisture would have in a closed-mold process. Compression-molded blanks, 12 × 12 ⅛ in. thick were made for this purpose. In this case, a flexible isophthalic resin was chosen. The internal mold release used was calcium stearate, and the catalyst was t-butyl peroctoate. No promoter was used. The die temperature was 290°F, and the pressure was 300 psi.

No pigments of any kind were used in these tests. Fillers were dried to a point where there was no detectable moisture with the equipment available for testing them. They were packaged in sealed polyethylene bags to prevent moisture pickup from the air.

The resin was catalyzed all in one batch and the internal mold release added, so that all batches were made with the identical resin mix.

In order to obtain flow and mold fill-out, clay is an absolute necessity in a batch of this kind. Since the consistency of the mix had to be such that it would be a heavy putty for this process, the total filler content per batch had to vary somewhat. Each batch contained 3 lb premixed resin and 2 lb clay, and the rest was made up of one of the other fillers.

The following formulations were used:

Batch 1

Resin-monomer–catalyst-mold release	3.0 lb
Clay	2.0
Silica, 100 mesh	18.0
Silica, 200 mesh	3.0
	26.0 lb

Batch 2

Resin	3.0 lb
Clay	2.0
Talc	18.0
	23.0 lb

Batch 3

Resin	3.0 lb
Clay	2.0
Barytes, No. 1 bleached	20.0
	25.0 lb

Batch 4

Resin	3.0 lb
Clay	2.0
Ground marble, 40–200 mesh	19.0
	24.0 lb

The difference in the filler contents will give an idea as to the difference in absorptivity of the fillers, but of course these compounds were not made up with optimum particle-size selection.

Each batch was divided into two equal parts and placed in polyethylene bags to prevent any moisture from getting into the mix and to prevent monomer evaporation.

Then, eight more batches were mixed, which were identical in every way to the above, except for water content.

Batch 5: Exactly as batch 1, with 0.18 oz water added
Batch 6: Exactly as batch 1, with 0.36 oz water added
Batch 7: Exactly as batch 2, with 0.18 oz water added
Batch 8: Exactly as batch 2, with 0.36 oz water added
Batch 9: Exactly as batch 3, with 0.18 oz water added
Batch 10: Exactly as batch 3, with 0.36 oz water added
Batch 11: Exactly as batch 4, with 0.18 oz water added
Batch 12: Exactly as batch 4, with 0.36 oz water added

Thus, batches 5, 7, 9, and 11 had 0.5% water (by weight of the resin content) and batches 6, 8, 10, and 12 had 1.0% water (by weight of the resin).

These batches were also divided into two equal parts and all placed in polyethylene bags. They were numbered 1A, 1B, 2A, 2B, etc.

The A bags were allowed to stand for 1 hr before molding. Charges were weighed out at 27 oz each for convenience, although the part thicknesses varied according to the specific gravity of the major filler material.

The cycle time on the press was set for 30 sec closed time. All the A batches were molded in the same sequence that they had been mixed. Each batch was stacked separately, and each piece was marked 1A, 2A, etc.

A surface pyrometer was used to check temperatures of the parts as soon as they came out of the mold and at 15-min intervals thereafter.

Four blanks were molded from each *A* batch. Some material was left over, and this was replaced in the polyethylene bags.

The 12 stacks of 4 blanks each were allowed to cool to room temperature; the total time from molding was recorded, and temperatures were taken on the surface of each stack every 15 min during this time.

The *B* batches were allowed to stand for 4 hr before molding. These were done in exactly the same manner as the *A* batches. Four blanks from each *B* batch were stacked, and the temperatures were checked as soon as they came out of the dies and each 15 min thereafter until they reached room temperature.

Of the total 96 blanks, there were no broken parts or total rejects, until batch No. 12*B* was molded. Two of the four parts stuck to the lower die sufficiently so that they were badly damaged when they were removed with a small vacuum cup. None of the four parts entirely filled out the dies. All were most obviously reject parts.

The results of the tests on these parts were quite similar in some ways to the tests that had been run by casting. In every case, Barcol hardness was reduced with the addition of water to the mix, and the greatest effect was shown with the calcium carbonate filler.

Gel times, peak exotherms, and the time to peak were reduced in every case where water was present, and, again, the most drastic effects occurred where the calcium carbonate was present.

The longer the time a compound was allowed to set before processing, the more effect the water had in all cases, but, again, the most drastic effects occurred with the calcium carbonate.

The 12 bags marked *A* and the 12 bags marked *B* were checked for the consistency of the small amounts of material still remaining in them each hour. At the end of 5 hr after mixing, all were still unchanged except batches 12*A* and *B*. In these, hard lumps were forming, indicating partial polymerization. At the end of 6 hr, these two small quantities were almost completely gelled. At the end of 7 hr, they were fairly hard, and lumps had begun to form in batches 11*A* and *B*. At the end of 10 hr batches 11*A* and *B* had hardened.

In 24 hr, all the batches containing water had begun to form hard lumps, and in 48 hr they had solidified. They were removed from the bags and placed in the oven, well marked so they would not be mixed up. They were baked out 30 min at 250° and sawed in half for examination. Barcol hardness was checked, and solvent resistance was checked on a small piece of each batch.

Batches 1 through 4, with no water added, were still of good consistency at the end of 4 days.

The results of all tests on the blanks made by compression-molding were compared to those made by casting the small pieces earlier, both those cast at room temperature and those that had been heat cured.

In the compression-molded pieces, there were no pores or pinholes. The pressure had prevented these from forming. The surface appearance of all blanks containing 1% water were not good, but the samples with calcium carbonate were extremely bad. Under a microscope, there were many tiny voids and depressions in the surface, ringed with a lighter-colored formation. The surface looked quite like pumice before it is crushed and ground.

One blank of each batch was cut into 1×2 in. pieces to check water absorption, solvent resistance, Barcol hardness, and other tests.

Following are the conclusions drawn from these series of tests:

1. Water acts as an accelerator, or promoter, for all peroxide catalysts.

2. When calcium carbonate or other highly alkaline filler is present, the promotion is greatly accelerated.

3. The optimum properties of the polyester are affected by any amount of water present, regardless of the percentage. The tolerable percentage is probably below 0.25% (by weight of the resin) when there are no calcium carbonates or alkaline fillers in the compound. With calcium carbonates present, permissible water levels must be very nearly zero.

4. The addition of higher levels of catalysts does not in any way improve the ultimate cure of the resin. It merely causes faster gel where water is present. Raising water content or calcium carbonate content of a compound equally reduces gel times and at the same time reduces all properties.

5. A postcure of parts containing water above the 0.25% level will not improve properties in any way. No additional polymerization can be attained.

6. The effect of water on a compound cured at ambient temperatures in open molds is less pronounced than in closed molds at elevated temperatures.

7. The worst effects of low concentrations of water in casting are pin-holes and pores.

8. Concentrations of water may be much higher in compounds not containing calcium carbonates or other alkalies.

There may be many ways by which the effects of water on a polyester compound may be reduced so that permissible levels of moisture content can be higher.

The most obvious method, of course, is to eliminate all calcium carbonate fillers and aggregates from a compound. This is not possible in the manufacture of terrazzo-type flooring.

Another way in which improvements can be made is to use only resins with an acid number of zero. This will reduce the total acidity of the compound drastically, even though the catalyst and mold release are acidic.

It can be helpful if the resin manufacturer will azeotrope the maximum amount of water from the resin during manufacture.

Of maximum importance is that the filler suppliers use proper drying equipment so that all fillers and aggregates can be furnished at the lowest possible moisture levels. The materials must be packaged in airtight polyethylene bags, with paper or burlap outer bagging, to protect the inner liner. In cases where fillers and aggregates are shipped by bulk, only completely sealed containers can be used.

The use of desiccants is possible but impractical in applications calling for filler loadings in the 90% range. The desiccant silicas and the molecular sieves are too expensive to use in such quantities as would be necessary, and the amount of these materials would affect the viscosity of the mix to a great extent. They are practical in compounds involving as high as 50% fillers, but, above this, they would be too expensive for most of the lower-cost compounds. The drying of the fillers is the easiest and most practical route to take.

Wherever possible, other materials must be substituted for the calcium carbonate fillers, particularly in the finer particle sizes. The larger particle sizes have far less effect than the fines. Talc and asbestine can be substituted very well for the finer calcium carbonates. They are both very slightly more absorptive than the ground marble but not to a great extent.

The clays, which are among the most difficult fillers to dry completely, must be used in minimum quantities, and these should be the clays of least absorption.

In applications calling for wood flour, wherever possible such materials as rice hulls and bagasse should be substituted since these materials have water levels far below those of wood flour.

Very close controls must be kept on the moisture content of all these fillers and aggregates, both at the supplier's end and at the processor's end. Good, accurate equipment is available for checking these materials. This is a most important part of the manufacture of any polyester product having very high filler levels. The additional cost of purchasing dry materials, the cost of the control equipment, and the time spent will be a very good investment for any manufacturer. The low percentage of reject parts will pay for this additional expense, and the quality of the products manufactured will depend to a very large extent on this phase of the production.

There are signs of partial saponification of the polyesters resin in com-

CHART 20. REINFORCING MATERIALS: PROPERTIES AND EFFECTS IMPARTED TO POLYESTERS

Legend:
L—low E—excellent
M—medium X—not recommended
H—high O—no known effect
P—poor
F—fair
G—good

Material	Cost	Specific gravity	Resin absorption	Reactivity	Exterior exposure	Abrasion resistance	Shrinkage	Tensile strength	Compressive strength	Flexural modulus	Flexural strength	Impact strength	Elongation	Hardness (Barcol)	Dielectric properties	Electrical conductivity	Water resistance	Heat resistance	Flame resistance	Organic-acid resistance	Inorganic-acid resistance	Alkali resistance	Salt resistance	Sulfides resistance	Thermal conductivity	Thixotrophy to resin	Pigmenting effect
Glass filament	H	M	L	O	E	E	*	E	E	**	E	E	***	G	E		E	E	F	G	G	G	E	E	G	>	O
Glass surface mat	H	M	L	O	E	E	*	E	E	**	E	E	***	G	E		E	E	F	G	G	G	E	E	G		O
Glass flake	M	M	L	O	E	E	*	E	E	**	E	E	***	G	E		E	E	F	G	G	G	E	E	G		O
Glass, chopped	M	M	L	O	E	E	*	G	G	**	E	E	***	G	E		E	E	F	G	G	G	E	E	G		O
Glass roving	H	M	L	O	E	E	*	E	E	**	E	E	***	G	E		E	E	F	G	G	G	E	E	G		O
Glass mat	H	M	L	O	E	E	*	G	G	**	E	E	***	G	E		E	E	F	G	G	G	E	E	G		O
Glass fabric	M	M	H	O	E	E	*	E	E	**	E	E	***	G	E		E	E	F	G	G	G	E	E	G	>	O
Asbestos fiber, long	H	L	H	O	E	G	*	G	G	**	G	E	***	P	F		P	E	F	P	P	F	G	G	P	>	M
Asbestos fiber, short	L	L	H	O	F	G	*	F	G	**	F	F	***	P	F		P	E	F	P	P	G	F	G	P	>	M
Asbestos fabric	M	L	M	O	G	G	*	G	G	**	G	G	***	P	F		P	E	F	P	P	F	F	G	P	>	M
Sisal	L	L	M	O	F	F	*	F	F	**	F	F	***	P	F		P	E	E	P	P	F	F	G	P	>	M
Hemp	L	L	M	O	F	F	*	F	F	**	F	F	***	P	F		F	E	E	P	P	F	F	G	P	>	M
Coconut fiber	L	L	H	O	F	L	*	L	F	**	L	L	***	P	F		F	E	E	P	P	L	L	G	P	>	M
Rice hulls	L	L	H	O	L	L	*	L	F	**	L	F	***	P	F		F	E	P	P	P	F	G	G	P	>	M
Bagasse fiber	L	L	M	O	F	F	*	F	G	**	F	F	***	P	F		F	E	P	P	P	F	F	G	P	>	M
Cotton fiber	M	L	M	O	L	L	*	G	G	**	F	F	***	F	F		M	E	P	P	P	F	P	F	P	>	H
Cotton fabric	H	L	H	O	L	L	*	G	G	**	F	F	***	P	F		M	E	P	P	P	F	P	F	P	>	H
Metallic fiber	H	H	L	O	G	G	*	E	E	**	E	E	***	E	P	E	G	E	E	X	X	G	P	G	E		H
Wire mesh, steel	M	H	L	O	P	F	*	E	E	**	E	E	***	E	X	E	G	E	E	X	X	G	P	G	E		L
Steel rods	H	H	L	O	P	L	*	E	E	**	E	E	***	E	X	E	G	E	E	X	X	G	P	G	E		L
Nylon 66	H	L	L	O	P	G	*	G	G	**	G	G	***	E	E		G	E	P	P	P	G	P	F	P		L
Nylon 6	H	L	L	O	P	G	*	G	G	**	G	G	***	E	E		G	E	P	P	P	E	P	F	P		L
Nylon 610	H	L	L	O	P	G	*	G	G	**	G	G	***	E	E		G	E	P	P	P	E	P	F	P		L
Polyester, terephthalic	H	L	L	O	G	G	*	G	G	**	G	G	***	E	E		E	E	P	G	G	G	G	E	P		O
Polypropylene fiber	H	L	L	O	G	G	*	G	G	**	G	G	***	E	E		G	E	P	G	G	E	G	E	P		O
Polypropylene fabric	H	L	L	O	G	F	*	G	G	**	G	G	***	E	E		G	E	P	G	G	E	G	E	P		O
Acrylic fiber	H	L	L	O	E	F	*	G	G	**	G	G	***	E	E		E	E	P	G	G	E	E	E	P		O
Acetate fiber	H	L	L	O	E	F	*	G	G	**	G	G	***	E	E		E	E	P	G	G	E	E	E	P		O
Rayon fiber	M	L	L	O	M	P	*	F	G	**	F	G	***	P	E		G	P	P	P	P	P	G	F	P		O

Notes:
* Shrinkage: Reduce shrinkage, according to % absorption
** Flexural modulus: All increase modulus, according to its own modulus
*** Elongation: All reduce elongation

pounds with some moisture content in closed-mold operations. This should be explored further.

When thinking of reinforcing materials for polyesters, most people think immediately of glass and asbestos fibers, in one form or another. A great many materials are available that will reinforce polyesters very well.

In glass fiber, most people think of E glass because this is the most common glass reinforcing for plastics. This material is reasonable in cost and has excellent properties for most applications. In applications requiring extremely good dielectric properties, heat and flame resistance, S glass is far better than the E glass. It has a far higher percentage of silica and will give superior results in these applications. The additional cost of this glass can be justified in extreme environments.

Glass is available in so many forms today, and more forms are being introduced on the market constantly. The individual fibers are available from 0.00010 to 0.002 in. in diameter. These fibers are marketed in the form of roving, in single and multiple strands. They are available in gossamer-surface mats, veil mats, coarse random mats, and in woven fabrics of all types. In the woven fabrics, the weight per square foot and the direction of the weaving determine the ultimate strengths of the products manufactured from them. The ratio of glass to resin alone does not determine this ultimate strength. The size of the individual strands, the type of size used in treating the glass, and many factors enter into the ultimate strength of a finished product.

The manufacturers of these materials can furnish detailed information on their products and the types of treatments best suited to a particular polyester resin. They will work with a manufacturer and supply all necessary technical aid in finding the proper glass product for his needs.

Glass flake is a rather new addition to the glass reinforcing market. It has an adaptability to many applications where chopped glass cannot be used. It is particularly adaptable for use in heavy protective coatings in marine and other such environments. When properly used and applied, it can form a virtual glass shield, together with polyester resin.

Asbestos has long been known as an excellent reinforcing material for polyester resins, particularly in applications calling for good heat and flame resistance. The shorter fibers are economical for use also in many applications where high resin absorption would be an asset rather than a detriment. A product where high flexibility is needed can utilize these short fibers to good advantage. Very high strengths can be obtained, with minimum effect on the modulus of the resin.

Asbestos is available in many forms, though not in as many as glass. Woven asbestos cloths are available; roving and mat are available in a number of weights and in a number of different asbestos materials.

The crocidolite type of fiber is the most resistant to chemicals and has the best mechanical properties. The other types of asbestos are lower in cost but are also lower in mechanical properties and in chemical resistance.

Sisal has been used in a great many applications for polyester resin. It is quite adequate as a reinforcing material in many products for the building-materials market. It is low in cost and readily available.

Hemp has been used in fewer applications because of its relatively high cost and shorter supply. If and when available, it can be used to good advantage. It can impart good mechanical properties to polyesters.

In the United States we know little of coconut fiber as a reinforcing material for polyesters. In much of the world, this material is one of the most readily available fibers known. It can be substituted very well for glass fiber in many applications requiring somewhat lesser mechanical properties. In building materials of all types, it would be a most adequate and appropriate reinforcing fiber.

Along the Gulf Coast, rice hulls are considered a waste material. Some of this material is ground and used in fertilizers and livestock feeds, mostly as a filler material, because it has no real value in either application. The rest is a detriment to the rice industry because of the expense in hauling it away and dumping it. This material is a source of a plentiful supply of fillers and reinforcing materials for polyester resins. It has a very low resin absorption, and it has excellent mechanical properties. Because of its low absorption, very high percentages of this material can be incorporated into polyester compounds. It can be most useful in the manufacture of building products. Rice hulls impart very good properties to such products.

In a few areas of the United States and all over Latin America, huge quantities of bagasse are available. This is the waste product from sugar cane, left over from the manufacture of sugar, molasses, and rum. The fiber has a very low resin absorption and excellent mechanical properties. Because of its nature it is easily dried, shredded, and turned into individual fibers. This fiber can compare very well with sisal, hemp, cotton, and many other fibers in the mechanical properties imparted to polyester products.

Cotton fiber is rarely considered as a reinforcing fiber for use in plastic products. It is rather high in cost, and its mechanical properties are not the best. However, there are many low-cost cotton products that can be used to good advantage in many polyester products. Waste cotton—the part which is full of hulls—and other waste materials that are too expensive to remove can be used well in many applications as reinforcing fiber when combined with other fillers and aggregates.

A number of metallic fibers are available for specific purposes. Some of these are excellent for imparting electrical conductivity to polyester. Others are very good for extremely high temperature applications. All have excellent mechanical properties and can be used where very high strengths are necessary. The costs of these fibers are very high, but they may be justified in certain uses.

Many kinds of metallic fabrics and mesh already on the market are ideal as reinforcing materials for polyesters in applications calling for extreme mechanical properties. Wire mesh is available in black iron, carbon steel, stainless steel, monel, and many other metals and alloys. Even coarse highway-reinforcing mesh can be used in applications calling for very large parts, such as metal-forming dies for shaping steel and aluminum.

Resistance wires can be imbedded into polyester compounds for heating applications for interior or exterior use. Entire buildings can be heated in this manner, and airfields, sidewalks, streets, and bridges may be kept free of ice and snow in this way.

Special graphite and carbon fibers are available for use in polyester compounds for both reinforcing and heating applications. These conductive fibers are used many times in the curing of polyester compounds. The resistance fibers are incorporated into the compound and attached to a source of electrical current. The heat given off by these fibers will cure polyesters in a few minutes.

Nylon fiber and fabrics are useful in the reinforcing of many polyester compounds and products where high tensile strengths are desirable, without raising the flexual modulus of the polyester too much. Polyester fiber, of the terephthalic type, and polypropylene fibers and fabrics are often used for these same purposes. Although these fibers do not have the high tensile strengths of glass fibers, often much higher volume ratios of reinforcing to resin can be incorporated into a product than with glass materials. This fact, together with the lower specific gravity of these synthetic fibers, can produce laminates, castings, and lay-ups with mechanical properties quite comparable to polyester-glass combinations (on a strength-to-weight basis).

These synthetic fibers all can be used to great advantage in certain applications. Each product, process, and application will differ in the end requirements. The reinforcing material is a most important part of the finished product and must be chosen to best fit the needs of the application, taking into consideration each and every end property the product must possess.

Reinforcing steel, such as that used in concrete construction, is seldom considered for use in plastics reinforcing. It can be put to excellent use in the manufacture of light-weight polyester beams, columns, and other structural members. Such products may be prestressed or post-stressed, quite as concrete members are produced.

Reinforcing steel may be used in large polyester products of any kind. It is useful in large metal-forming dies, large vacuum-forming dies for thermosetting plastics, and very large polyester molds and dies for producing polyester products.

Steel angles, I beams, H beams, and channels may be put to very good use as parts of a finished polyester product. In large marine vessels, such beams can form the framework around which polyester is laid up to form the hulls. These members may be used as framework supports for very large polyester-cast dies and other products.

Steel of any kind to be used in polyesters must be well cleaned by either phosphoric acid or sandblasting and primed with a primer such as that described in Chart 5. The steel thus treated can become an integral part of large polyester products.

Many times steel pipe can be incorporated into polyester products, either for its own reinforcing value or as channels for future wiring. Pipe can be incorporated into polyester beams and structural members, and later wire cable in these conduits may be poststressed to give extremely high mechanical strengths to these members.

Steel, aluminum, and other metals may be used to good advantage in many polyester products.

Manufacturing Procedures and Techniques

When a manufacturer of polyester products has the proper resin, catalyst, promoter, mold release, reinforcing materials, pigments, and fillers for his product and the proper equipment for his process, most of his problems are solved.

Very few processing techniques from one product can be applied to other products. During the first few weeks of production, almost every production line will require small changes in these techniques to improve coordination of all phases of the process, to speed up production, and to turn out better products at lower plant costs.

Many techniques and variations of these techniques will be very minor, but sometimes a very small change in the methods used can make very large differences in both the amount of total production and the quality of the product. Often, the cost per unit can be appreciably reduced.

Some parts are more easily processed than others. Small, plane parts are by far the simplest. Any part that can be stacked flat as it comes off the production line while still hot should never give any major problems.

Such parts should be stacked on a very flat, level surface until they reach room temperature. The height of the stacks will depend to a large extent on the thickness of each part and the degree of cure that the part has reached in the dies. Sometimes a process will call for only a partial cure of the parts in the dies—enough to give sufficient strength for further handling and processing. In such cases, the parts should be stacked in larger quantities in order to utilize both the exotherm heat and the heat that has been introduced into the part in the dies to complete the cure.

In a process where the parts are fully cured in the dies, they should then be stacked is lesser quantities so they may cool to room temperature at an even but faster rate.

In some production lines, it is necessary to install conveyor belts to carry the molded parts to other operations or to the packaging area. Particularly in thin parts, in such a production line where they cannot be stacked for cooling, arrangements must be made so that they do not cool too rapidly or from one side only. There is always some danger of warping from the stresses that are set up by one side of a part cooling much faster than the other.

Conveyor belts may be totally enclosed, and, when necessary, heating elements may be installed in them so that cooling of the parts may be carried out at an even rate.

More complex-shaped products can create problems during the cooling stages. Parts that will "nest" together, thus supporting each other as they cool, will present few problems. Parts that are too complex to nest must be cooled over a template to prevent any undue stresses as they cool and shrink.

The more complex the shape of a part, the more problems that are possible, but this does not mean that the problems cannot be solved. Shapes requiring sharp radii, particularly when the walls are very thin, can present problems at the radii. Often these parts will show very tiny hairline cracks in these radii, which may be caused by too little reinforcing material at these points or overcure of the parts in the dies. Any part, and in particular a large part, with right-angle forms and deep draws must not be cured to complete optimum cure in the dies. The shrinkage of the part as it cures will be greatest during the last few seconds of the curing cycle. The part must be cured in the dies to a point where it has sufficient strength for removal and handling; however, if allowed to reach full cure, it will form cracks from shrinkage stresses at the radii, at which point all such forces will be concentrated. Very little or no shrinkage will occur during the gel and precure stages.

Roughly 40% will occur during the final few seconds of cure, and the other 60% will occur during the cooling stages of the part. These percentages will vary slightly, according to the filler or reinforcement percentages the thickness of the part, but they will not vary greatly.

It is during the first 40% of the shrinkage that the stresses that can damage the part occur, so the part must be removed from the dies just before the final stages of the cure takes place. A properly formulated compound will have more than enough strength to be removed and handled at this point. This is usually referred to as "hot strength," and it is a very important aspect of proper formulation.

Any irregular part that may have ribs or other obstructions on the plane surfaces can present this same problem. However, it is easy to solve by setting cycle times so that the part is removed before critical shrinkage takes place.

The thickness of parts will usually influence considerably the total cycle time. The thicker the part, the longer it takes for the endotherm or applied heat to be absorbed by compound. This can be minimized to a great extent by the proper choice of filler materials with good thermal conduction and by the addition of small amounts of promoters to the formulation. The heat in the dies may also be raised in many cases to reduce the cycle time.

The size of polyester products can have considerable effect on the exact techniques, formulas, etc., to be used. In compression-molding, injection-molding, and other matched-die processes, the compound must be formulated so as to flow much better and to gel much slower than smaller products.

A compound formulated for parts 12×12 in. square that are plane can be formulated to gel and cure very fast; the smaller the part, the less flowability it will need to be able to fill the dies completely. In compression-molding and transfer-molding, the speed of the closing of the dies will have much to do with how a compound is formulated to flow and gel. The faster the action of the press, the faster the compound may be formulated to gel.

Parts with angles, curves, sharp radii, and very thin wall swill need a compound with much better flow than plane parts; the larger the area of the part, the more flow will be necessary, with correspondingly slower gel.

Lubricants are often used in formulating compounds for very large articles. Few of the prepared internal mold releases have good lubricating properties when used alone, but when combined with one of the stearates or one of the very high molecular weight polyethylene glycol monostearates, exceedingly good combinations of both flow and mold release can be obtained.

The dies themselves will have much to do with the proper fill-out and flow. Design of the dies should give maximum radii wherever possible, and the dies should be polished to a 5-μ finish or less for the very best surface possible. The better the die surface, the better will be the finished part, and the easier it will be to obtain good fill-out and release.

Polyester resin itself is a very good lubricant and will flow well until it begins to gel. The kaolin clays are excellent fillers for obtaining good flow. Talc is also a very good filler for incorporation into a compound requiring maximum flow. The silicas and calcium carbonates are among the poorer-flowing fillers.

The dimensional tolerances of polyester products are one of the most important factors that must be considered. Many parts require extremely close tolerances, while others may vary considerably in dimensions.

Whatever the dimensional tolerances may be in the finished product, these must be clearly defined before molds or dies are made. Where dimensions must be very close—within plus or minus 0.1%—the best procedure is to make one set of dies to calculated dimensions, allowing for probable shrinkage in a given compound. With this set of test dies, compound formulations may be tested until the exact end product is obtained and the exact amount of shrinkage determined, before proceeding to make up full sets of dies.

When tolerances must be held to such close standards, formulations may not be changed in any way after the dies have been made up. Die temperatures also may not be changed. Every single factor must be considered.

At room temperature, a hardened steel die cavity may be 12.025 in. At 275°F, it can be 12.036 in., and at 350°F, it can be 12.046 in., depending on the steel alloy, the method of hardening used, and the amount of hardening of the metal. The coefficient of thermal expansion will vary quite drastically in different metals of quite similar chemical content.

If a compound is formulated to give parts at 12 in. in such a die, allowing a plus or minus 0.015-in. tolerance, at a given die temperature, any slight change in either formulation or die temperature can change the overall dimensions by as much as 0.010 in.

When compounding such formulations for products where very close tolerances must be held, weights and measures of the components going into the formulation must be very close indeed. A 1% error in the amount of a given ingredient can make a dimensional change in parts up to 0.5%, depending on which ingredient is in error.

Human error is perhaps the cause of most reject parts in polyester manufacture. Wherever possible, weights and measures should be calculated automatically with the excellent equipment available today for this purpose. Properly maintained machinery can do the job with less chances of error than if these calculations were made by a workman.

In the manufacture of products where such close tolerances are unnecessary, slight changes in temperatures and formulations may be made after molds and dies are made. A change in temperature can be offset by a slight change in filler content, or the reverse.

Even in casting operations, contact-molding, hand and gun lay-up, and pressure-casting, the tolerances in dimensions of a product can be held to very reasonable levels. Again, it is advisable to make a sample mold first, on which final formulations, temperatures, and other factors may be tested. The sample mold need not be full size. The mold may be scaled down to $\frac{1}{4}$ size or even smaller, as long as the material with which it is made is identical to the material to be used in the ultimate molds.

In such test molds, formulations may be perfected and the end properties of the product obtained. The amount of total shrinkage may be measured with vernier calipers in the scale size mold and projected to the ultimate molds. Tolerances of 0.5% accuracy can be held in very large products in this manner.

Thickness dimensions never present much of a problem in matched-die processes. Many times the dies must be shimmed, leveled, and adjusted in order to have all corners of a part within the allowed tolerances, but this is usually routine, with few problems experienced. If the dies are properly designed and made, and if the equipment and platens are accurate, little trouble is encountered.

In hand and gun lay-up or in casting operations, sometimes thickness dimensions can present a few problems; however, in products manufactured by these methods, this is usually not a critical dimension, and quite large plus or minus factors are generally allowed.

A production line for the processing of any polyester product could well be compared to a fine timepiece. If one minute part does not function properly, the entire cycle is interrupted. Each small part must do its prescribed job in the prescribed amount of time with the prescribed accuracy, or the rest of the equipment is prevented from doing its job.

The programming of each piece of equipment in a polyester production line is much more critical than with any other thermosetting material because of the great difference in cycle time. A production line producing phenolic or epoxy parts may be programmed for 20-, 30-, or even 40-min cycles, where each piece of equipment has some considerable time in which to perform its function. But in a polyester production line, total cycle time may be as low as 15 sec in many cases. Production such as this will not allow for any equipment error or human error.

CHART 21. PRODUCTS AND SOME PROCESSING METHODS

Product	Compression molding	Transfer molding	Injection molding	Extrusion	Calendering	Hand layup	Gun layup, chopper	Casting in place	Casting, vibrating	Cell casting	Casting, Press autoclave	Bag molding	Plunger molding	Vacuum injection mold.	Diamond blade sawing	Flow coating	Web dip, process, conv.	Sprayup	Conveyor-belt casting	Centrifugal casting	Rotational casting	Filament winding	Blow molding	Surface grinding	Sealer	Gel coating	Mandrel
Floor tile terrazzo, small	>	>	>		>				>										>					>	>		
Floor tile marbelized	>	>	>		>				>										>								
Floor tile terrazzo, medium	>	>	>						>		>								>					>	>		
Floor tile terrazzo, large									>		>				>				>					>	>		
Flooring, calendered					>											>	>		>								
Flooring, rolled					>																						
Flooring, in-place								>																			
Wall paneling				>																						>	
Wall slabs, marble, granite									>																	>	
Modular panels																										>	
Bathroom fixtures									>									>	>							>	
Vanity, bar, table tops									>																	>	
Laminates, pressure	>		>								>	>	>														
Ceramic tile, 4" x 4"										>																	
Glass, clear, decorative			>							>																>	
Roofing materials, panels																>	>										
Roofing materials, rolled																											
Roofing materials, sprayup						>	>											>									
Pipe, high-pressure				>																>		>					>
Tubular goods, low-pressure																											>
Corrosion coatings																											
Elect. insulators	>	>	>								>																
Elect. fixtures	>	>	>																								
Optical lenses										>			>														
Auto. component parts	>																									>	
Furniture	>						>																			>	
Tooling							>																			>	
Large marine craft						>	>							>												>	
Vessels, chemical							>		>												>	>				>	
Swimming pools							>																			>	>

Any small part of the entire line that cannot perform its function in this prescribed time will hold up every other part of the line.

Every time a production cycle is interrupted for any reason—whether it be faulty formulation, faulty equipment, or a man not at his post—production for that period is reduced, and each part produced during that time increases sharply in plant cost.

A difference in 1 or 5% reject parts can easily mean the difference between profit and loss in many manufacturing operations. A difference of a 5 or 6% increase in total daily production can very often mean that the plant will break even or make a good profit. A downtime of 10 hr per month for repairs and adjustments can often cancel out any profits for the month. In mass-production procedures and products, the profit margin per part is usually very small. Profits are made through volume. Every phase of the operation must be synchronized like the parts in a fine watch. Raw materials must be readily available as needed. They must be weighed and batched exactly on schedule. The compound must be fed into the molding process at the right rate of material per minute, and after molding, these parts must be further processed or packaged on schedule. Not a single phase of the operation may lag behind even for a few seconds.

A single raw material that a purchasing agent forgot to order, or that did not arrive on schedule, can shut down an entire plant and layoff all its workmen for days. One piece of equipment that breaks down can have the same effect.

Every possible eventuality must be foreseen, and everything possible must be done to correct that eventuality before it happens. Raw-material storage must be adequate for all possible delays in arrival of materials. Spare parts must be on hand for all equipment. Trained men must be ready to take over for any absent or ill key men in the production line. Every possible precaution must be taken against faulty formulation. Each piece of equipment that is purchased must be completely adequate for its function.

With proper planning and foresight, a polyester production plant can run as smoothly as a fine watch, with high production and profits. The equipment and materials are available today with which to accomplish this. The markets are waiting for new and better products. There are almost no limit to the opportunities whereby a new or established and expanding industry may manufacture some of these products.

Appendix

SUPPLIERS OF RAW MATERIALS, INTERMEDIATES, RESINS, ADDITIVES, PIGMENTS, FILLERS, REINFORCING MATERIALS, EQUIPMENT, AND MACHINERY

Polyester Resin Manufacturers

1. Allied Chemical Corp., 61 Broadway, New York, N.Y. 10006
2. Alpha Chemical Corp., P. O. Drawer A, Colliersville, Tenn. 38017
3. American Cyanamid Co., Wallingford, Conn. 06492
4. Archer-Daniels-Mildland Co., 700 Investor's Bldg., Minneapolis, Minn. 55440
5. Atlas Chemical Industries, Inc., Wilmington, Del. 19899
6. American Petrochemicals Corp., Mol-Rez Div., 3134 California St., N.E., Minneapolis, Minn. 55418
7. Cook Paint and Varnish Co., Kansas City, Mo. 66141
8. Durez Plastics Div., Hooker Chemical Corp., 1967 Walck Rd., North Tonawanda, N.Y. 14121
9. Freeman Chemical Corp., 222 E. Main St., Port Washington, Wis. 53074
10. The Glidden Co., 900 Union Commerce Bldg., Cleveland, Ohio 44115
11. Koppers Co., Inc., Koppers Bldg., Pittsburgh, Pa. 15219

12. Interchemical Corp., 1255 Broad St., Clifton, N.J. 07011
13. Naftone, Inc., 425 Park Ave., New York, N.Y 10022
14. Pittsburgh Plate Glass Co., 632 Ft. Duquesne Blvd., Pittsburgh, Pa. 15222
15. Reichold Chemicals, Inc., 525 N. Broadway, White Plains, N.Y. 10602
16. Resins Systems Div., Tra-Con Inc., 25 Ship Ave., Medford, Mass. 02155
17. Isochem Resin Co., Cook St., Lincoln, R.I., 02865
18. Witco Chemical Co., Inc., 277 Park Ave., New York, N.Y. 10017
19. Chevron Chemical Co., 200 Rusk St., San Francisco, Calif.
20. Goodyear Tire and Rubber Co., Chemical Div., 1485 Archwood Ave., Akron, Ohio 44316
21. Diamond Alkali Co., 300 Union Commerce Bldg., Cleveland, Ohio 44115

There are many more manufacturers of polyester resins. They are not listed simply because of lack of names and addresses.

Hydroxyl Components

1. A.I.D. Chemical Co., Inc., 26 Broadway, New York, N.Y. 10004
2. Archer-Daniels-Midland, 733 Marquette Ave., Minneapolis, Minn. 55440
3. Baker Castor Oil Co., 40 Avenue A., Bayonne, N.J. 07002
4. Celanese Corp. of America, Dept. 560, 522 Fifth Ave., New York, N.Y 10036
5. Dow Chemical Co., Midland, Mich. 48640
6. Eastman Chemical Co., Kingsport, Tenn. 37662
7. Browning Chemical Corp., 17876 St. Clair Ave., Cleveland, Ohio 44110
8. Chemical Solvents, 60 Park Pl., Newark, N.J. 07102
9. Fallek Chemical Corp., 4 W. 58th St., New York, N.Y. 10019
10. C. P. Hall Co., 414–418 S. Broadway, Akron, Ohio 44308
11. Van Waters and Rodgers, Inc., P.O. Box 3200, Rincon Annex, San Francisco, Calif. 94119
12. Wyandotte Chemical Corp., Wyandotte, Mich. 48193
13. Reichold Chemicals, 525 N. Broadway, White Plains, N.Y. 10602
14. F. H. Ross, 3920 Glenwood Rd., Charlotte, N.C. 28201
15. Sonford Chemical Co., 1100 State Natl. Bank, 412 Main St., Houston, Tex. 77002
16. Enjay Chemical Co., 60 W. 49th St., New York, N.Y. 10020
17. Harshaw Chemical Co., 1945 E. 97th St., Cleveland, Ohio 44106
18. Hooker Chemical Co., 1300 47th St., Niagara Falls, N.Y. 14302
19. Jefferson Chemical Co., Inc., P.O. Box 53300, Houston, Tex. 77052
20. J. T. Baker Chemical Co., Phillipsburgh, N.J. 08865
21. McKesson and Robbins, Inc., 155 E. 44th St., New York, N.Y. 10017
22. Mercury Chemical Corp., Rt. 1, Metuchen, N.J. 08840
23. Olin, Chemicals Div., 745 Fifth Ave., New York, N.Y. 10022
24. Phillips Petroleum Co., Chemicals Dept., Barletsville, Okla. 74003
25. Sinclair Petrochemicals, Inc., 600 Fifth Ave., New York, N.Y. 10020
26. Union Carbide Corp., Chemicals Div., 270 Park Ave., New York, N.Y. 10017
27. Wilson-Martin Div., Synder Ave. and Swanson St., Philadelphia, Pa. 19148
28. Tenneco Chemicals, Inc., 300 E. 42nd St., New York, N.Y. 10017

There are many manufacturers of these materials that cannot be listed because of lack of space and names and addresses. There are two excellent buyers' guides available, which list all these materials: One is Chemical Week Buyer's Guide, published by McGraw-Hill Book Co., 330 West 42nd St., New York, N.Y. 10036. The other is the OPD Chemical Buyer's Guide, published by Schnell Publishing Co., Inc., 100 Church St., New York, N.Y. 10007.

Saturated Acids

1. A.I.D. Chemical Co., Inc., 26 Broadway, New York, N.Y. 10004
2. American Cyanamid Co., Intermediates Dept. Bound Brook, N.J. 08805
3. Allied Chemical Corp., P.O. Box 365, Morristown, N.J. 07960
4. Ciba Products Co., Fairlawn, N.J. 07410
5. Chevron Chemical Co., Orosite Div., 1695 W. Crescent Ave., Anaheim, Calif. 92801
6. Celanese Corp. of America, Dept. 560, 522 Fifth Ave., New York, N.Y. 10036
7. E. I. DuPont de Nemours and Co., Inc., Wilmington, Del. 19898
8. J. T. Baker Chemical Co., Phillipsburg, N.J. 08865
9. Fallek Chemical Corp., 4 W. 58th St., New York, N.Y. 10019
10. General Mills, Inc., Chemical Div., P.O. Box 191, Kankakee, Ill. 60901
11. Hooker Chemical Co., 1300 47th St., Niagara Falls, N.Y. 14302
12. International Chemical Corp., 500 Fifth Ave., New York, N.Y. 10036
13. Harshaw Chemical Co., 1945 E. 97th St., Cleveland, Ohio 44106
14. Koppers Co., Tar and Chem. Div., Koppers Bldg., Pittsburgh, Pa. 15219
15. McKesson and Robbins, Inc., 155 E. 44th St., New York, N.Y. 10017
16. Mercury Chemical Co., Inc., 2443 N. Claybourne Ave., Chicago, Ill. 60614
17. Monsanto Co., 800 N. Lindberg Blvd., St. Louis, Mo. 63166
18. Petro Tex Chemical Corp., 8660 Park Place, Houston, Tex., 77017
19. Prior Chemical Corp., 420 Lexington Ave., New York, N.Y. 10017
20. Reichold Chemicals, Inc., 525 N. Broadway, White Plains, N.Y. 10602
21. Rohm and Haas Co., Independence Mall West, Philadelphia, Pa. 19105
22. Sinclair Koppers Co., Koppers Bldg., Pittsburgh, Pa. 15219
23. Tenneco Chemicals, Inc., 300 E. 42nd St., New York, N.Y. 10017
24. W. R. Grace and Co., Hatco Chemicals Div., King George Post Rd., Fords, N.J. 08863
25. Van Waters and Rodgers, Inc., P.O. Box 3200, Rincon Annex, San Francisco, Calif. 94119
26. Union Carbide, Chemicals Div., 270 Park Ave., New York, N.Y. 10017
27. USS Chemicals, Div. of U.S. Steel, 5 Gateway Center, Pittsburgh, Pa. 15230
28. Witco Chemical Co., Inc., 277 Park Ave., New York, N.Y. 10017
29. Veliscol International Corp., P.O. Box 1687, Nassau, Bahamas

Unsaturated Acids

1. Agrichem Corp., 99 Park Ave., New York, N.Y. 10016
2. Allied Chemical Corp., National Analine Div., 40 Rector St., New York, N.Y. 10006
3. Asher-Moore Co., 801 East Canal St., Richmond, Va. 23219
4. Barclay Chemical Co., Inc., 75 Varick St., New York, N.Y. 10013
5. California Chemical Co., Inc., 200 Bush St., San Francisco, Calif. 94120
6. Cemco, Inc., 50 E. 41st St., New York, N.Y. 10017

7. Cheamator, Inc., 40 Exchange Plaza, New York, N.Y. 10005
8. M. W. Hardy and Co., Inc., 141 Broadway, New York, N.Y. 10006
9. Fallek Chemical Corp., 4 W. 58th St., New York, N.Y. 10019
10. International Chemical Corp., 500 Fifth Ave., New York, N.Y. 10036
11. Koppers Co., Inc., Tar & Chemicals Div., Koppers Bldg., Pittsburgh, Pa. 15219
12. McKesson and Robbins, Inc., 155 E. 44th St., New York, N.Y. 10017
13. A. Millner Co. Inc., 71 Mercer St., New York, N.Y. 10012
14. Monsanto Co., 800 N. Lindberg Blvd., St. Louis, Mo. 63166
15. Petro Tex Chemical Company, 8600 Park Place, Houston, Tex. 77017
16. Chas. Pfizer and Co., Inc., Chemical Div., 235 E. 42nd St., New York, N.Y. 10017
17. Pittsburgh Chemical Co., 2027 Grant Bldg., Pittsburgh, Pa. 15219
18. Prior Chemicals, Inc., 420 Lexington Ave., New York, N.Y. 10017
19. Reichold Chemicals, Inc., 525 N. Broadway, White Plains N.Y. 10602
20. Tenneco Chemicals, Heyden Div., 300 E. 42nd St., New York, N.Y. 10017
21. Tar Residuals, Inc., 420 Lexington Ave., New York, N.Y. 10017

Monomers

1. Alleghany Solvents and Chemical Co., Box 477, Carnegie, Pa. 15106
2. Amoco Chemicals Corp., 130 E. Randolph Dr., Chicago, Ill. 60601
3. American Cyanamid Co., Bound Brook, N.J. 08805
4. Amsco Solvents and Chemical Co., 4619 Reading Rd., Cincinatti, Ohio 45229
5. Buffalo Solvents and Chemical Corp., P. O. Box 73, Station B, Buffalo, N.Y. 14207
6. Borden Chemical Co., 350 Madison Ave., New York, N.Y. 10017
7. Cosden Oil and Chemical Co., Box 1311, Big Springs, Tex. 10036
8. Celanese Corporation, 522 Fifth Ave., New York, N.Y. 10036
9. Dow Chemical Co., Midland, Mich. 48640
10. E. I. DuPont de Nemours and Co., Inc., Wilmington, Del. 19898
11. Eastman Chemical Co., Kingsport, Tenn. 37662
12. Escambia Chemical Corp., 261 Madison Ave., New York, N.Y. 10016
13. Interchemical Corp., 150 Wagaraw Rd., Hawthorne, N.J.
14. FMC Corp., 633 Third Ave., New York, N.Y. 10017
15. General Aniline and Film Corp., 140 W. 51st St., New York, N.Y. 10020
16. Kingston Chemical Co., Inc., 97–99 Hudson St., New York, N.Y. 10013
17. Jefferson Chemical Co., Inc., P.O. Box 53300, Houston, Tex. 77052
18. McKesson and Robbins, Inc., 155 E. 44th St., New York, N.Y. 10017
19. Rohm and Haas Co., Independence Mall West, Philadelphia, Pa. 19105
20. Monsanto Co., 800 N. Lindberg Blvd., St. Louis, Mo. 63166
21. Kay-Fries Chemicals Inc., 360 Lexington Ave., New York, N.Y. 10017
22. Shell Chemical Co., 50 W. 50th St., New York, N.Y. 10020
23. Sinclair Koppers Co., Koppers Bldg., Pittsburgh, Pa. 15219
24. Sartomer Resins, Inc., P.O. Box 56, Essington, Pa. 19029
25. Union Carbide Co., 270 Park Ave., New York, N.Y. 10017
26. U.S. Industrial Chemicals Co., 99 Park Ave., New York, N.Y. 10016
27. U.S. Industries, Inc., 250 Park Ave., New York, N.Y. 10017

Almost all the companies listed have more than one plant, well distributed all over the entire country. There materials are available from one or more companies fairly near any given location.

Additives—Antistatic Agents

1. American Cyanamid Co., Dye and Textile Div., Bound Brook, N.J. 08805
2. Carlisle Chemical Works, Inc., Reading, Ohio 45215
3. Ciba Chemical and Dye Co., Route 208, Fairlawn, N.J. 07410
4. E. I. DuPont de Nemours and Co., Wilmington, Del. 19898
5. Giegy Dyestuffs Div., Saw Mill River Rd., Ardsley, N.Y. 10502
6. General Aniline and Film Corp., 140 W. 51st St., New York, N.Y. 10020
7. General Mills, 9200 Wayzata Blvd., Minneapolis, Minn. 55440
8. Sonneborn Chemical and Refining Co., 277 Park Ave., New York, N.Y. 10017
9. Standard Chemical Products, Inc., 1301 Jefferson St., Hoboken, N.J. 07030
10. Union Carbide Corp., Chem. Div., 270 Park Ave., New York, N.Y. 10017

Ultraviolet Agents: Absorbers and Blocking

1. American Cyanamid Co., Intermediates Dept., Bound Brook, N.J. 08805
2. Carlisle Chemical Works, Reading, Ohio 45215
3. Ferro Chemical Div., P.O. Box 349, Bedford, Ohio 44014
4. Geigy Ind., Chem. Div., Saw Mill River Rd., Ardsley, N.Y. 10502
5. General Aniline and Film Corp., 140 W. 51st St., New York, N.Y. 10020
6. Interchemical Corp., Organic Chem. Dept., 150 Wagaraw Rd., Hawthorne, N.J. 07506
7. Monsanto Co., 800 N. Lindberg Blvd., St. Louis, Mo. 63166
8. M and T Chemicals, Inc., Rahway, N.J. 07065
9. Naftone, Inc., 425 Park Ave., New York, N.Y. 10022
10. Tenneco Chemicals, Inc., Nuodex Div., P.O. Box 242, Elizabeth, N.J. 07207
11. Mantrose Co., 99 Park Ave., New York, N.Y. 10016

Flame Retarders

1. American Cyanamid Co., Bound Brook, N.J. 08805
2. Diamond Alkali, 300 Union Commerce Bldg., Cleveland, Ohio, 44114
3. General Aniline and Film Corp., 140 W. 51st St., New York, N.Y. 10020
4. Harshaw Chemical Co., 1945 E. 97th St., Cleveland, Ohio 44106
5. M and T Chemicals, Inc., Rahway, N.J. 07065
6. Michigan Chemical Corp., 500 N. Bankson St., St. Louis, Mich. 48880
7. Monsanto Chemical Co., 800 N. Lindberg Blvd., St. Louis, Mo. 63166
8. Sun Chemical Corp., 441 Tompkins Ave., Rosebank, Staten Island, N.Y. 10305

Flatting Agents

1. Cabot Corp., 125 High St., Boston, Mass. 02110
2. W. R. Grace Co., Davidson Div., 101 N. Charles St., Baltimore, Md. 21203
3. Monsanto Co., 800 N. Lindberg Blvd., St. Louis, Mo. 63166
4. Nopco, 60 Park Place, Newark, N.J. 07102
5. Tenneco Chemicals, Nuodex Div., P.O. Box 242, Elizabeth, N.J. 07207
6. Whittaker, Clark and Daniels, Inc., 100 Church St., New York, N.Y. 10007
7. Witco Chemical Co., Inc., 277 Park Ave., New York, N.Y. 10017

Treated Silicas, Aerogels, Colloidal, Thixotropic Agents

1. Cabot Corp., 125 High St., Boston, Mass. 02110
2. Berkshire Chemicals, Inc., 155 E. 44th St., New York, N.Y. 10017
3. Chemwest, Inc., 600 S. 4th St., Richmond 4, Calif. 94804
4. Illinois Minerals Co., 218 10th St., Cairo, Ill. 62914
5. Gallard-Schlesinger Chemical Mfg. Corp., 580 Mineola Ave., Carle Place, Long Island, N.Y. 11514
6. Johns Mansville, 22 E. 40th St., New York, N.Y. 10016
7. McKesson and Robbins, Inc., 155 E. 44th St., New York, N.Y. 10017
8. Tamms Industries Co., P.O. Box 64, Lyons, Ill. 60534
9. Monsanto Co., 800 N. Lindberg Blvd., St. Louis, Mo. 63166
10. Van Waters and Rodgers, Inc., P.O. Box 3200, Rincon Annex, San Francisco, Calif. 94119
11. Whittaker, Clark, and Daniels, Inc., 100 Church St., New York, N.Y. 10007
12. G. S. Robins and Co., 126 Chouteau Ave., St. Louis, Mo. 63102

Cellulose Acetate Butyrate:
$\frac{1}{2}$ sec, $\frac{1}{10}$ sec

1. Eastman Chemical Products Co., Kingsport, Tenn. 37662

Triphenyl Phosphite, Stabilizers

1. Cemco, Inc., 50 E. 41st St., New York, N.Y. 10017
2. Hooker Chemical Corp., 1300 47th St., Niagara Falls, N.Y. 14302
3. Monsanto Co., 800 N. Lindberg Blvd., St. Louis, Mo. 63166

Silicones, Special, for Polyesters

1. Dow-Corning, Midland, Mich. 48641
2. General Electric, Silicones Products Div., Waterford, N.Y. 12183
3. C. P. Hall Co., 414–418 S. Broadway, Akron, Ohio 44308
4. Union Carbide Corp., Silicones Div., 270 Park Ave., New York, N.Y. 10017

Fungacides and Biocides

1. Allied Chemical Corp., General Chemical Div., P.O. Box 70, Morristown, N.J. 07960
2. Barlow Chemical Corp., Barlow Lane, Ossining, N.Y. 10562
3. Browning Chemical Corp., 295 Madison Ave., New York, N.Y. 10017
4. California Chemical Co., Ortho Div., 200 Bush St., San Francisco, Calif. 94120
5. Carlisle Chemical Works, Inc., Reading, Ohio 45215
6. Chemical Industries Corp., 30 Whitmore Ave., Metuchen, N.J. 08840
7. Chemwest, Inc., 600 S. 4th St., Richmond, Calif. 94804
8. Cosan Chemical Co., 481 River Rd., Clifton, N.J. 07013

9. Metalsalts Corp., 2 Wagaraw Rd., Hawthorne, N.J. 07506
10. Dow Chemical Co., Midland, Mich. 48640
11. E. I. DuPont de Nemours and Co., Wilmington, Del. 19898
12. General Aniline and Film Corp., 140 W. 51st St., New York, N.Y. 10020
13. Hercules Powder Co. 910 Market St., Wilmington, Del. 19899
14. Monsanto Co., 800 N. Lindberg Blvd., St. Louis, Mo. 63166
15. Pennsalt Chemical Corp., 3 Penn Center, Philadelphia, Pa. 19102
16. Rohm and Haas Co., Independence Mall West, Philadelphia, Pa. 19105
17. Stauffer Chemical Co., 3940 Summit St., Weston, Mich. 49289
18. Tenneco Chemicals, Nuodex Div., P.O. Box 242, Elizabeth, N.J. 07207
19. Union Carbide Corp., Chem. Div., 270 Park Ave., New York, N.Y. 10017

Copper Polymerization Inhibitors, Color Clarifiers

1. Advance Div., Carlisle Chemical Works, 500 Jersey Ave., New Brunswick, N.J. 08903
2. Ferro Chemicals Div., P.O. Box 349, Bedford, Ohio 44014
3. Harshaw Chemical Co., 1945 E. 97th St., Cleveland, Ohio 44106
4. Witco Chemical Co., Inc., 277 Park Ave., New York, N.Y. 10017

Coumarin Compounds, Clarifiers

1. Advance Div., Carlisle Chemical Works, 500 Jersey Ave., New Brunswick, N.J. 08903
2. Dow Chemical Co., Midland, Mich. 48640
3. McKesson and Robbins, Inc., Chem. Div., 155 E. 44th St., New York, N.Y. 10017
4. Monsanto Co., 800 N. Lindberg Blvd., St. Louis, Mo. 63166

Semiconductors, Organic

1. Electronic Space Products, Inc., 854 S. Robertson Blvd., Los Angeles, Calif. 90035
2. Allied Chemical Corp., General Chemical Div., P.O. Box 70, Morristown, N.J. 07960
3. Mallinkrodt Chemical Works, St. Louis, Mo. 63160
4. J. T. Baker Chemical Co., Phillipsburg, N.J. 08865
5. E. I. DuPont de Nemours and Co., Electro-Chemical Dept., Wilmington, Del. 19898
6. Sylvania Electrical Products, Inc., Chem. and Metal. Div., Tanawanda, Pa. 18848

Inhibitors: Catechol

1. J. H. DeLamar and Sons, Inc., 4529 N. Kedzie Ave., Chicago, Ill. 60625
2. Grant Chemical Co., Inc., 1911 N. 4th St., Baton Rouge, La. 70821
3. Koppers Co., Koppers Bldg., Pittsburgh, Pa. 15219
4. Tucker Chemical Co., Inc., 185 Foundry St., Newark, N.J. 07105

Inhibitors: Hydroquinones

1. Allied Chemical Corp., General Chemical Div., P.O. Box 70, Morristown, N.J. 07960
2. J. T. Baker Chemical Co., Phillipsburgh, N.J. 08865
3. Eastman Chemical Products, Inc., Kingsport, Tenn. 37662
4. Carus Chemical Co., Inc., 1372 8th St., La Salle, Ill. 60004
5. Naftone, Inc., 425 Park Ave., New York, N.Y. 10022

Inhibitors: Quaternary Ammoniums

1. Archer Daniels Midland Co., 733 Marquette Ave., Minneapolis, Minn. 55440
2. Barlow Chemical Corp., Barlow Lane, Ossining, N.Y. 10562
3. Cargill Inc., Industrial Chemical Div., Cargill Bldg., Minneapolis, Minn. 55402
4. Geigy Industrial Chemicals, Saw Mill River Rd., Ardsley, N.Y. 10502
5. Rohm and Haas, Independence Mall West, Philadelphia, Pa. 19105
6. Witco Chemical, 277 Park Ave., New York, N.Y. 10017
7. Aceto Chemical Co., Inc., 40-40 Lawerence St., Flushing, N.Y. 11354

Promoters, Accelerators

1. Aceto Chemical Co., Inc., 40-40 Lawerence St., Flushing, N.Y. 11354
2. Advance Div., Carlisle Chemical Works, 500 Jersey Ave., New Brunswick, N.J. 08903
3. Allied Chemical, Natl. Analine Div., 40 Rector St., New York, N.Y. 10006
4. American Cyanamid Co., Intermediates Dept., Bound Brook, N.J. 08805
5. Cardinal Chemical Co., RFD No. 4, Box 779, Columbia, S.C. 29209
6. Carlisle Chemical Works, Inc., Reading, Ohio, 45215
7. Ferro Chemicals, P.O. Box 349, Bedford, Ohio 44014
8. Gallard-Schlisinger Chemical Mfg. Corp., 580 Mineola Ave., Carle Place, Long Island, N.Y. 11514
9. M and T Chemical Co., Inc., Rahway, N.J. 07065
10. R. T. Vanderbilt and Co., Inc., 230 Park Ave., New York, N.Y. 10017
11. Union Carbide Corp., 270 Park Ave., New York, N.Y. 10017
12. U.S. Peroxygen Corp., 850 Morton Ave., Richmond, Calif. 94804
13. Witco Chemical Co., Inc., Organics Div., 277 Park Ave., New York, N.J. 10017

Catalysts: Initiators, Peroxides, Hydroperoxides, Perethers, Peresters, Peracetates, Percarbonates, Etc.

1. A.I.D. Chemical Co., Inc., 26 Broadway, New York, N.Y. 10004
2. Cadet Chemical Corp., 2153 Lockport-Olcott Rd., Burt, N.Y. 10428
3. Lucidol Div., Wallace and Tiernan, Inc., 1740 Military Rd., Buffalo, N.Y. 14240
4. McKesson and Robbins, Inc., Industrial Chemical Dept., 155 E. 44th St., New York, N.Y. 10017
5. Philipp Bros. Chemicals, Inc., 10 Columbus Circle, New York, N.Y. 10019
6. Pittsburgh Plate Glass Co., One Gateway Center, Pittsburgh, Pa. 15222

7. Reichold Chemicals, Inc., 525 N. Broadway, White Plains, N.Y. 10602
8. U.S. Peroxygen Corp., 850 Morton Ave., Richmond, Calif. 94814

Alloying Polymers

1. Allied Chemical Corp., P.O. Box 365, Morristown, N.J. 07960
2. American Cyanamid Co., Berden Ave., Wayne, N.J. 07470
3. Archer Daniels Midland Co., 733 Marquette Ave., Minneapolis, Minn. 55440
4. Ciba Products Co., Fairlawn, N.J. 07410
5. Celanese Chemical Co., 522 Fifth Ave., New York, N.Y. 10036
6. Dow Chemical Co., Midland, Mich., 48640
7. Eastman Chemical Corp., Kingsport, Tenn. 37662
8. FMC Corp., 633 Third Ave., New York, N.Y. 10017
9. General Mills, Inc., P.O. Box 191, Kankakee, Ill. 60901
10. Hercules Powder Co., Inc., 910 Market St., Wilmington, Del. 19899
11. Isocyanate Products, Inc., 900 Wilmington Rd., New Castle, Del. 19720
12. Carlisle Chemical Works, Inc., Reading, Ohio 45215
13. Mobay Chemical Co., Penn Lincoln Parkway West, Pittsburgh, Pa., 15205
14. Monsanto Chemical Co., 800 N. Lindberg Blvd., St. Louis, Mo. 63166
15. Mohawk Industries, Inc., P.O. Box 177, 44 Station Rd., Sparta, N.Y.
16. Pennsylvania Industrial Chemicals Corp., 120 State St., Clairton, Pa. 15025
17. Pittsburgh Plate Glass Co., One Gateway Center, Pittsburgh, Pa. 15222
18. Reichold Chemicals, 525 N. Broadway, White Plains, N.Y. 10602
19. Sinclair Petrochemicals, Inc., 600 Fifth Ave., New York, N.Y. 10020
20. Spencer-Kellogg, 120 Delaware Ave., Buffalo, N.Y. 14240
21. Shell Chemical Co., 50 W. 50th St., New York, N.Y. 10020
22. Union Carbide Corp., Plastics Div., 270 Park Ave., New York, N.Y. 10017
23. Upjohn Co., Kalamazoo, Mich. 48001

Mold Releases (Internal and External), Lubricants

1. Axel Plastics Research Laboratories, 41–14 29th St., Long Island City, N.Y. 11101
2. Brulin and Co., Inc., 2939 Columbia Ave., Indianapolis, Ind. 46207
3. Crown Industrial Products Co., 158 State Line Rd., Hebron, Ill. 60034
4. C. P. Hall Co., 414–418 S. Broadway, Akron, Ohio 44308
5. Harshaw Co., 1945 E. 97th St., Cleveland, Ohio 44106
6. Kraft Chemical Co., 917 W. 18th St., Chicago, Ill. 60608
7. Mitchell-Rand Mfg. Corp., 51 Murray St., New York, N.Y. 10007
8. Miller-Stephenson Chemical Co., Inc., Route 7, Danbury, Conn. 06810
9. Mallinckrodt Chemical Works, St. Louis, Mo. 63160
10. McKesson and Robbins, Inc., Chemical Dept., 155 E. 44th St., New York, N.Y. 10017
11. M. W. Parsons-Plymouth Div., 100 Church St., New York, N.Y. 10008
12. Nopco Chemical Co., 60 Park Place, Newark, N.J. 07102
13. Price-Driscoll Corp., 75 Milbar Blvd., Farmingdale, N.Y. 11735
14. Specialty Products Co., 15 Exchange Place, Jersey City, N.J. 07302
15. Tenneco Chemicals, Inc., Nuodex Div., P.O. Box 242, Elizabeth, N.J. 07207
16. Ram Chemicals, Inc., 210 E. Alondra Blvd., Gardena, Calif. 90247
17. Whittaker, Clark, and Daniels, Inc., 100 Church St., New York, N.Y. 10007
18. Witco Chemical Co., Inc., 277 Park Ave., New York, N.Y. 10007

Pigment, Color, and Dye Manufacturers

1. Aceto Chemical Co., 40–40 Lawerence St., Flushing, N.Y. 11354
2. American Hoecht Corp., 270 Sheffield St., Mountainside, N.J. 07091
3. Allied Chemical Corp., Natl. Analine Div., P.O. Box 14, Hawthorne, N.J. 07506
4. C. K. Williams and Co., Div. of Pfizer, 2001 Lynch Ave., East St. Louis, Ill. 62204
5. Chemical Service Corp., 82 Beaver St., New York, N.Y. 10005
6. E. I. DuPont de Nemours and Co., Pigments Dept., Wilmington, Del. 19898
7. Fallek Chemical Corp., 4 W. 58th St., New York, N.Y. 10019
8. Ferro Corp., P.O. Box 349, Bedford, Ohio 44014
9. Harshaw Chemical Corp., 1933 E. 97th St., Cleveland, Ohio 44106
10. Imperial Color and Chemical Dept., Hercules, Glen Falls, N.Y. 12801
11. Naftone, Inc., 425 Park Ave., New York, N.Y. 10020
12. National Lead Co., 111 Broadway, New York, N.Y. 10006
13. Kohnstamm H. and Co., Inc., 161 Ave. of the Americas, New York, N.Y. 10013
14. The Mearl Corp., 41 E. 42nd St., New York, N.Y. 10017
15. Plastic Molders Supply Co., Inc., South Ave., Fanwood, N.J. 07023
16. Plastic Color Co., Inc., 20 Commerce St., Chatham, N.J. 07928
17. Riverdale Color Co., Inc., 5 Ohio St., Newark, N.J. 07103
18. Rona Pearl Corp., East 21st St. and E. 22nd St., Bayonne, N.J. 07002
19. C. J. Osborne Co., 1301 W. Balnache St., Linden, N.J. 07036
20. Ciba Chemical Co., Inc., Pic. Div., State Highway 208, Fairlawn, N.J. 07410
21. Witco Chemical Co., Inc., 122–24 E. 42nd St., New York, N.Y. 10017
22. Western Dry Color Co., 600 W. 52nd St., Chicago, Ill. 60609
23. The Glidden Co., Pigments Div., Baltimore, Md. 21226
24. American Cyanamid Co., Pigments Div., Bound Brook, N.J. 08805
25. The New Jersey Zinc Co., 160 Front St., New York, N.Y. 10038
26. R. T. Vanderbilt and Co., Inc., 230 Park Ave., New York, N.Y. 10017
27. Barclay Chemical Co., Inc., 75 Varick St., New York, N.Y. 10013
28. Reichold Chemicals, Inc., 525 N. Broadway, White Plains, N.Y. 10602
29. Smith Color and Chemical Co., Inc., 121 Commerce St., Brooklyn, N.Y. 11281
30. Chemore Corp., 100 E. 42nd St., New York, N.Y. 10017
31. Keystone Color Works, Inc., 151 W. Gay Ave., York, Pa. 17403
32. General Aniline and Film Corp., 140 W. 51st St., New York, N.Y. 10020
33. Sun Chemical Corp., 441 Tompkins Ave., Rosebank, Staten Island, N.Y. 10305
34. McKesson and Robbins, Inc. 155 E. 44th St., New York, N.Y. 10017
35. Verona Dyestuffs Co., P.O. Box 385, Springfield Road, Union, N.J. 07083
36. American Analine Products, Inc., P.O. Box 2086, Patterson, N.J. 07509
37. St. Joseph's Lead Co., 250 Park Ave., New York, N.Y. 10017

Silicas, 20–400 Mesh (See Additives for Finer Silicas)

1. C. K. Williams and Co., 2001 Lynch Ave., East St. Louis, Ill. 62204
2. Crystal Silica Co., Oceanside, Calif. 92054
3. Illinois Minerals Co., 218 10th St., Cairo, Ill. 62914
4. Chas. Pfizer and Co., 235 E. 42nd St., New York, N.Y. 10017
5. Ottawa Silica Co., Ottawa, Ill. 61350

6. Pennsylvania Glass Sand Co., 375 Park Ave., New York, N.Y. 10022
7. Silica Products Co., Guion, Ark. 72540
8. Tamms Industries, Inc., P.O. Box 64, Lyons, Ill. 60534
9. Charles A. Wagner Co., Inc., 4455 N. 6th St., Philadelphia, Pa. 19140
10. Whittaker, Clark and Daniels, Inc., 100 Church St., New York, N.Y. 10007
11. McKesson and Robbins, Inc., 155 E. 44th St., New York, N.Y. 10017
12. Raw Materials Co., Inc., 140 Federal St., Boston, Mass. 02110

Perlite: Blown Silica

1. Johns-Mansville Perlite Corp., 504 Railroad St., Joilet, Ill. 60436
2. Sil-Flow Corp, P.O. Box 7086, Ft. Worth, Tex. 76111
3. Great Lakes Carbon Corp., 630 Shatto Place, Los Angeles, Calif. 90005

Vermiculite: Blown Mica

1. Aschcraft-Wilkinson Co., 601 Trust Co. of Georgia Bldg., Atlanta, Ga. 30303
2. C. R. Graybeal and Sons, Roan Mountain, Tenn. 37687

Bentonite

1. Archer Daniels Midland Co., 733 Marquette Ave., Minneapolis, Minn. 55440
2. American Colloid Co., 5100 Suffield Court, Skokie, Ill. 60077
3. Baroid Div., Natl. Lead, P.O. Box 1675, Houston, Tex. 77001
4. Georgia Kaolin Co., 443 N. Broad St., Elizabeth, N.J. 07208
5. Johns-Mansville Co., 22 E. 40th St., New York, N.Y. 10016
6. Harshaw Chemical Co., 1945 E. 97th St., Cleveland, Ohio 44106
7. McKesson and Robbins, Inc., 155 E. 44th St., New York, N.Y. 10017
8. Minerals and Chemicals, Phillip, 350 Park Ave., New York, N.Y. 10022
9. Chas. Pfizer and Co., Inc., 235 E. 42nd St., New York, N.Y. 10017
10. Tamms Industries, Inc., P.O. Box 64, Lyons, Ill. 60534
11. Whittaker, Clark and Daniels, Inc., 100 Church St., New York, N.Y. 10007

China Clay, Kaolin, Aluminum Silicate

1. Burgess Pigment Co., P.O. Box 349, Sandersville, Ga. 31082
2. Minerals and Chemicals Phillip Corp., 27 Essex Turnpike, Menlo Park, N.J. 08837
3. Freeport, Kaolin Co. Div., 405 Lexington Ave., New York, N.Y. 10017
4. Thompson-Weinman and Co., Box 1009, Cartersville, Ga. 30120
5. United Clay Mines Corp., Box 1201, Trenton, N.J. 08607
6. Whittaker, Clark and Daniels, Inc., 100 Church St., New York, N.Y. 10007
7. Georgia Kaolin Co., 433 N. Broad St., Elizabeth, N.J. 07208
8. R. T. Vanderbilt, Inc., 230 Park Ave., New York, N.Y. 10017
9. Tamms Industries, Inc., P.O. Box 64, Lyons, Ill. 60534

Alumina, Tabular

1. Alkan Sales, Inc., 111 West 50th St., New York, N.Y. 10020
2. Aluminum Corp. of America, 1501 Alcoa Bldg., Pittsburgh, Pa. 15219

Barytes, Barium Sulfate

1. Baroid Div., Natl. Lead, P.O. Box 1675, Houston, Tex. 77001
2. Harshaw Chemicals Co., 1945 E. 97th St., Cleveland, Ohio 44106
3. Chas. Pfizer and Co., 235 E. 42nd St., New York, N.Y. 10017
4. Thompson, Weinman and Co., Box 1007, Cartersville, Ga. 30120
5. Charles A. Wagner and Co., Inc., 4455 N. 6th St., Philadelphia, Pa. 19140
6. Whittaker, Clark and Daniels, Inc., 100 Church St., New York, N.Y. 10007

Calcium Carbonates, Treated and Untreated

1. Allied Chemicals Div., P.O. Box 70, Morristown, N.J. 07960
2. Diamond Alkalie Co., 300 Union Commerce Bldg., Cleveland, Ohio 44114
3. Georgia Marble Co., Tate, Ga. 07207
4. Harshaw Chemical Co., 1945 E. 97th St., Cleveland, Ohio 44106
5. Mallinckrodt Chemical Works, St. Louis, Mo. 63160
6. McKesson and Robbins, Inc., 155 E. 44th St., New York, N.Y. 10017
7. National Gypsum Co., 325 Delaware Ave., Buffalo, N.Y. 14202
8. C. K. Williams Co., 2001 Lynch Ave., East St. Louis, Ill. 62204
9. Chas. Pfizer and Co., Inc., 235 E. 42nd St., New York, N.Y. 10017
10. Thompson Hayward Co., P.O. Box 768, Kansas City, Mo. 64141
11. Thompson, Weinman and Co., Box 1009, Cartersville, Ga. 30120
12. U.S. Gypsum, 101 South Wacker Dr., Chicago, Ill. 60606
13. Marble Products Co., 67 Peachtree Park Dr., Atlanta, Ga. 30309
14. Dezendorf Marble Co., P.O. Box 6032, Austin, Tex. 78702
15. Jamison Black Marble Co., P.O. Box 1198, Roanoke, Va. 24006

Mica, Biotite, and Muscovite

1. The English Mica Co., Ridgeway Center Bldg., Stamford, Conn. 06905
2. Baroid Div., Natl. Lead, P.O. Box 1675, Houston, Tex. 77001
3. Carolina-Southern Mining Co., P.O. Box 429, Spruce Pine, N.C. 28777
4. Industrial Minerals, Inc., 3 South Congress St., York, S.C. 29745
5. Kraft Chemical Co., 917 W. 18th St., Chicago, Ill. 60608
6. Thompson Hayward Co., P.O. Box 768, Kansas City, Mo. 64141
7. Thompson, Weinman and Co., Box 1009, Cartersville, Ga. 30120
8. U.S. Gypsum Co., Industrial Div., 101 S. Wacker Dr., Chicago, Ill. 60606
9. Whittaker, Clark, and Daniels, Inc., 100 Church St., New York, N.Y. 10007

Synthetic Mica

1. Mycalex Corp. of America, Clifton Blvd., Clifton, N.J. 07011

Talc, Magnesium Silicate

1. J. T. Baker Co., Phillipsburgh, N.J. 08865
2. Charles B. Chrystal Co., Inc., 53 Park Place, New York, N.Y. 10017

3. Harshaw Chemical Co., 1945 E. 97th St., Cleveland, Ohio 44106
4. International Talc Co., 420 Lexington Ave., New York, N.Y. 10017
5. Kraft Chemical Co., 917 W. 18th St., Chicago, Ill. 60608
6. McKesson and Robbins, Inc., 155 E. 44th St., New York, N.Y. 10017
7. The Milwhite Co., P.O. Box 15038, Houston, Tex. 77020
8. Chas. Pfizer and Co., Inc., 235 E. 42nd St., New York, N.Y. 10017
9. Tamms Industries Co., P.O. Box 63, Lyons, Ill. 60534
10. R. T. Vanderbilt Co., Inc., 230 Park Ave., New York, N.Y. 10017
11. Westex Talc Corp, P.O. Box 15038, Houston, Tex. 77020
12. Whittaker, Clark and Daniels, Inc., 100 Church St., New York, N.Y. 10007

Graphite

1. Asbury Graphite Mills, Inc., Asbury, Warren County, N.J. 08802
2. Frank D. Davis Co., 3285 E. 26th St., Los Angeles, Calif. 90023
3. Kraft Chemical Co., 917 W. 18th St., Chicago, Ill. 60608
4. Los Angeles Chemical Co., 4545 Ardine St., South Gate, Calif. 90280

Wood Flour

1. American Colloid Co., 5100 Suffield Court, Skokie, Ill. 60077
2. Acme Sawdust Co., 4927 W. Commerce, San Antonio, Tex. 78207
3. Archer Daniels Midland Co., 2191 W. 110 St., Cleveland, Ohio 44102
4. Miller-Stephenson, Route 7, Danbury, Conn. 06810

Molecular Sieves

1. Linde Div., Union Carbide Corp., 270 Park Place, New York, N.Y. 10017
2. Norton Co., Worchester, Mass. 01606

Aggregates: Marble Chips, Granite, Quartz, Etc.

1. C. K. Williams Co., Emeryville, Calif. 94608
2. Tamms Industries, 228 N. La Salle St., Chicago, Ill. 60601
3. Georgia Marble Co., Tate, Ga. 30177
4. Marble Products Co., First National Bank Bldg., Atlanta, Ga. 30303
5. Jamison Black Marble Co., P.O. Box 1198, Roanoke, Va. 24006
6. Texas Terrazzo and Marble Supply Co., 5713 Armour Dr., Houston, Tex. 77020
7. Vermont Marble Co., Procter, Vt. 05765
8. Minerals and Chemicals, 20 Essex Turnpike, Menlo Park, N.J. 08837
9. Bilbrough Marble Co., Burnet, Tex. 78611
10. National Gypsum Co., Gold Bond Bldg., Buffalo, N.Y. 14202
11. Rocky Mountain Aggregates, P.O. Box 771, Golden, Colo. 80401
12. Silica Products Co., Guion, Ark. 72540
13. Minerals, Pigments, and Metals Div., Chas. Pfizer Co., P.O. Drawer AD, Victorville, Calif. 90394
14. Heart of Texas Mining Corp., 2510 Fidelity Union Tower, Dallas, Tex. 75201

Metallic Fillers for Color and Conductivity

1. Reynolds Chemicals, P.O. Box 2346, Richmond, Va. 23218
2. Alcoa, 1209 Alcoa Bldg., Pittsburgh, Pa. 15219
3. Kaiser Chemicals, 300 Lakeside Dr., Oakland, Calf. 94604
4. Aluminum Co. of America, 1501 Alcoa Bldg., Pittsburgh, Pa. 15219
5. Metals Disintegrating Corp., P.O. Box 290, Elizabeth, N.J. 07207
6. Indussa Corp., 605 Third Ave., New York, N.Y. 10016

Metallic Fillers, Hard, for Abrasion Resistance

1. Carborundum Metals Co., P.O. Box 32, Akron, N.Y. 14001
2. Norton Co., Worchester, Mass. 01606
3. Belmont Smelting and Refining Works, Inc., 316 Belmont Ave., Brooklyn, N.Y. 10007
4. American Metal Climax, Inc., 1270 Ave. of the Americas, New York, N.Y. 10020
5. Atomergic Chemetals Co., 580 Mineola Ave., Carle Place, Long Island, N.Y. 11514
6. Shieldalloy Corp., West Blvd., Newfield, N.J. 08344
7. Aluminum Metalurgical Granules, P.O. Box 11430 D, Kansas City, Mo. 642112
8. Minnesota Mining and Mfg. Co., St. Paul, Minn. 55119
9. Chas. Pfizer and Co., Inc., Minerals, Pigments and Metals Div., 235 E. 45th St., New York, N.Y. 10017
10. Reade Mfg. Co., Inc., Ridgeway Road, Lakehurst, N.J. 07306
11. Atlantic Powdered Metals, Inc., 38 Park Row, New York, N.Y. 10038

Glass Powder, Beads, Colored, Reflecting

1. Cataphote Corp., Box 28, Station F, Toledo, Ohio 73610
2. Flex-O-Lite Mfg. Corp., P.O. Box 4366, St. Louis, Mo. 63123
3. Sinclair Minerals and Chemicals Co., 6441 Ridge St., Chicago, Ill. 60626

Flourescent Fillers, Pigments, and Aggregates

1. Dee-Lite Industries, Inc., 7016 Twentieth Ave., Brooklyn, N.Y. 11204
2. C. P. Hall Co., 414–418 S. Broadway, Akron, Ohio 44308

Asbestos, Powdered

1. Carey-Canadian Mines, Ltd., P.O. Box 15095, Cincinnati, Ohio 45215
2. C. P. Hall Co., 414–418 S. Broadway, Akron, Ohio 44308
3. Johns-Mansville Co., 22 E. 40th St., New York, N.Y. 10016
4. Miller-Stephenson Chemical Co., Inc., Route 7, Danbury, Conn. 06810

5. Whittaker, Clark and Daniels, Inc., 100 Church St., New York, N.Y. 10007
6. National Gypsum Co., 325 Delaware Ave., Buffalo, N.Y. 14202
7. Huxley Development Corp., 1271 Ave. of the Americas, New York, N.Y. 10020

Zinc Oxide, Powdered

1. St. Josephs Lead Co., 250 Park Ave., New York, N.Y. 10017
2. New Jersey Zinc Co., 160 Front St., New York, N.Y. 10038
3. American Zinc Co., 1600 Paul Brown Bldg., St. Louis, Mo. 63101

Zirconium Fillers and Pigments

1. Tam Div. Natl. Lead Co., Box C, Bridge Station, Niagara Falls, N.Y. 14305
2. Foote Mineral Co., Route 100, Exton, Pa. 19341
3. Carborundum Metals Co., P.O. Box 32, Akron, N.Y. 14001

Keytone Solvents for Cleaning Equipment

1. Allied Chemicals Corp., P.O. Box 365, Morristown, N.J. 07960
2. Ashland Oil and Refining Co., 1409 Winchester Ave., Ashland, Ky. 41101
3. Buffalo Solvents and Chemical Co., P.O. Box 73, Station B, Buffalo, N.Y. 14207
4. California Chemical Co., 200 Bush St., San Francisco, Calif. 94120
5. Celanese Chemical Co., Dept 560, 522 Fifth Ave., New York, N.Y. 10030
6. Eastman Chemical Products Co., Kingsport, Tenn. 37662
7. Enjay Chemical Co., 60 W. 49th St., New York, N.Y. 10020
8. Hercules Powder Co., Wilmington, Del. 19899
9. Union Carbide Corp., 270 Park Ave., New York, N.Y. 10017
10. U.S. Industrial Chemicals, 99 Park Ave., New York, N.Y. 10016

Glass-fiber Reinforcing Materials: Filaments, Strands, Chopped Fiber, Roving, Mat, Surfacing Mat, Fabrics, Flake, and Others

1. Aerojet-General Corp., P.O. Box 296, Azuza, Calif. 91702
2. American Air Filter Co., Inc., 215 Central Ave., Louisville, Ky. 40208
3. Cadillac Plastics Co., Broad and 14th St., Carlstadt, N.J. 07072
4. Famco, Inc., 6200 Strawberry Lane, Louisville, Ky. 40214
5. Ferro Corp., 4150 Fiber Glass Road, Nashville, Tenn. 37211
6. Fiber Glass Industries, Amsterdam, N.Y. 12010
7. Foss Mfg. Co., 225 2nd Ave., S. Twin Falls, Idaho 83301
8. Johns-Mansville Corp., 22 E. 40th St., New York, N.Y. 10016
9. Miller-Stephenson Chemical Co., 16 Sugar Hollow Rd., Danbury, Conn. 06810
10. Modiglas Fibers, Inc., P.O. Box 86, Bremen, Ohio 43107
11. Owens-Corning Fiberglass Corp., 608 Madison Ave., Toledo, Ohio 43604
12. Owens-Illinois Glass Co., P.O. Box 1035, Toledo, Ohio 43601

13. Pittsburgh Plate Glass Co., One Gateway Center, Pittsburgh, Pa. 15222
14. Schramm Fiberglass Products, Inc., 3010 Montrose Ave., Chicago, Ill. 60618
15. A. O. Smith Corp., 3533 N. 27th St., Milwaukee, Wis. 53216
16. J. C. Stephens and Co., 1460 Broadway, New York, N.Y. 10036
17. H. Thompson Fiberglass Co., 1600 W. 135th St., Gardena, Calif. 90249

Asbestos Reinforcing Materials, Fiber, Mat, Cloth

1. American Asbestos Textile Corp., Stanbridge, St., Norristown, Pa. 19401
2. Asbestos Corp. of America, 31 North Ave., Garwood, N.J. 07027
3. Phillip Carey Mfg. Co., 320 Wayne Ave., Cincinnati, Ohio 45215
4. Carolina Asbestos Co., Davidson, N.C. 28036
5. Johns-Mansville Corp., 22 E. 40th St., New York, N.Y. 10016
6. North American Asbestos Corp., Board of Trade Bldg., Chicago, Ill. 60604
7. Raybestos-Manhattan Corp., Manheim, Pa. 17545
8. Tallman-McClusky Fabrics, 236 E. Monroe, Kirkwood, Mo. 63122
9. Carey-Canadian Mines, Ltd., P.O. Box 190, East Broughton Station, Quebec, Canada
10. National Gypsum Co., 325 Delaware Ave., Buffalo, N.Y. 14202
11. Miller-Stephenson Chemical Co., Route 7, Danbury, Conn. 06810
12. The C. P. Hall Co., 414–418 S. Broadway, Akron, Ohio 44308

Miscellaneous Natural Fiber, Mat, and Fabrics

1. Albany Felt Co., Broadway, Albany, N.Y. 12202
2. American Felt Co., 110 Glenville Rd., Glenville, Conn. 06830
3. Continental Felt Co., 26 W. 15th St., New York, N.Y. 10011
4. The Carborundum Co., Graphite Prod. Div., Blank and Walmore Rd., Sanborne, N.Y. 14132
5. The Philip Carey Mfg. Co., 320 S. Wayne Ave., Cincinnati, Ohio 45215
6. General Electric Co., 1 Plastics Ave., Pittsfield, Mass. 01201
7. W. R. Grace and Co., 7 Hanover Sq., New York, N.Y. 10005
8. Hitco Materials Div., 1600 W. 135th St., Gardena, Calif. 90249
9. The Mead Corp., South Lee, Mass. 01260
10. National Gypsum Co., 325 Delaware Ave., Buffalo, N.Y. 14202
11. Refractory Products Co., 910 Custer Ave., Evanston, Ill. 60202
12. Bridgeport Fabrics, Inc., 125 Holland Ave., Bridgeport, Conn. 06605
13. Raybestos-Manhattan, Inc., 6010 Northwest Highway, Chicago, Ill. 60631

Synthetic Fiber, Mat, and Fabric

1. Southern Silk Mills, Spring City, Tenn. 37381
2. Burlington Industries, Inc., 1430 Broadway, New York, N.Y. 10018
3. The Vectra Co., Odenton, Md. 21113
4. Chicapee Mills, Inc., Cornelia, Ga. 30531

5. Ferro Corp., P.O. Box 781, East Liverpool, Ohio 43920
6. Tallman-McClusky Fabrics Co., 236 E. Monroe, Kirkwood, Mo. 63122
7. U.S. Rubber Co., Textile Div., 1220 Ave. of the Americas, New York, N.Y. 10020
8. Troy Mills, Inc., 200 Madison Ave., New York, N.Y. 10016
9. Wellington Sears Co., 111 W. 40th St., New York, N.Y. 10018
10. Minnesota Mining and Mfg. Co., 2501 Hudson Rd., St. Paul, Minn. 55119
11. Haveg Industries, Inc., 336 Weir St., Taunton, Mass. 02780
12. General Tire and Rubber Co., P.O. Box 875, Toledo, Ohio 43601
13. B. F. Gooodrich, Industrial Products Co., 500 S. Main St., Akron, Ohio 44311
14. U.S. Polymeric Chemicals, Inc., 700 E. Dyer Rd., Santa Ana, Calif. 92705

Metal-wire Reinforcing

1. Cambridge Wire Cloth Co., Goodwill Rd., Cambridge, Md. 21613
2. Englehard Industries, Inc., 113 Astor St., Newark, N.J. 07114
3. Keystone Steel and Wire Co., 700 S. Adams St., Peoria, Ill. 61602
4. Michigan Wire Cloth Co., 2100 Howard Ave., Detroit, Mich. 48216
5. Newark Wire Cloth Co., 350 Verona Ave., Newark, N.J. 07104
6. Phelps Dodge Aluminum Products Corp., P.O. Box 38, Florence, Ala. 35630
7. Technit Industries Wire Products, Inc., 129 Dermody St., Cranford, N.J. 07016
8. Semrow Products Co., Inc., 755 Seegars Rd., Des Plaines, Ill. 60616
9. National Standard Co., 601 N. 8th St., Niles, Mich. 49120
10. Kawecki Chemical Co., 220 E. 42nd St., New York, N.Y. 10017

Mold- and Die-making Materials: Fluorocarbon Materials for Molds, Dies, and Belts

1. Allied Chemical Corp., P.O. Box 70, Morristown, N.J. 02960
2. Cadillac Plastics and Chemical Co., 15111 Second Ave., Detroit, Mich. 48203
3. Chemplast, Inc., 150 Deyroad, Wayne, N.J. 07470
4. Commercial Plastic and Supply Co., 630 Broadway, New York, N.Y. 10012
5. Crane Packing Co., Teflon Div., 6400 Oakton St., Morton Grove, Ill. 60053
6. Dixon Corp., Metacom Ave., Bristol, R.I. 02809
7. John L. Dore Co., P.O. Box 7772, Houston, Tex. 77007
8. E. I. DuPont de Nemours and Co., Wilmington, Del. 19898
9. Emerson Plastics Corp., 1383 Seabury Ave., Bronx, N.Y. 10461
10. The Fluorocarbon Co., P.O. Box 3339, Anaheim, Calif. 92803
11. Minnesota Mining and Mfg. Co., 2501 Hudson Rd., St. Paul, Minn. 55116
12. Plastics and Rubber Products Co., 2100 Hyde Park Blvd., Los Angeles, Calif. 19102
13. The Polymer Corp., Reading, Pa. 19603
14. Raybestos Manhattan, Inc., 6010 Northwest Highway, Chicago, Ill. 60631
15. Sparta Mfg. Co., P.O. Box 128, Dover, Ohio 44622
16. Thiokol Chemical Corp., P.O. Box 1296, Trenton, N.J. 08607
17. Westlake Plastics Co., West Lenni Blvd., West Lenni, Pa. 19152

Mold- and Die-making
Materials: Silicones and
Elastomers for Molds and Belts

1. Dow Corning Corp., Midland, Mich. 48640
2. Emerson and Cummings, Inc., 869 Washington Sq., Canton, Mass. 02021
3. American Cyanamid Co., 4614 Spring Grove Ave., Cincinnati Ohio, 45232
4. General Electric Co., Silicones Div., Waterford, N.Y. 12188
5. Smooth-On Mfg. Co., Inc., 572 Comminpaw Ave., Jersey City, N.J. 07304
6. Chicago Rubber Co., 651 Market St., Waukegan, Ill. 60085
7. Connecticut Hard Rubber Co., 407 E. St., New Haven, Conn. 06509
8. Firestone Industrial Products Div., Firestone Bldg., Noblesville, Ind. 46060
9. Illinois Industrial Rubber Co., Box 456, Ladd, Ill. 61329
10. Quantum, Inc., Lufbery Ave., Wallingford, Conn. 06492
11. Toledo Industrial Rubber Co., Box 456, Ladd, Ill. 61329
12. Union Carbide Corp., Silicones Div., 270 Park Ave., New York, N.Y. 10017

Mold-making Materials:
Miscellaneous Castable Plastics

1. Smooth-On Mfg. Co., 572 Comminpaw, Jersey City, N.J. 07304
2. Marblett Corp., 37–31 Thirtieth Ave., Long Island City, N.Y. 11102
3. Magnolia Plastics Inc., 5547 Peachtree Ind. Blvd., Chamblee, Ga. 30005
4. Hysol Corp., Olean, N.Y. 14760
5. General Mills, Kankakee, Ill. 60901
6. Thiokol Chemical Corp., P.O. Box 1296, Trenton, N.J. 08607
7. General Electric Co., Waterford, Conn. 12188
8. Adhesives Products, Inc., 1660 Boone Ave., New York, N.Y. 10060
9. Archer Daniels Midland, 733 Marquette Ave., Minneapolis, Minn. 55440
10. Ciba Products Co., Fairlawn, N.J. 07410
11. Union Carbide Corp., Plastics Div., 270 Park Ave., New York, N.Y. 10017

Glass for Molds and Dies:
High-temperature, Etc.

1. Corning Glass Co., Corning, N.Y. 14830
2. Libbey-Owens-Ford Glass Co., 811 Madison Ave., Toledo, Ohio 43624

Metals for Mold and Die
Making: Hardened, Stainless,
Plated, Prefinished, and Polished

1. Youngstown Sheet and Tube Co., P.O. Box 900, Youngstown, Ohio 44501
2. United States Steel Corp., 525 William Penn Pl., Pittsburgh, Pa. 15230
3. Vanadium Alloy Steel Co., Latrobe, Pa. 15650
4. Wheeling Steel Corp., 1134 Market St., Wheeling, W. Va. 26003
5. Lukens Steel Co., Coatsville, Pa. 19320
6. Republic Steel Corp., 1441 Republic Bldg., Cleveland, Ohio 44101

7. Joseph T. Ryerson and Son, Inc., P.O. Box 8000 A, Chicago, Ill. 60680
8. Armco Steel Corp., 700 Curtis St., Middletown, Ohio 45042
9. Bethlehem Steel Corp., 701 E. Third St., Bethlehem, Pa. 18016
10. Crucible Steel Co., P.O. Box 88, Pittsburgh, Pa. 15230
11. Phoenix Steel Corp., Claymont, Del. 19703
12. Allegheny Ludlem Steel Corp., Oliver Bldg., Pittsburgh, Pa. 15222
13. International Metals Co., Inc., 67 Wall St., New York, N.Y. 10005
14. John and Laughlin Steel Corp., P.O. Box 4606, Detroit, Mich. 48234
15. Latrobe Steel Co., 2626 Ligonier St., Latrobe, Pa. 15650

Most of these companies will finish steel to any specifications the customer desires. Metals can be plated, polished, and shipped free of stress. Many of them have tool steel as a normal product, already pre-finished to a plus or minus 5-μ finish. It is shipped packaged so as to preserve the finish.

Special Materials: Blowing Agents for Foam

1. E. I. DuPont de Nemours and Co., Wilmington, Del. 19898
2. Naugatuck Chemical Div., U.S. Rubber Co., Naugatuck, Conn. 06770

Printed Imbedment Papers and Membranes

1. Morart Gravure, 7 N. Bridge St., Holyoke, Mass. 01040
2. Decotone Products Div., Fitchburg Paper Co., Westminster, Mass. 01473
3. Di-Noc. Chemical Arts, Inc., 1700 London Rd., Cleveland, Ohio 44112
4. The Orchard Corp., 1154 Reco Ave., St. Louis, Mo. 63126

Textured Releasing Papers

1. S. D. Warren Co., 225 Franklin St., Boston, Mass. 02101

Equipment Manufacturers and Suppliers: Hydraulic Presses, Compression- and Transfer-molding

1. Adamson United Co., 730 Carrol St., Akron, Ohio 44304
2. Baker Brothers, Inc., 1000 Post St., Toledo, Ohio 43610
3. Bipel International, Inc., 20 Nutmeg Drive, Trumbull, Conn. 06611
4. Dake Corporation, Grand Haven, Mich. 49417
5. Danly Machine Specialties, Inc., 2100 S. Laramie Ave., Chicago, Ill. 60650
6. Dunning and Boschert Press Co., Inc., 329 W. Water St., Syracuse, N.Y. 13202
7. El-Tronics, Inc., Warren Components Div., 11 S. Irvine St., Warren, Pa. 16365
8. Erie Engine and Mfg. Co., 953 East 12th St., Erie, Pa. 16512

9. Farrel Corp., 565 Blossom Rd., Rochester, N.Y. 14610
10. Fjellman American, Inc., 105 Republic Ave., Joilet, Ill. 60435
11. HPM Div., Koehring Co., Marion Rd., Mount Gilead, Ohio, 43338
12. Hannifin Press Co., Div. Parker-Hannifin, 501 S. Wolf Rd., Des Plaines, Ill. 60016
13. Hull Corporation, Hatboro, Pa. 19040
14. Kard Manufacturing Co., Inc., 5304 Valley Blvd., Los Angeles, Calif. 90032
15. Nordberg Mfg. Co., Box 383, Milwaukee, Wis. 53201
16. Pasadena Hydraulics, Inc., 1433 Lidcombe, El Monte, Calif. 91733
17. Rodgers Hydraulics, Inc., 7401 Walker St., Minneapolis, Minn. 55426
18. Stokes Equipment Div., Pennsalt Chem. Corp., 5500 Tabor Rd., Philadelphia, Pa. 19120
19. The Lewis Welding and Engineering Corp., 113 St. Clair Ave. N.E., Cleveland, Ohio 44114
20. C. A. Lawton Co., DePere, Wis. 54115
21. Williams-White and Co., 600 Third Ave., Moline, Ill. 61265

Injection-molding Equipment

1. Beloit Eastern Corp., Dowingtown, Pa. 19335
2. Battenfeld Corp. of America, 7301 N. Monticello Ave., Skokie, Ill. 60076
3. Bipel International, Inc., 20 Nutmeg Dr., Trumbull, Conn. 06611
4. Buhler Corp., 8925 Wayzata Blvd., Minneapolis, Minn. 55426
5. Farrel Corp., 565 Blossom Rd., Rochester, N.Y. 14610
6. The Fellows Gear Shaper Co., Springfield, Vt. 05156
7. HPM Div. of Koehring Co., Marion Rd., Mount Gilead, Ohio 43338
8. Improved Machinery, Inc., Nashua, N.H. 03060
9. Lester Engineering Co., 2711 Church Ave., Cleveland, Ohio 44113
10. Lombard Industries, Inc., 300 Main St., Ashland, Mass. 01721
11. Modern Plastics Machinery Co., 64 Lakeview Ave., Clifton, N.J. 07011
12. National Automatic Tool Co., Inc., National Rd., W. Richmond, Ind. 47374
13. New Britain Machine Co., New Britain, Conn. 06051
14. Pasedena Hydraulics, Inc., 1433 Lidcombe, El Monte, Calif. 91733
15. Reed-Prentice Co., East Longmeadow, Mass. 01028
16. Rocheleau Tool and Die Co., 650 N. Main St., Leominster, Mass. 01453
17. Standard Tool Co., 217 Hamilton St., Leominster, Mass. 01453
18. Stokes Equipment Co., 5500 Tabor Rd., Philadelphia, Pa. 19120
19. Van Dorn Plastics Machinery Co., 2685 E. 79th St., Cleveland, Ohio 44104
20. R. H. Windsor of Canada Ltd., 56 Advance Rd., Toronto, Ontario, Canada

Extruders

1. Akron Extruders, 1119 Milan St., Canal Fulton, Ohio 43321
2. Baker-Perkins, Inc., Saginaw, Mich. 48605
3. Beloit Eastern Corp., Bowingtown, Pa. 19335
4. The Black-Clawson Co., Second and Vine St., Hamilton, Ohio 45011
5. The Bonnot Co., Canton, Ohio 44701
6. Davis-Standard Co., P.O. Box 202, Mystic, Conn. 06355
7. Frank W. Egan Co., S. Adamsville Rd., Sommerville, N.J. 08876
8. Farrel Corp., Ansonia, Conn. 06401

 9. Foremost Machine Builders, Inc., 23 Spielman Rd., Fairfield, N.J. 07006
10. Killon Extruders, Inc., 56 Depot St., Verona, N.J. 07044
11. Modern Plastic Machinery Corp., 64 Lakeview Ave., Clifton, N.J. 07011
12. NRM Corp., 47 W. Exchange St., Akron, Ohio 44308
13. Olimpia Tool and Machine Co., 119–121 Delancy St., Newark, N.J. 07105
14. Prodex Div. of Koehring Co., King George Post Rd., Fords, N.J. 08863
15. John Royle and Sons, 10 Essex St., Paterson, N.J. 07501
16. Sterling Extruder Corp., 1537 W. Elizabeth Ave., Linden, N.J. 07036
17. Stewart Boling and Co., 3190 E. 65th St., Cleveland, Ohio 44127
18. Waldron-Hartig Co., P.O. Box 531, Westfield, N.J. 07090

Calenders and Rolls

1. Farrel-Birmingham Co., Inc., Ansonia, Conn. 06401
2. Allis-Chalmers Mfg. Co., Box 512, Milwaukee, Wis. 53201
3. Waldron-Hartig, Box 791, New Brunswick, N.J. 08913
4. Goulding Mfg. Co., Inc., 2929 River St., Saginaw, Mich. 48601
5. Adamson United Co., 730 Carrol St., Akron, Ohio 44304

Autoclaves

1. Bethlehem Steel Corp., 701 E. 3rd St., Bethlehem, Pa. 18015
2. Adamson United Co., 730 Carrol St., Akron, Ohio 44304
3. Blaw-Knox Co., 43 Winchester Ave., Buffalo, N.Y. 14211
4. Stewart-Bolling and Co., 3190 E. 65th St., Cleveland, Ohio 44127
5. Hull Corp., Hatboro, Pa. 19040
6. Struthers Wells Corp., P.O. Box 300, Warren, Pa. 10365
7. Tenney Engineering, Inc., 1090 Springfield Rd., Union, N.J. 07083

Pressure Heads for Low-pressure Autoclaves

1. Welding and Steel Fabricators Co., Inc., 7 Hackett Dr., Tonawanda, N.Y. 14150
2. Tube Turns, Div. of Chemetron Corp., Louisville, Ky. 40201

Filament-winding Equipment

 1. Davis-Standard Co., 14 Waters St., Mystic, Conn. 06355
 2. Engineering Technology, Inc., 145 W. 2950 St., Salt Lake City, Utah 84115
 3. I. G. Brenner Co., 100 Manning St., Newark, Ohio 43055
 4. Dynetics, Inc., P.O. Box 127, Mountain Lakes, N.J. 07046
 5. KPT Mfg. Co., Plastics Div., 11 Locust Ave., Roseland, N.J. 07068
 6. McLean-Anderson, Inc., 120 W. Melvina St., Milwaukee, Wis. 53212
 7. Monkley Corp., 8 Grafton St., Worchester, Mass. 01604
 8. E. Parkinson Mfg. Co., Maple and Oak St., Esmond, R.I. 02917
 9. Progressive Machine Co., 165–169 Marion St., Paterson, N.J. 07522
10. Roblex Industries, Inc., 177 Bangor St., Lindenhurst, N.Y. 11757

11. Victor Industries, 330 Wagaraw Rd., Hawthorne, N.J. 07506
12. John L. Wilson Associates, 285 S. Main St., Cohasset, Mass. 02025

Heavy-duty Mixers, Compound Mixers

1. Adamson United Co., 730 Carroll, Akron, Ohio 44304
2. Baker-Perkins, Saginaw, Mich. 48005
3. Allis-Chalmers, P.O. Box 512, Milwaukee, Wis. 53201
4. The Cleveland Mixer Co., P.O. Box 197, Bedford, Ohio 44014
5. J. H. Day Co., 4932 Beech St., Cincinnati, Ohio 45212
6. Hobart Mfg. Co., Troy, N.Y. 45373
7. Mixing Equipment Co., 135 Mt. Read Blvd., Rochester, N.Y. 14611
8. Read Corp., 901 S. Richland Ave., York, Pa. 17405
9. Charles Ross and Son, 710–718 Old Willets Path. Hauppauge, Long Island, N.Y. 11788
10. Sprout, Waldron and Co., Muncy, Pa. 17756
11. The Patterson-Kelley Co., Inc., East Stroudsburg, Pa. 18301
12. Barber-Greene Co., Aurora, Ill. 60507
13. The Patterson Foundry and Machine Co., East Liverpool, Ohio 43920
14. Paul O. Abbe Co., Little Falls, N.J. 07424

High-shear, High-speed Mixers for Liquids

1. Gifford-Wood Co., 420 Lexington Ave., New York, N.Y. 10017
2. Charles Ross and Son Co., 710–718 Old Willets Path, Hauppauge, Long Island, N.Y. 11788
3. J. H. Day Co., 4932 Beech St., Cincinnati, Ohio 45212
4. Kinetic Dispersion Corp., 95 Botsford Place, Buffalo, N.Y. 14216
5. Morehouse-Cowles, Inc., 1150 San Fernando Rd., Los Angeles, Calif. 90065
6. Abbe Engineering Co., 420 Lexington Ave., New York, N.Y. 10017
7. The Cleveland Mixer Co., P.O. Box 197, Bedford, Ohio 44014
8. The Patterson Foundry and Machine Co., East Liverpool, Ohio 43920
9. Mixing Equipment Co., Inc., 147 Mt. Read Blvd., Rochester, N.Y. 14611

Miscellaneous Process Equipment: Timers

1. Eagle Signal Co., 736 Federal St., Davenport, Iowa 52803
2. Giannini Controls Corp., Old Saybrook, Conn. 06475
3. Controls Co. of America, 9655 Soreng Ave., Schiller Park, Ill. 60176
4. A. W. Haydon Co., 220 N. Elm St., Waterbury, Conn. 06720
5. Precision Timer Co., Inc., 100 Wesley Ave., Westbrook, Conn. 06498
6. Standard Electric Co., 85 Logan St., Springfield, Mass. 01101
7. Tork Time Controls, Inc., 100 Grove, Mount Vernon, N.Y. 10550

Vibrators, Electric and Pneumatic

1. Jeffrey Mfg. Co., 956 N. 4th St., Columbus, Ohio 43201
2. Hewitt-Robins Div., Littleton Ind., Stamford, Conn. 06904
3. Martin Engineering Co., Neoponset, Ill. 61345
4. Chicago Pneumatic Tool Co., 8 E. 44th St., New York, N.Y. 10017
5. Cannon Vibrator Co., 467 Literary Rd., Cleveland, Ohio 44113
6. Kassnel Vibrator Co., 1400 N. Odgen Ave., Chicago, Ill. 60610
7. Syntron Co., 1938 Black St., Hoover City, Pa. 15748
8. Vibco Inc., 23 A Vreeland Ave., Lodi, N.J. 07644
9. Vibro-Plus Products, Inc., P.O. Box T-368, Standhope, N.J. 07874
10. Cleveland Vibrator Co., 2827 Clinton Ave., Cleveland, Ohio 44113
11. Thor Power Tool Co., Aurora, Ill. 60507

Ultrasonic Vibrators

1. Transducer Products, 97 Wolcott Ave., Torrington, Conn. 06780
2. E. Kitching and Co., 505 Shawmut, La Grange, Ill. 60525
3. Micromat Co., 550 Piedmont Ave., Hillsdale, N.J. 07642
4. Alcar Instruments, Inc., 200 Elm, Trenton, N.J. 08611
5. Heat Systems Co., 62 Broad Hollow Ave., Melville, N.Y. 11746

Vibrators, Portable

1. Marvel Equip. Co., 217 Eagle St., Brooklyn, N.Y. 11222
2. Stow Mfg. Co., 400 State St., Binghamton, N.Y. 13901
3. Viber Co., S. Flower St. & Almeda, Burbank, Calif. 91502
4. National Air Vibrator Co., 6807 Wynwood, Houston, Tex. 77008

Electrical Automation Controls

1. Allen Bradley Co., 1201 S. Second St., Milwaukee, Wis. 53204
2. Cutler-Hammer Co., Milwaukee, Wis. 53201

Electrical and Thermal Controls: Instruments

1. Minneapolis-Honeywell, Minneapolis, Minn. 55440
2. Partlow Co., New Hartford, N.Y. 13413
3. Mercoid Corp., 4201 Belmont Ave., Chicago, Ill. 60641
4. Foxboro Industrial Instruments, Foxboro, Mass. 02035
5. West Instrument Corp., 4363 W. Montrose Ave., Chicago, Ill. 60641
6. General Controls Co., 8080 McCormick Blvd., Skokie, Ill. 70076

Automatic Valves, Solenoid

1. Republic Mfg. Co., 15655 Brookpark Rd., Cleveland, Ohio 44142
2. AAA Products Inc., P.O. Box 35482 Dallas, Tex. 75235
3. Ross Operating Valve Co., Detroit, Mich. 48203
4. Beckett-Harcum Co., Wilmington, Ohio 45177
5. Skinner Electric Valve Co., New Britain, Conn. 06050
6. Hanna Eng. Works, 1765 Elston Ave., Chicago, Ill. 60622
7. Versa Products Co., Inc., 249 Scholes St., Brooklyn, N.Y. 11206

Cylinders, Air and Oil, for Automation

1. Ortman-Miller Co., 19 143rd St., Hammond, Ind. 46320
2. Hanna Engineering Works, 1765 Elston Ave., Chicago, Ill. 60622
3. AAA Products, Inc., P.O. Box 35482, Dallas, Tex. 75235
4. A. Schrader Co., 470 Vanderbilt Ave., Brooklyn, N.Y. 11218
5. Be-Gee Mfg. Co., P.O. Box 67, Gilroy, Calif. 95020
6. Cleveland Hydraulics Co., 5055 Richmond Ave., Cleveland, Ohio 44105
7. Hannifin Cylinder Div., 150 S. Wolf Ave., Del Plaines, Ill. 60016
8. Miller Fluid Power Div., Bensenville, Ill. 60106

Pumps for Viscous Plastics: Compounds

1. Dorr-Oliver Co., Stamford, Conn. 06904
2. Moyno Pump Div., Robbins and Myers, Springfield, Ohio 45501

Valves for Viscous Plastics: Compounds

1. Red Jacket Co., Inc., 500 Bell Ave., Carnegie, Pa. 15106

Weighing and Batching Equipment, Automated

1. B.I.F. Industries, 345 Harris Ave., Providence, R.I. 02909
2. Cutler-Hammer, Thayer Scale Div., Pembroke, Mass. 02359
3. The Exact Scale Co., Columbus, Ohio 43212
4. Blaw-Knox Co., 1543 Fillmore Ave., Buffalo, N.Y. 14211
5. Howe Richardson Scale Co., 680 Van Houten Ave., Clifton, N.J. 07013
6. Kane Air Scales Co., Glassboro, N.J. 08028
7. Wallace and Tiernan, Inc., 25 Main St., Belleville, N.J. 07109

Speed Control for Conveyors, Webs

1. Wagner Electric Brake and Clutch Co., Beloit, Wis. 53511

Bulk-materials Handling and Storage Equipment

1. Sprout Waldron Mfg. Co., Muncy, Pa. 17756
2. Salina Manufacturing Co., Inc., 606 N. Front St., Salina, Kans. 67401
3. Systems Engineering Co., P.O. Box 18013, Dallas, Tex. 75218
4. SEMCO, P.O. Box 7643, Houston, Tex. 77007
5. The J. H. Day Co., 4932 Beech St., Cincinnati, Ohio 45212
6. Whitlock Associates, Inc., 21020 Coolidge Hwy., Oak Park, Mich. 48237
7. Waldron Hartig Co., P.O. Box 791, New Brunswick, N.J. 09801
8. Fuller Co., 124 Bridge St., Catasauqua, Pa. 18032
9. The Black Clawson Co., Second & Vine St., Hamilton, Ohio 45011
10. Apex Welding Co., 30 Interstate St., Bedford, Ohio 44014

Steam Boilers

1. Continental Boiler Div., 7 Manavon St., Philadelphia, Pa. 19460
2. Oswego Package Boiler Co., 440 E. First St., Oswego, N.Y. 13126
3. Erie City Iron Works, 1500 East Ave., Erie, Pa. 16503
4. Vapor Corp., 80 E. Jackson Blvd., Chicago, Ill. 60604
5. American Standard, Tireman Ave. at Rosedown, Detroit, Mich. 48204
6. Fulton Boiler Works, Inc., 33 Port, Pulaski, N.Y. 13142
7. Orr and Sembower, Inc., 620 Morgantown Rd., Reading, Pa. 19602
8. Johnson Bros., 1944 Thomas St., Ferrysburg, Mich. 49409
9. Texsteam Corp., P.O. Box 9127, Houston, Tex. 77011

Dowtherm Heating

1. Struthers-Wells, P.O. Box 300, Warren, Pa. 16365

Hot-oil Heating

1. Vapor Corp., 80 E. Jackson Blvd., Chicago, Ill. 60604
2. Childers Mfg. Co., P.O. Box 6185, Albuquerque, N. Mex. 87107
3. Texsteam Corp., P.O. Box 9127, Houston, Tex. 77011
4. Hy-Way Heat Systems, Inc., P.O. Box 2494, Youngstown, Ohio 44509

Proportioning Equipment

1. John R. Nalbach Engineering Co., 6139 W. Ogden Ave., Chicago, Ill. 60650
2. F. L. Burt Co., 1144 Howard St., San Francisco, Calif. 94103
3. G. Diehl Mateer Co., 776 W. Lincoln Hwy., Wayne, Pa. 19087
4. Lincoln Engineering Co., 4010 Goodfellow Blvd., St. Louis, Mo. 63120
5. Progressive Machine Co., 165 Marion St., Paterson, N.J. 07522
6. BIF, Div. N.Y. Air Brake Co., 376 Harris Ave., Providence, R.I. 02909
7. Whitlock Associates, Inc., 21020 Coolidge Hwy., Oak Park, Mich. 48237
8. The Foxboro Co., Foxboro, Mass. 02035
9. American Meter Co., 13500 Philmont Ave., Philadelphia, Pa. 19116

10. Novo, Mitchell Specialty Div., Philadelphia, Pa. 19136
11. Madden Corp., 1345 Jarvis Ave., Chicago, Ill. 60626

Vacuum Equipment

1. Whiting Corp., Harvey, Ill. 60426
2. Gast Mfg. Corp., P.O. Box 117, Benton Harbor, Mich. 49022
3. Chicago Pneumatic Tool Co., 6 E. 44th St., New York, N.Y. 10017
4. Stokes Plastics, Equip. Div., 5500 Tabor Rd., Philadelphia, Pa. 19120
5. Allis-Chalmers, P.O. Box 512, Milwaukee, Wis. 53201
6. General Electric Co., Ind. Sales Div., 1 River Rd., Schenectady, N.Y. 12305
7. Gardner-Denver Co., Quincy, Ill. 62302

Ovens, Infrared and Electric

1. Fostoria Corp., 1200 N. Main St., Fostoria, Ohio 44830
2. Infra-Red Systems, Route 23, Riverdale, N.J. 07457
3. Radiant Heat Enterprises, Inc., P.O. Box 540, Caldwell, N.J. 07006
4. Edwin L. Wiegand Co., 7500 Thomas Blvd., Pittsburgh, Pa. 15208

Ovens, Convection and Others

1. Despach Oven Co., Minneapolis, Minn. 55414
2. Automation Products Corp., RFD 2, Box 120, Ashland, Ohio 44805
3. DeVilbiss Co., 300 Phillips Ave., Toledo, Ohio 43601
4. Cleveland Process Corp., 1773 E. 21st St., Cleveland, Ohio 44114
5. Falcon Equipment Co., 13th St., & 11th Ave., New Brighton, Pa. 15066
6. Farrel Corp., Ansonia, Conn. 06401
7. Industrial Ovens, Inc., 13825 Triskett Rd., Cleveland, Ohio 44111
8. George Koch and Sons, Inc., Box 358, Evansville, Ind. 47704
9. Michigan Oven Co., 415 Brainard St., Detroit, Mich. 48201
10. Young Bros. Co., 1832 Columbus Rd. N.W., Cleveland, Ohio 44113

Grinding Equipment: Large, Stationary

1. Timesavers Sanders, Inc., 5270 Hanson Court, Minneapolis, Minn. 55429
2. Curtis Div., The Carborundum Co., Niagara Falls, N.Y.
3. Ty-Sa-Man Machine Co., Box 1269, Knoxville, Tenn. 37901
4. Hammond Machinery Builders, 1600 Douglas Ave., Kalamazoo, Mich. 49007
5. The Gardner Co., Beloit, Wis. 53511
6. Mattison Machine Works, Rockford, Ill. 61105
7. Tri-Matic Co., 2363 University Ave., St. Paul, Minn. 55114

Diamond-grinding Wheels

1. Most of the above grinding-equipment manufacturers
2. W. F. Meyers Co., Bedford, Ind. 47421

Grinders: Portable, Floor

1. Terro, Terrazzo Machine and Supply Co., Inc., 2536 24th Ave., South Minneapolis, Minn. 55405

Diamond Saws: Large, Stationary—Production

1. Ty-Sa-Man Machine Co., Box 1269, Knoxville, Tenn. 37901
2. Patch-Wegner Co., Inc., Rutland, Vt. 05701

Masonry Saws: Portable, Cutoff

1. Omark Industries, Inc., 10515 Reading Rd., Cincinnati, Ohio 45241

Diamond Blades, All Sizes

1. W. F. Meyers Co., Bedford, Ind. 47421

Air Compressors

1. Gardner-Denver Co., Quincy, Ill. 62301
2. Chicago Pneumatic Tool Co., 6 E. 44th St., New York, N.Y. 10017
3. Ingersoll-Rand Co., 11 Broadway, New York, N.Y. 10004
4. Allis-Chalmers, P.O. Box 512, Milwaukee, Wis. 53201
5. The Devilbiss Co., Toledo, Ohio 43601
6. Binks Mfg. Co., 3114 W. Carrol Ave., Chicago, Ill. 60612
7. Joy Manufacturing Co., Henry W. Oliver Bldg., Pittsburgh, Pa. 15222

Railroad-car Pullers and Spotters

1. Jeffrey Mfg. Co., 956 N. 4th St., Columbus, Ohio 43201
2. Hewitt-Robins Div., Littleton Ind., Stamford, Conn. 06904
3. Link-Belt Co., Moline, Ill. 61265
4. Whiting Corp., Harvey, Ill. 60426

Automatic Boxing Equipment

1. Crompton and Knowles Packaging Corp., Holyoke, Mass. 01040
2. General Corrugated Mach. Co., Inc., West Central Blvd., Palisades, N.J. 10964
3. Textile Mach. Works, Reading, Pa. 19603
4. Lee Associates, 47 A River St., Wellesley Hills, Mass. 02181
5. Ekhart Mfg. Co., 3522 North Grove, Ft. Worth, Tex. 76106
6. United Shoe Mach. Corp., 140 Federal St., Boston, Mass. 02110

Automatic Paletizing Equipment

1. Lampson Corp., Syracuse, N.Y. 13201

Box Glueing and Closing Equipment

1. Baker and Associates, 8400 Westchester, Dallas, Tex. 75225

Rotary Kiln Dryers for Fillers and Aggregates

1. Allis-Chalmers Mfg. Co., Box 512, Milwaukee, Wis. 53201
2. Norberg Mfg. Co., P.O. Box 383, Milwaukee, Wis. 53201
3. Lindberg Engineering Co., 2456 W. Hubbard, Chicago, Ill. 60612
4. Ferro Corp., 4170 E. 56th St., Cleveland, Ohio 44105
5. Despach Oven Co., 611 S. E. 8th St., Minneapolis, Minn. 55414
6. Louisville Mfg. Corp., 205 Lincoln Ave., Louisville, Ohio 44641
7. Brill Equipment Corp., 37–45 Jabes, Newark, N.J. 07105
8. Bethlehem Steel Corp., Div., 25 Broadway, New York, N.Y. 10004
9. Fuller Co., Dept. N. 124 Bridge St., Catasanqua, Pa. 15032
10. F. L. Schmidt and Co., 1270 Ave. of the Americas, New York, N.Y. 10020
11. Ohio Kiln, Inc., Granville, Ohio 43023
12. Bellview Industrial Furnace Co., 2622 Crane Ave., Detroit, Mich. 48214

Mold and Die Manufacturers

1. Akron Standard Mold Co., 1624 Englewood Ave., Akron, Ohio 44305
2. All Bright Mold Co., 600 E. Franklin St., Bloomfield, Iowa 52537
3. Accurate Steel Rule and Die Co., 26–28 W. 21st St., New York, N.Y. 10010
4. Atlas Machine and Tool Corp., 255 Highland Cross, Rutherford, N.J. 07070
5. Atols Tool and Mold Corp., 3828 N. River Rd., Shiller Park, Ill. 60176
6. Beacon Die and Mold Co., 57 Crooks Ave., Clifton, N.J. 07011
7. Bermer Tool and Die Co., Golf St., Southbridge, Mass. 01551
8. Byrd Tool and Mold Corp., 2953 W. 12th St., Erie, Pa. 16505
9. Crown Machine and Tool Co., 540 Great Southwest Parkway, Arlington, Tex. 76010
10. D-M-E Corp., 6686 E. McNichols Rd., Detroit, Mich. 48212
11. Damen Tool and Eng. Co., 4621 N. Olcott Ave., Chicago, Ill. 60656
12. El Monte Mold Eng. Co., 1923 Hoyt Ave., S., El Monte, Calif. 91733
13. F&F Mold and Die Works, Inc., Commerce St., Verona, Ohio 45378
14. Globe Tool and Gauge Works, 575 Albany St., Boston, Mass. 02118
15. Hansen Pattern and Mold Corp., P.O. Box 384, Ludlow, Mass. 01056
16. Leominster Tool Co., 272 Whitney St., Loeminsher, Mass. 01432
17. Newark Die Co., Inc., 24 Scott St., Newark, N.J. 07102
18. Plastic Cast Mold and Products Co., 1430 Archwood Ave., Akron, Ohio 44036
19. Plastic Molds Tool and Die Co., 1 Maple St., E. Rutherford, N.J. 07073

20. Plating Engineering Co., 252 Lake Ave., Yonkers, N.Y. 10701
21.' Springfield Cast Products, Inc., 616 Berkshire Ave., Springfield, Mass. 01109
22. Standard Tool Co., 217 Hamilton St., Leominster, Mass. 01453
23. Overmeyer Mold Co., Box 487, Windchester, Ind., 47394
24. Perfect Mold Co., 1500 N. Crooks Rd., Clawson, Mich. 48017
25. Kerrco, Inc., 2731 N. 58th St., Lincoln, Neb. 68529
26. Hull Corp., Hatboro, Pa. 19040

Moisture-control Equipment

1. Moisture Register Co., 1510 W. Chestnut St., Alhambra, Calif. 91802
2. Boonton Polytechnic Co., 14 Union St., Rookaway, N.J. 07866
3. Pacific Scientific Co., 702 E. Abram, Arlington, Tex. 76010
4. Soil Test, Inc., 2205 Lee St., Evanston, Ill. 60202
5. Daystrom, Inc., Div. of Weston Instruments, Newark, N.J. 07114
6. Consolidated Electrodynamics Corp., 360 Sierra Madre Villa, Pasadena, Calif. 91109

Spray-up Equipment, with and without Glass Choppers

1. Binks Mfg. Co., 3114 W. Carroll Ave., Chicago, Ill. 60612
2. Devilbiss Co., 300 Phillips Ave., Toledo, Ohio 43601
3. Glass-Craft Co., 3225 N. Verdugo Rd., Glendale, Calif. 91208
4. Grayco, Inc., 1000 P.T. Sibley St. N.E., Minneapolis, Minn. 55413
5. National Mfg. Corp., P.O. Box 189, Tonawanda, N.Y. 14150
6. Plastics Eng. and Chemical Co., 3501 N.W. 9th St., Ft. Lauderdale, Fla. 33309
7. Progressive Equipment Co., 8625 Mackinaw, Detroit, Mich. 48204
8. Pyles Industries, Inc., 28990 Wixom Rd., Wixom, Mich. 48096
9. Rezolin, Inc., 1651 18th St., Santa Monica, Calif. 90404
10. Spray-Bilt, Inc., P.O. Box 158, Ojus, Fla. 33163
11. Venus Products, 15820 Benson Rd., Benton, Wash. 98055
12. Tool Chemical Co., 29 E. 8 Mile Rd., Hazel Park, Mich. 48038
13. Reiter Eng. Co., 3 Clearview Rd., Mountainside, N.J. 07092
14. Decker Industries, Inc., P.O. Box 1318 Stuart, Fla. 33494

Some of the above equipment is available in conventional, air-atomized spray, and other equipment is available in airless atomization. Most of it is two-component pump fed, with the mixing chamber at the gun.

Flow-coating Equipment

1. Kohler Coating Machine Corp., 9701 Cleveland Ave., N. W. Greentown, Ohio 44630

Prestressing Equipment for Members, Beams

1. Intercontinental Equipment Co., 120 Broadway, New York, N.Y. 10005

Special Conveyor Equipment, Open-chain Type

1. Link Belt Co., Moline, Ill. 61265
2. Rex Chain Belt, Milwaukee, Wis. 53201

Metal Conveyor Belts

1. Cambridge Wire Cloth Co., Cambridge, Md. 21613

Specialized Equipment for Coating Manufacture

1. The J. H. Day Co., 4932 Beech St., Cincinnati, Ohio 45212
2. Paul O. Abbe Co., Little Falls, N.J. 07424
3. The Patterson Foundry and Machine Co., East Liverpool, Ohio 43920
4. Kinetic Dispersion Corp., 95 Botsford Place, Buffalo, N.Y. 14216
5. Moorehouse-Cowles Co., 1150 San Fernando Rd., Los Angeles, Calif. 90065

Used Plastics Equipment Dealers

1. Perry Equipment Corp., 1421 North Sixth St., Philadelphia, Pa. 19122
2. Brill Equipment Co., 35–63 Jabez St., Newark, N.J. 07105
3. Union Standard Equipment Co., 801–825 E. 141st St., Bronx, N.Y. 10454
4. Madison Equipment Co., Inc., 1724 W. Arcade, Chicago, Ill. 60612
5. R. Gelb and Sons, Inc., U.S. Highway 22, Union, N.J. 07083
6. Equipment Clearing House, Inc., 111 33rd St., Brooklyn, N.Y. 11232
7. Keith Machinery Corp., 52 Ninth St., Brooklyn, N.Y. 11215
8. Ferro Equipment Co., 5454 Bellvue, Detroit, Mich. 48211
9. Baje Equip. Co., 5875 N. Lincoln Ave., Chicago, Ill. 60645
10. Chemical and Process Machinery Corp., 52 Ninth St., Brooklyn, N.Y. 11215
11. Herman M. Newman, 27 P Hayne Ave., Newark, N.J. 07114
12. Reliable Rubber and Plastics Machinery Co., Inc., 2014 Union Turnpike, North Bergen, N.J. 07047
13. S and S Machinery Co., 140 P 53rd St., Brooklyn, N.Y. 10032
14. First Machinery Corp., 209–289 Tenth St., Brooklyn, N.Y. 10015
15. Machinery Unlimited Bldg., 115 Port Kearney, Kearney, N.J. 07032
16. Johnson Machinery Co., Inc., 245 Frelinghuysen Ave., Newark, N.J. 07114
17. Machinery and Equipment Co., 123 Townsend St., San Francisco, Calif. 94107
18. Santa Fe Hydraulics, 4901 S. Santa Fe Ave., Los Angeles, Calif. 90058
19. Chem-Oil Equipment Corp., 4823 Alum Rd., Houston, Tex. 77045

Among these used equipment dealers, almost any type of equipment necessary in polyester-resin manufacture, raw-materials handling, and polyester-products processing can be found. Almost every piece of equipment from the reactors to hydraulic presses and heavy-duty mixers may be found.

Index